Favorite Songs and Hymns

A COMPLETE

CHURCH HYMNAL

* * *

Compiled by

Homer F. Morris
Virgil O. Stamps
J. R. Baxter, Jr.
W. W. Combs

* * *

ROUND AND SHAPE NOTES

* * *

Prices:

Limp Binding

50c per copy; $5.50 per dozen;
$20.00 per 50; $35.00 per 100

Cloth Binding

$1.00 per copy; $10.00 per dozen;
$40.00 per 50; $75.00 per 100

* * *

MADE IN U. S. A.

Address:

Stamps-Baxter Music & Printing Co., Inc.

Dallas 8, Texas — Pangburn, Arkansas — Chattanooga 1, Tennessee

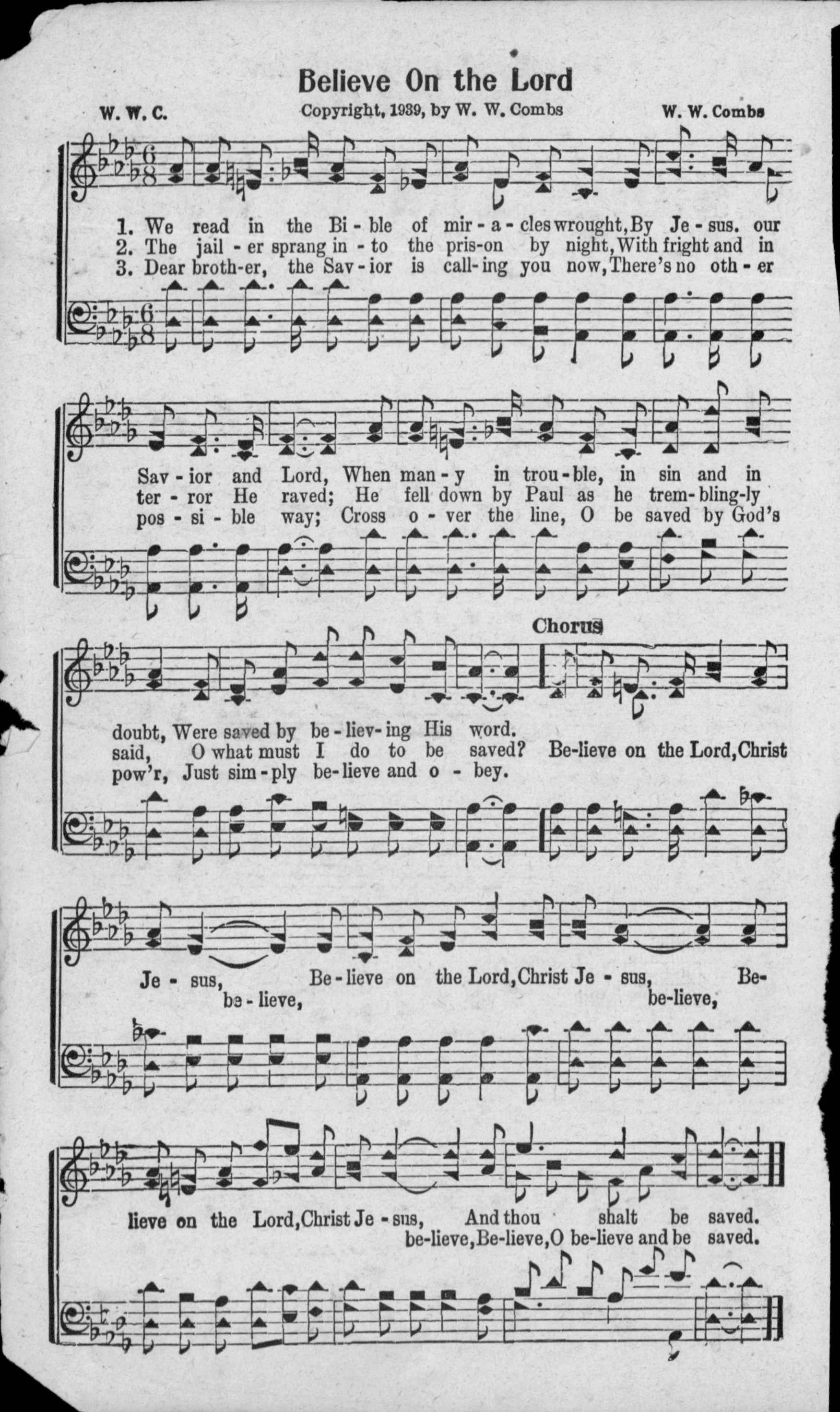
Believe On the Lord
W. W. C.
Copyright, 1939, by W. W. Combs
W. W. Combs
1. We read in the Bi - ble of mir - a - cles wrought, By Je - sus. our
2. The jail - er sprang in - to the pris-on by night, With fright and in
3. Dear broth-er, the Sav - ior is call - ing you now, There's no oth - er
Sav - ior and Lord, When man - y in trou - ble, in sin and in
ter - ror He raved; He fell down by Paul as he trem-bling-ly
pos - si - ble way; Cross o - ver the line, O be saved by God's
Chorus
doubt, Were saved by be - liev - ing His word.
said, O what must I do to be saved? Be-lieve on the Lord, Christ
pow'r, Just sim - ply be-lieve and o - bey.
Je - sus, Be-lieve on the Lord, Christ Je - sus, Be-
be - lieve, be-lieve,
lieve on the Lord, Christ Je - sus, And thou shalt be saved.
be-lieve, Be-lieve, O be-lieve and be saved.

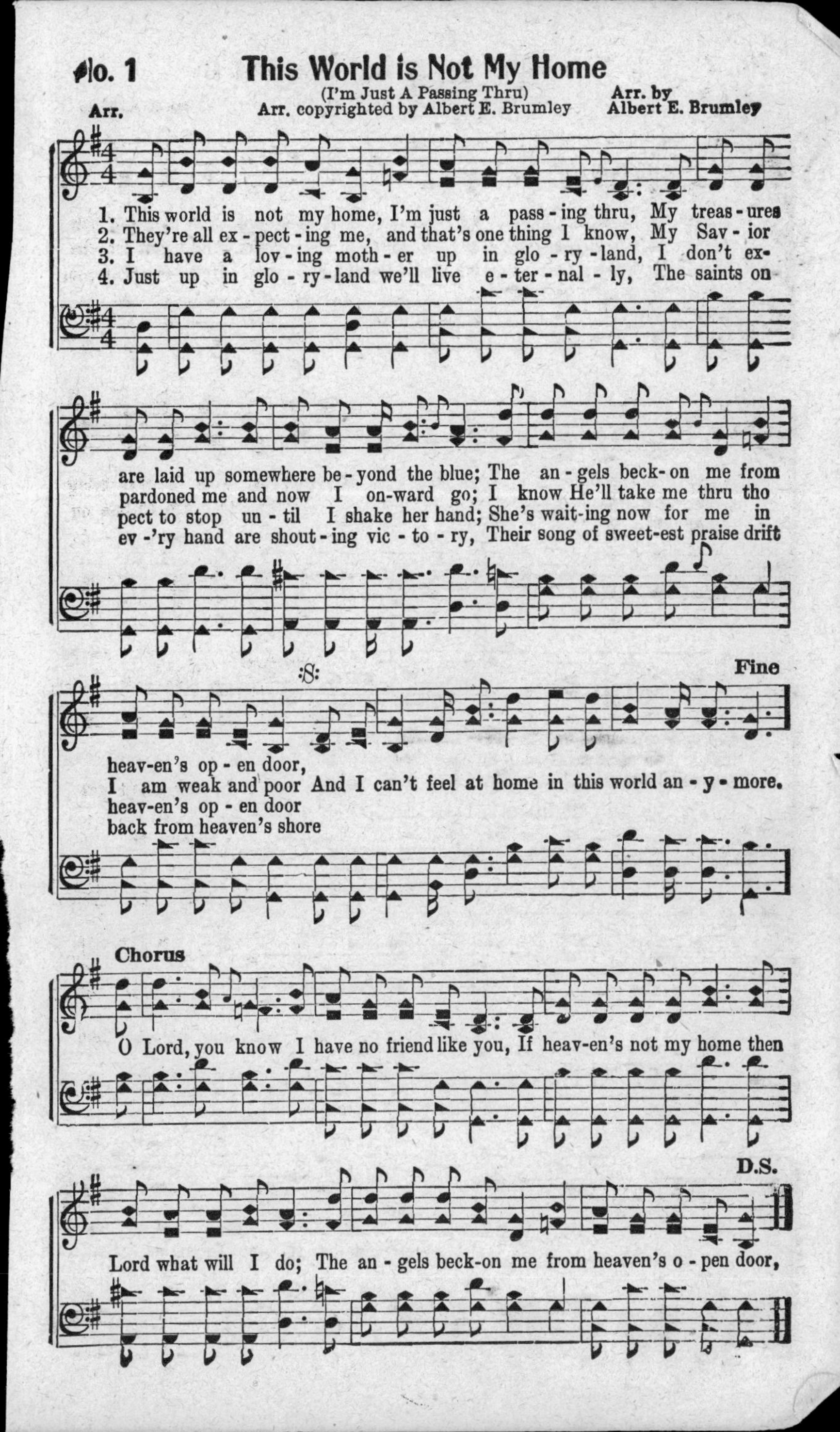
No. 1 This World is Not My Home
(I'm Just A Passing Thru)
Arr. copyrighted by Albert E. Brumley
Arr. by Albert E. Brumley
1. This world is not my home, I'm just a pass - ing thru, My treas - ures are laid up somewhere be - yond the blue; The an - gels beck - on me from heav-en's op - en door,
2. They're all ex - pect - ing me, and that's one thing I know, My Sav - ior pardoned me and now I on-ward go; I know He'll take me thru tho I am weak and poor
3. I have a lov - ing moth - er up in glo - ry - land, I don't ex - pect to stop un - til I shake her hand; She's wait - ing now for me in heav-en's op - en door
4. Just up in glo - ry - land we'll live e - ter - nal - ly, The saints on ev - 'ry hand are shout - ing vic - to - ry, Their song of sweet-est praise drift back from heaven's shore
And I can't feel at home in this world an - y - more.
Fine
Chorus
O Lord, you know I have no friend like you, If heav-en's not my home then Lord what will I do; The an - gels beck-on me from heaven's o - pen door,
D.S.

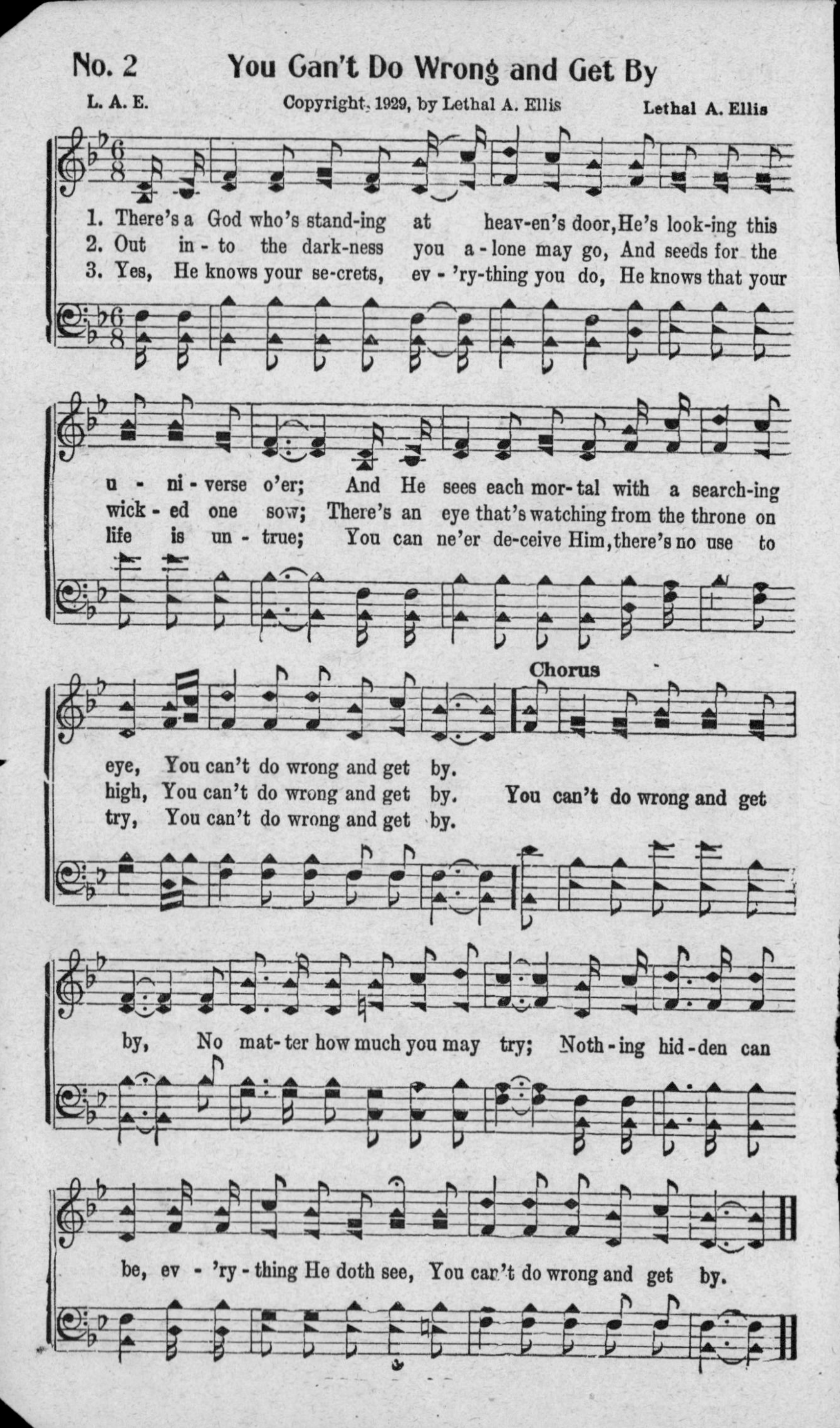
No. 2 You Can't Do Wrong and Get By
L. A. E.
Copyright, 1929, by Lethal A. Ellis
Lethal A. Ellis
1. There's a God who's stand-ing at heav-en's door, He's look-ing this u - ni - verse o'er; And He sees each mor-tal with a search-ing eye, You can't do wrong and get by.
2. Out in - to the dark-ness you a - lone may go, And seeds for the wick - ed one sow; There's an eye that's watching from the throne on high, You can't do wrong and get by.
3. Yes, He knows your se-crets, ev - 'ry-thing you do, He knows that your life is un - true; You can ne'er de-ceive Him, there's no use to try, You can't do wrong and get by.
Chorus
You can't do wrong and get by, No mat-ter how much you may try; Noth-ing hid-den can be, ev - 'ry - thing He doth see, You can't do wrong and get by.
3

No. 3
A Wonderful Time
Copyright, 1924, in "Crowning Hymns No. 4"
Mrs. C. D. Martin
H. F. Morris, owner
Pledger B. Jones
1. A won - der - ful time is just a - head, The Lord whom we
2. A won - der - ful time is just a - head, Our con - flicts and
3. A won - der - ful time is just a - head, The groans of cre-
love - and own Will o - pen the gates of glo - ry - land Re-
tri - als passed; Our wil - der - ness jour - ney at an end, Safe
a - tion cease; And all that is held in bond - age now The
Chorus
veal - ing His glo - ry throne.
home ev - 'ry one at last. A won - der - ful time for
Lord will that day re - lease.
you,...... A won - der - ful time for me,...... If we are pre-
for you, for me,
pared to meet Je - sus the King, A won - der - ful time 'twill be.

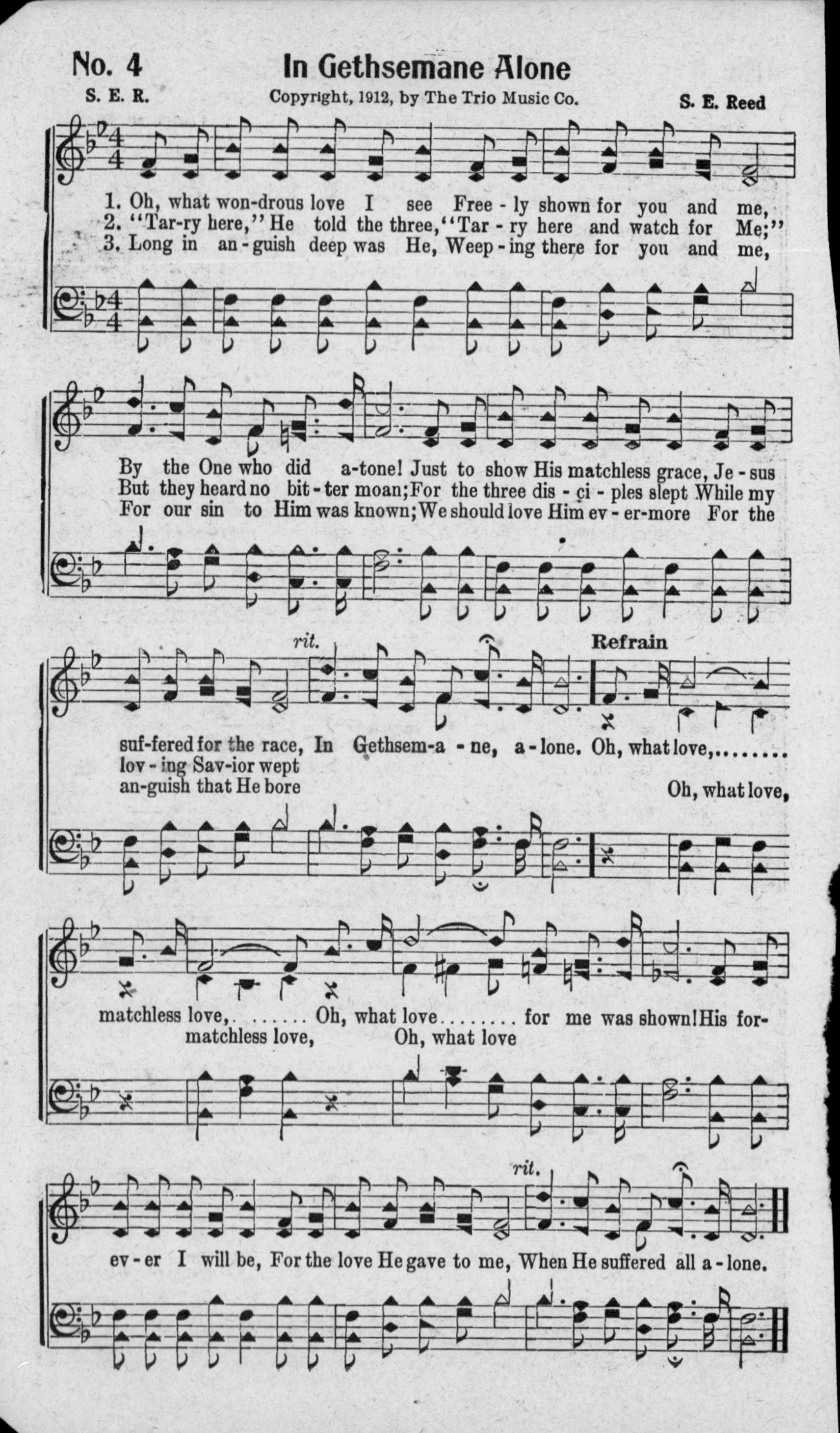
No. 4
In Gethsemane Alone
S. E. R.
Copyright, 1912, by The Trio Music Co.
S. E. Reed
1. Oh, what won-drous love I see Free - ly shown for you and me,
2. "Tar-ry here," He told the three, "Tar - ry here and watch for Me;"
3. Long in an - guish deep was He, Weep - ing there for you and me,
By the One who did a-tone! Just to show His matchless grace, Je - sus
But they heard no bit - ter moan; For the three dis - ci - ples slept While my
For our sin to Him was known; We should love Him ev - er-more For the
rit.
Refrain
suf-fered for the race, In Gethsem-a - ne, a - lone. Oh, what love,........
lov - ing Sav-ior wept
an-guish that He bore
Oh, what love,
matchless love,....... Oh, what love........ for me was shown! His for-
matchless love, Oh, what love
rit.
ev - er I will be, For the love He gave to me, When He suffered all a - lone.

No. 5
Look For Me at the Gate
Copyright, 1933, by The Stamps-Baxter Music Co.
in "Boundless Joy"
H. M. McKee
1. If you should reach heaven be - fore I ar - rive, And en - ter that
2. I've loved ones and friends who are hap - py up there, And they for my
3. Such won-der - ful sing - ing up there you will hear; And meet our dear
bless - ed es - tate, Re - mem - ber to meet you I'll ear - nest - ly strive,
com - ing a - wait; To join them and you I mean here to pre - pare,
Sav - ior so great; Be watch - ing for me as the cross - ing is near,
Chorus
Just look for me at the gate. Just look for me at the
gate,.... You'll not have long to wait;.... I'll sure - ly pre-pare
pearl-y gate, to wait;
to meet you there, Just look for me at the gate.........
beau-ti - ful gate.

No. 6 Love Lifted Me

James Rowe — Howard E. Smith

M. 69 = ♩
1. I was sink-ing deep in sin, Far from the peaceful shore, Ver - y deep-ly
2. All my heart to Him I give, Ev - er to Him I'll cling, In His bless-ed
3. Souls in dan-ger, look a-bove, Je - sus com-plete-ly saves; He will lift you
stained with-in, Sink - ing to rise no more; But the Mas-ter of the sea
pres - ence live, Ev - er His prais-es sing. Love so might-y and so true
by His love Out of the an - gry waves. He's the Mas-ter of the sea,
Heard my de-spair-ing cry, From the wa-ters lift-ed me, Now safe am I.
Mer - its my soul's best songs, Faith-ful, lov-ing serv-ice, too, To Him be - longs.
Bil - lows His will o - bey; He your Sav-ior wants to be—Be saved to - day.
CHORUS.
Love lift - ed me!...... Love lift - ed me!...... When noth - ing
e - ven me! e - ven me!
else could help, Love lift - ed me. Love lift - ed me.
1
2

No. 7 You Never Mentioned Him to Me

This arrangement copyrighted, 1939, by Stamps-Baxter Music & Ptg. Co.
in Favorite Songs and Hymns
J. W. Gaines
James Rowe
Arr. H. F. M.
Slow
1. When in the bet-ter land be - fore the bar we stand, How
2. O let us spread the word wher - e'er it may be heard, Help
3. A few sweet words may guide a lost one to His side, Or
deep - ly grieved our souls may be; If an - y lost one there should
grop - ing souls the light to see, That yon - der none may say, "you
turn sad eyes on Cal - va - ry; So work as days go by, that
cry in deep de-spair, "You nev - er mentioned Him to me."
showed me not the way," "You nev - er mentioned Him to me." "You never
yon-der none may cry, "You nev - er mentioned Him to me."
Refrain
mentioned Him to me, You helped me not the light to see; You met me
day by day and knew I was astray, Yet never mentioned Him to me."

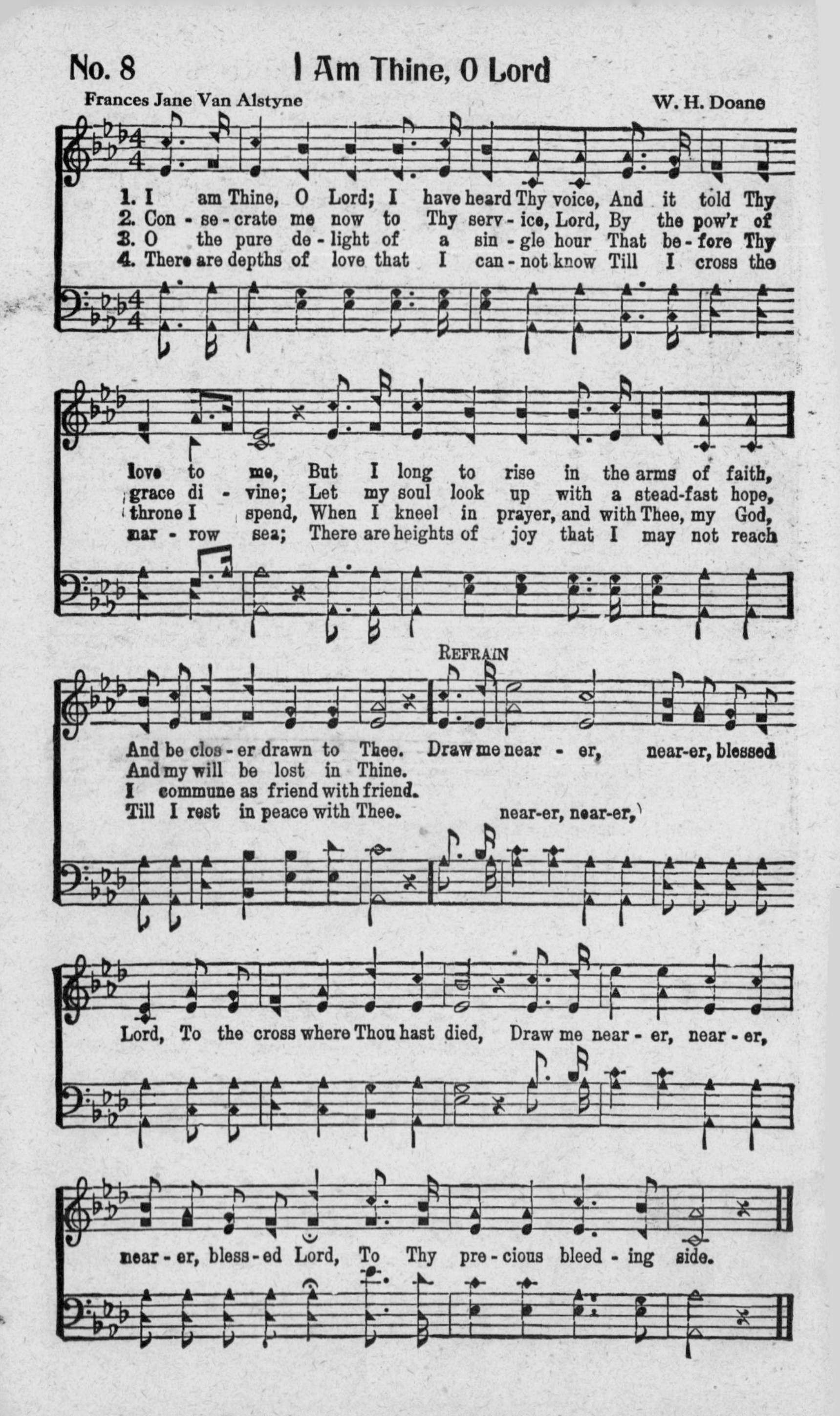
No. 8
I Am Thine, O Lord
Frances Jane Van Alstyne
W. H. Doane
1. I am Thine, O Lord; I have heard Thy voice, And it told Thy
2. Con - se - crate me now to Thy serv - ice, Lord, By the pow'r of
3. O the pure de - light of a sin - gle hour That be - fore Thy
4. There are depths of love that I can - not know Till I cross the
love to me, But I long to rise in the arms of faith,
grace di - vine; Let my soul look up with a stead-fast hope,
throne I spend, When I kneel in prayer, and with Thee, my God,
nar - row sea; There are heights of joy that I may not reach
Refrain
And be clos - er drawn to Thee. Draw me near - er, near-er, blessed
And my will be lost in Thine.
I commune as friend with friend.
Till I rest in peace with Thee. near-er, near-er,
Lord, To the cross where Thou hast died, Draw me near - er, near - er,
near - er, bless - ed Lord, To Thy pre - cious bleed - ing side.

No. 9 God's Tomorrow

A. H. A. — A. H. Ackley

Andante
1. God's tomorrow is a day of gladness, And its joys shall nev-er fade;
2. God's tomorrow is a day of greeting; We shall see the Sav-ior's face;
3. God's tomorrow is a day of glo - ry; We shall wear the crown of life;
No more weeping, no more sense of sadness, No more foes to make a - fraid.
And our long-ing hearts a-wait the meeting In that ho - ly, hap- py place.
Sing thru countless years love's old, old story, Free for-ev - er from all strife.
Chorus
God's to - mor-row, God's to-mor-row, Ev - 'ry cloud will pass a - way
At the dawn-ing of that day; God's to-mor-row, No more sor-row,
For I know that God's to-mor-row Will be bright - er than to-day!

No. 10 When I Make My Last Move

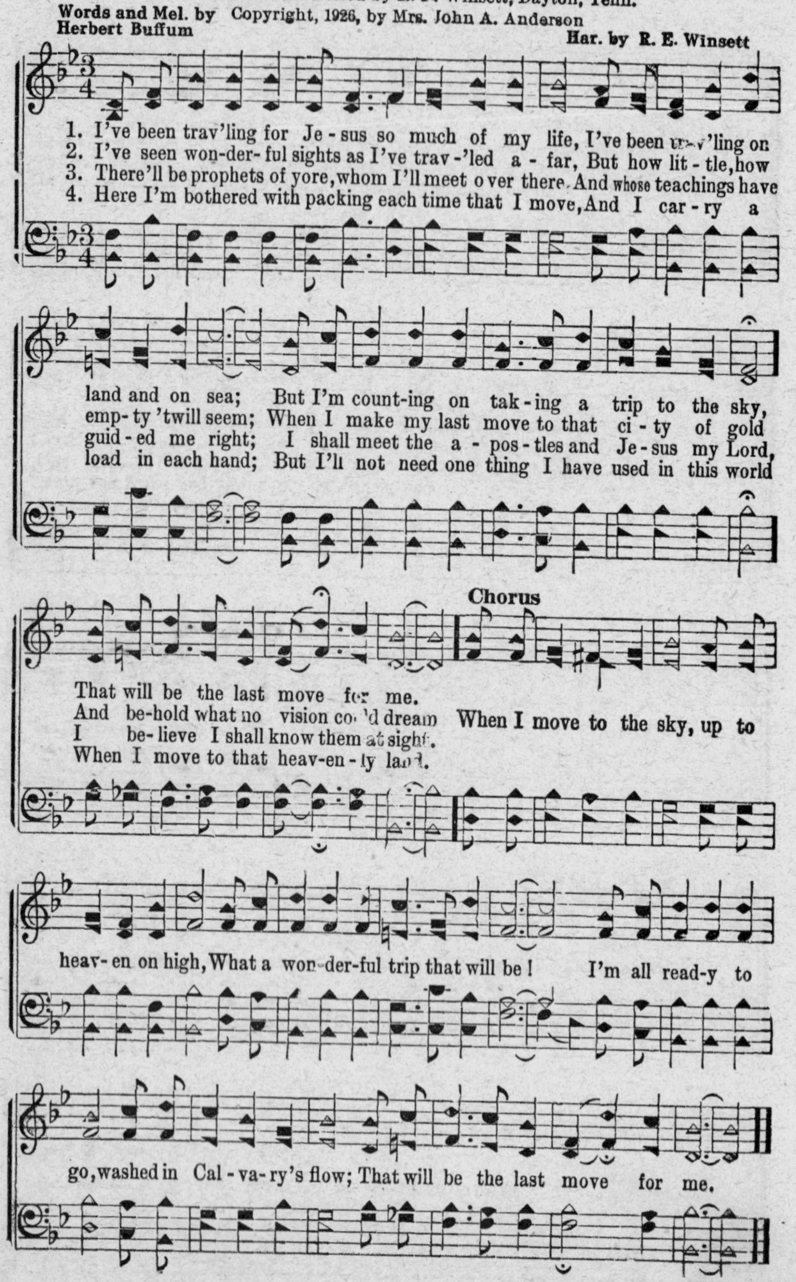
Words and Mel. by Herbert Buffum
Copyright, 1926, by Mrs. John A. Anderson
Har. by R. E. Winsett
1. I've been trav'ling for Je - sus so much of my life, I've been trav'ling on land and on sea; But I'm count-ing on tak-ing a trip to the sky, That will be the last move for me.
2. I've seen won-der-ful sights as I've trav-'led a - far, But how lit - tle, how emp-ty 'twill seem; When I make my last move to that ci - ty of gold And be-hold what no vision could dream
3. There'll be prophets of yore, whom I'll meet over there, And whose teachings have guid-ed me right; I shall meet the a - pos-tles and Je-sus my Lord, I be-lieve I shall know them at sight.
4. Here I'm bothered with packing each time that I move, And I car - ry a load in each hand; But I'll not need one thing I have used in this world When I move to that heav-en-ly land.
Chorus
When I move to the sky, up to heav-en on high, What a won-der-ful trip that will be! I'm all read-y to go, washed in Cal-va-ry's flow; That will be the last move for me.

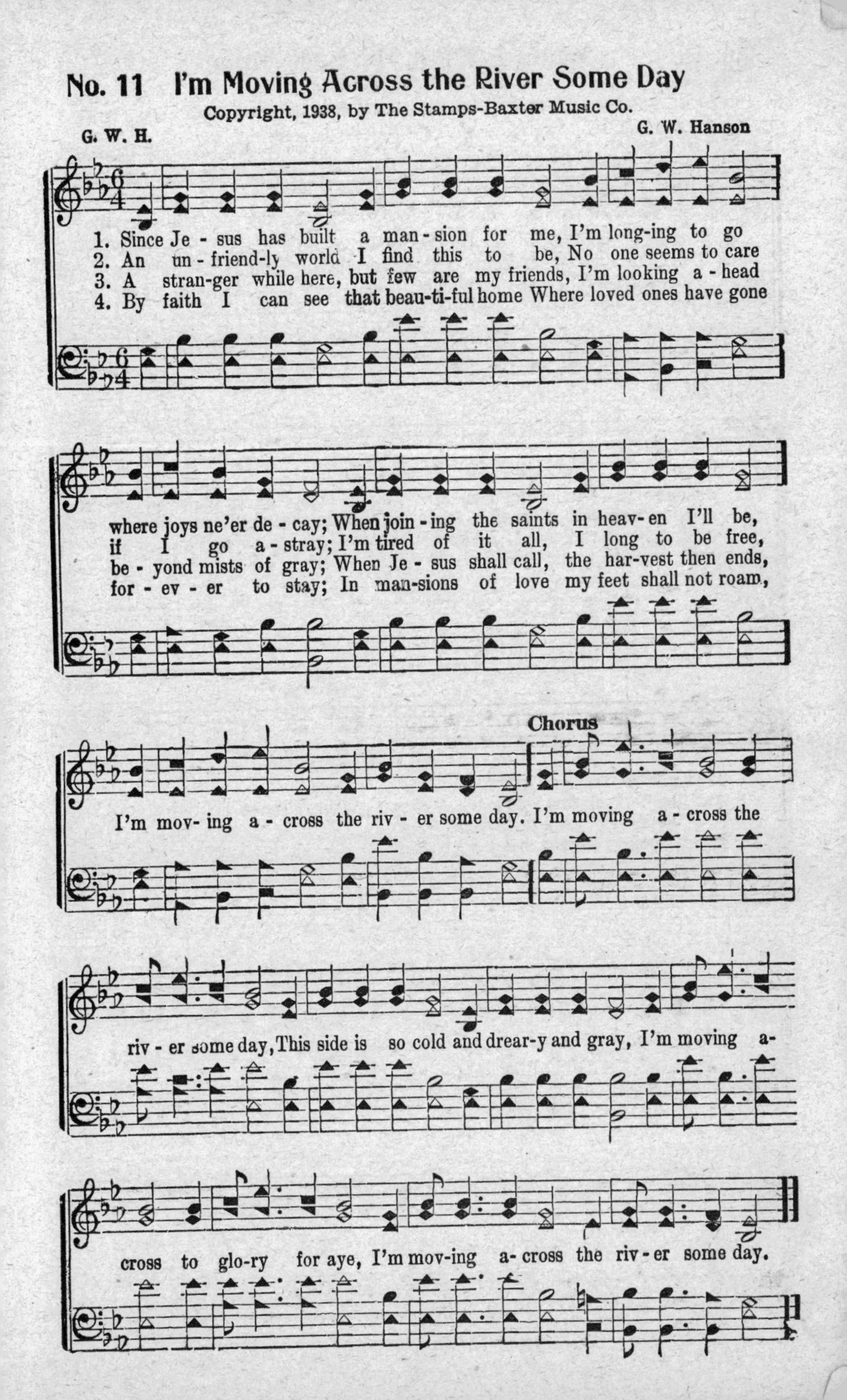
No. 11 I'm Moving Across the River Some Day
Copyright, 1938, by The Stamps-Baxter Music Co.
G. W. H.
G. W. Hanson
1. Since Je - sus has built a man - sion for me, I'm long-ing to go
2. An un - friend-ly world I find this to be, No one seems to care
3. A stran-ger while here, but few are my friends, I'm looking a - head
4. By faith I can see that beau-ti-ful home Where loved ones have gone
where joys ne'er de - cay; When join - ing the saints in heav- en I'll be,
if I go a - stray; I'm tired of it all, I long to be free,
be - yond mists of gray; When Je - sus shall call, the har-vest then ends,
for - ev - er to stay; In man-sions of love my feet shall not roam,
I'm mov- ing a - cross the riv - er some day.
Chorus
I'm moving a - cross the riv - er some day, This side is so cold and drear-y and gray, I'm moving a- cross to glo-ry for aye, I'm mov-ing a- cross the riv - er some day.

No. 12

In the Garden

C. A. M. Copyright, 1940, Renewal. Rodeheaver Co., owner C. Austin Miles

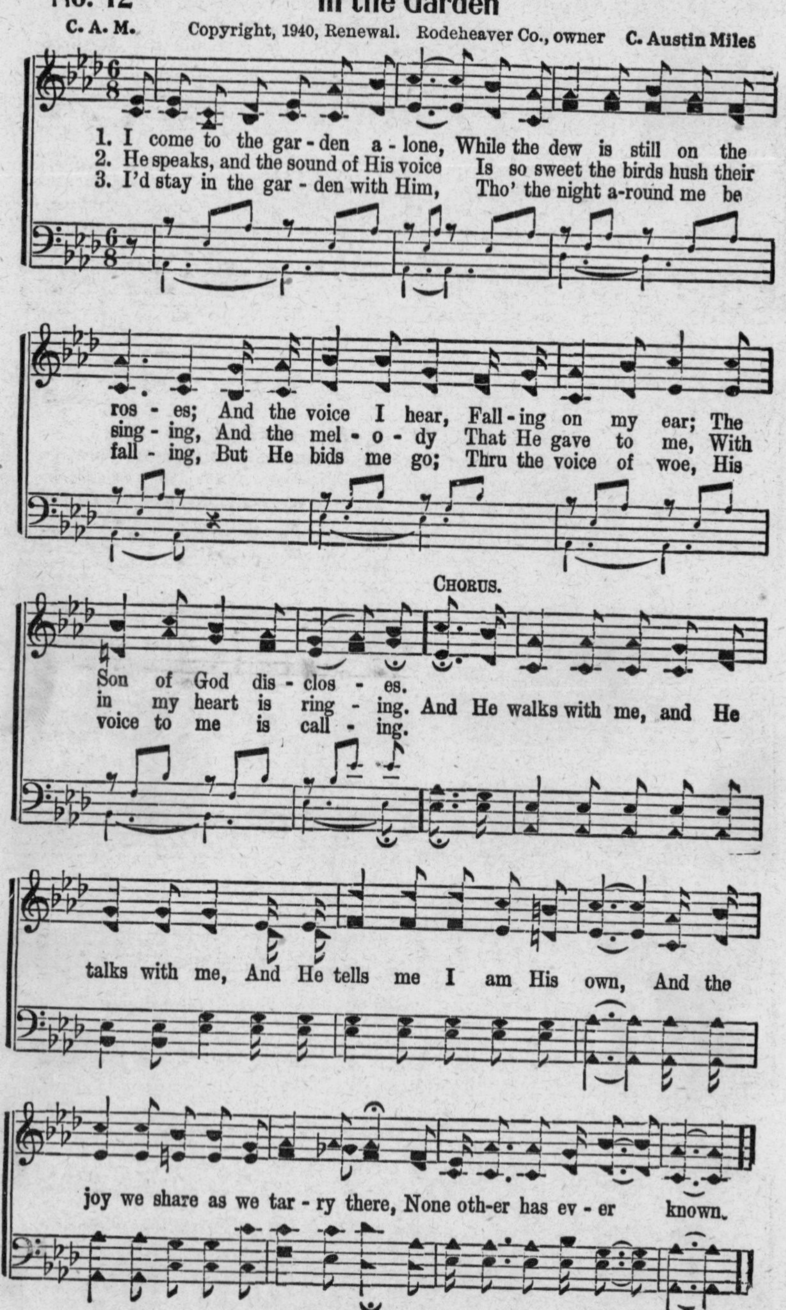
1. I come to the gar - den a - lone, While the dew is still on the
2. He speaks, and the sound of His voice Is so sweet the birds hush their
3. I'd stay in the gar - den with Him, Tho' the night a-round me be
ros - es; And the voice I hear, Fall - ing on my ear; The
sing - ing, And the mel - o - dy That He gave to me, With
fall - ing, But He bids me go; Thru the voice of woe, His
CHORUS.
Son of God dis - clos - es.
in my heart is ring - ing. And He walks with me, and He
voice to me is call - ing.
talks with me, And He tells me I am His own, And the
joy we share as we tar - ry there, None oth-er has ev - er known.

No. 13 Gethsemane

Rev. W. B. Waldrop, Sr. in "Gospel Tide" W. B. W., Arr. Mrs. E. H. Robinson

1. On a hill-side so lone-ly, Knelt Je-sus one day, Soul wound-ed and
2. On the hill-side and gar-den Such suff'ring I see, In hum-ble sub-
3. O the shad-ows are creep-ing, The Sav-ior in pain, The dark skies are
4. But a new day is break-ing, The vic-t'ry is won, The flow-ers re-
wea-ry, He went there to pray; By friends there for-sak-en, So lone-ly He
mis-sion, He's mak-ing His plea; His blood-streams are bursting, Come sinner, be
weep-ing, With dewdrops as rain; The an-gels bear wit-ness To Je-sus di-
joic-ing, A new day is born; The an-gels ex-claim-ing, Sweet mu-sic they
Fine
Chorus
feels, To heav-en He's cry-ing In help-less ap-peals.
true, His cheeks are stained crimson For me and for you.
vine, Sur-ren dered com-plete-ly, O Sav-ior of mine.
chime, For crown-ing of Je-sus, Your Sav-ior and mine.
But a gold-en day has
D.S.—With a ha-lo we're trav'ling The path-way to God.
brok-en In old Geth-sem-a-ne, The morn-ings all come sing-ing The
D.S.
songs of vic-to-ry; There's a new highway to glo-ry, The road that Je-sus trod,

No. 14 There is Power in the Blood

L. E. J. — L. E. Jones

1. Would you be free from your bur-den of sin? There's pow'r in the blood,
2. Would you be free from your passion and pride? There's pow'r in the blood,
3. Would you be whit-er, much whit-er than snow? There's pow'r in the blood,
4. Would you do serv-ice for Je-sus your King? There's pow'r in the blood,
pow'r in the blood; Would you o'er e - vil a vic - to - ry win?
pow'r in the blood; Come for a cleans-ing to Cal - va - ry's tide,
pow'r in the blood; Sin - stains are lost in its life - giv - ing flow,
pow'r in the blood; Would you live dai - ly, His prais - es to sing?
There's won - der - ful pow'r in the blood.
CHORUS.
There is pow'r, pow'r,
There is pow'r,
Wonder-working pow'r in the blood of the Lamb;
in the blood
of the Lamb;
There is pow'r, pow'r, Wonder-working pow'r In the pre-cious blood of the Lamb.
There is pow'r,

No. 15
I'll Live On
T. J. L.
Used by permission
Thos. J. Laney
1. 'Tis a sweet and glorious tho't that comes to me, I'll live on,
2. When my bod-y's slumb'ring in the cold, cold clay,
3. When the world's on fire and dark-ness veils the sun,
4. In the glo-ry-land, with Je-sus on the throne, I'll live on,
yes, I'll live on; Je-sus saved my soul from death and now I'm free,
yes, I'll live on; There to sleep in Je-sus till the judg-ment day,
yes, I'll live on; Men will cry and to the rocks and moun-tains run,
yes, I'll live on; Thru e-ter-nal a-ges sing-ing, home, sweet home,
Chorus
I'll live on, yes, I'll live on. I'll live on, yes, I'll live
I'll live on, and on,
on, Thru e-ter-ni-ty I'll live on, I'll live on,
and on, and on, and on,
yes, I'll live on, Thru e-ter-ni-ty I'll live on.
and on, yes, I'll live on.

No. 16 I Am So Glad

James Rowe — J. E. Thomas

1. I am so glad sal-va-tion's free to all who will re-ceive it,
Praise His dear name, I can pro-claim that tru-ly I be-lieve it,
2. I am so glad that I can tell to way-ward souls the sto-ry,
Find-ing de-light in serv-ice true, my soul is win-ning glo-ry,
3. I am so glad that all my heart to Je-sus I have giv-en,
I will be true un-til with all the hap-py throng in heav-en,

Glad that the news was bro't to me when I was lost and sad;
For I am now His child, (Omit.........................)
Glad that by grace from day to day a help-er I may be;
Glo-ry for Him who gave (Omit.........................)
Glad that at ev-en-tide my soul true sheaves to Him may bring;
Sweet-er and no-bler praise (Omit.........................)

D.S.-He has re-deemed this soul (Omit.........................)

I know, and I'm so glad.
His life to res-cue me.
I give to Christ, my King.

Fine. Refrain.

Glo-ry, hon-or, be to His name for-ev-er, Nev-er a great-er Friend the sin-ful race has had...
Glo-ry to Je-sus, glo-ry and hon-or,
Love Him, Praise Him, Je-sus, the matchless Saviour, (D. S.)
Love Him and serve Him, Love Him and praise Him,

of mine, and I'm so glad.

No. 17 In the Great Triumphant Morning

R. E. W. R. E. Winsett, owner R. E. Winsett

1. In the great triumphant morning, when we hear the Bridegroom cry, And the
2. In the great triumphant morning, what a hap-py time'twill be, When the
3. In the great triumphant morning, when the har-vest is com-plete, And the
4. In the great triumphant morning, all the kingdoms we'll pos-sess, Then the
dead in Christ shall rise, We'll be changed to life im-
When the Lord descends in
We'll be crowned with life im-
the ransomed dead, they all shall rise, Reign as kings and priests e-
mor-tal, in the twinkling of an eye, And meet Je - - - - sus in the
glo-ry, sets His waiting children free, And we meet.......... Him in the
mor-tal, Christ and all the loved ones meet, In the rap - - - ture in the
ter-nal, un-der Christ for-ev-er blest, Af-ter meet - - - ing in the
And meet Je-sus in the skies, up
skies, heav'nly skies.
Chorus
We shall all rise to meet Him, we shall all go to greet Him,
In the morning when the dead in Christ shall rise,
And shall have the marriage supper (Omit ....) in the skies, up in the skies.
1
2
dead shall rise,

No. 18
Home of The Soul
Copyright, 1939, Renewal. Stamps-Baxter Music & Ptg. Co., owners
James Rowe
Samuel W. Beazley
1. If for the prize we have striv-en, Af-ter our la-bors are o'er,
2. Yes, a sweet rest is re-main-ing For the true chil-dren of God,
3. Soon, the bright homeland a-dorn-ing, We shall be-hold the glad dawn;
Rest to our souls will be giv-en, On the e-ter-nal shore.
Where there will be no com-plain-ing, Nev-er a chast-'ning rod.
Lean on the Lord till the morn-ing, Trust till the night is gone.
Chorus
Home of the soul, beau-ti-ful home, there we shall rest,
Home........ of the soul,........ bless-ed king - - - dom of
nev-er to roam; Free from all care, hap-py and bright,
light,.... ..... Free .... from all care, ... and where
Je-sus is there, He is the light! Oft, in the storm,
fall - - - eth no night! .... Oft, ... in the

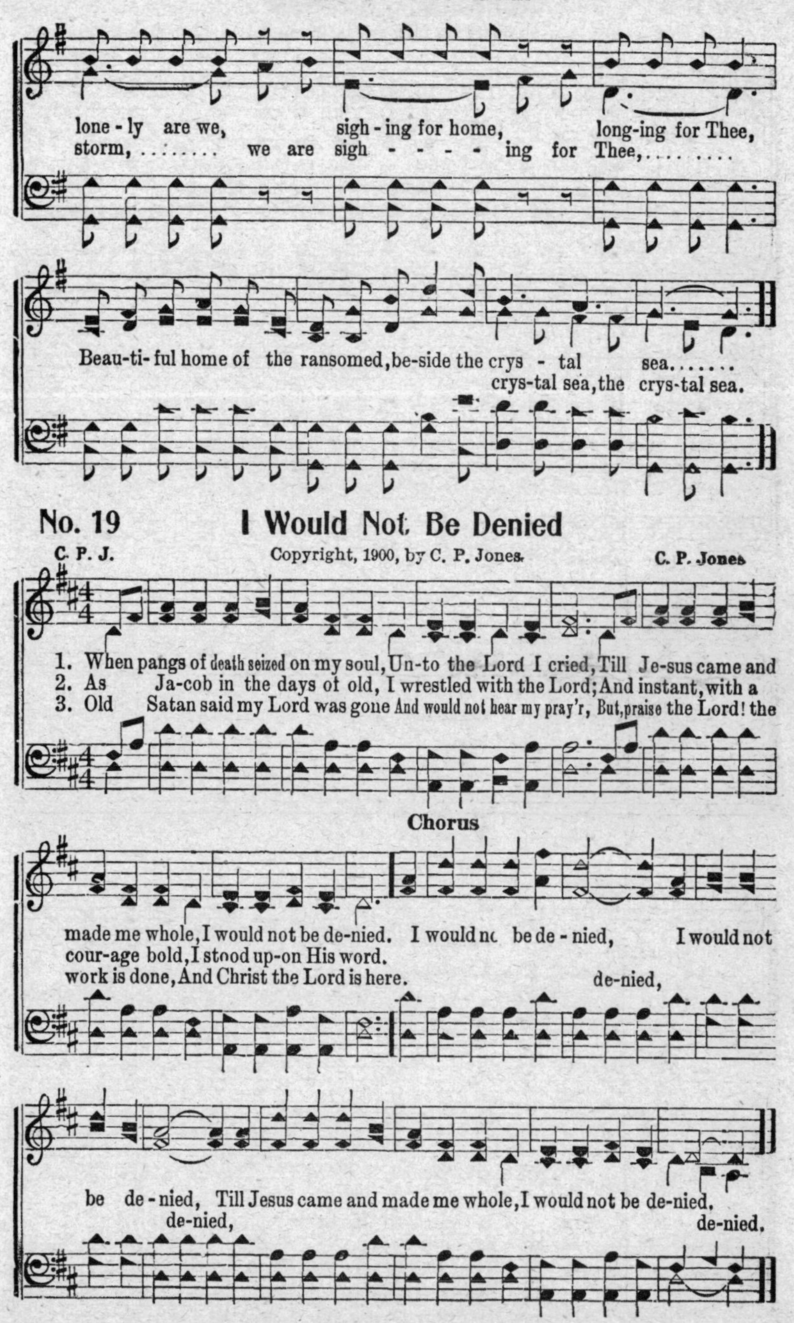
Home Of The Soul
lone - ly are we, sigh - ing for home, long-ing for Thee,
storm, ... we are sigh - - - - ing for Thee,.........
Beau-ti- ful home of the ransomed, be-side the crys - tal sea.......
crys-tal sea, the crys-tal sea.
No. 19 I Would Not Be Denied
C. P. J.
Copyright, 1900, by C. P. Jones.
C. P. Jones
1. When pangs of death seized on my soul, Un-to the Lord I cried, Till Je-sus came and
2. As Ja-cob in the days of old, I wrestled with the Lord; And instant, with a
3. Old Satan said my Lord was gone And would not hear my pray'r, But, praise the Lord! the
Chorus
made me whole, I would not be de-nied. I would not be de - nied, I would not
cour-age bold, I stood up-on His word.
work is done, And Christ the Lord is here. de-nied,
be de - nied, Till Jesus came and made me whole, I would not be de-nied.
de-nied, de-nied.

No. 20 Where We'll Never Grow Old

(To my father and mother.—J. C. M.)

J. C. M. Copyright, 1930, by Jas. C. Moore Jas. C. Moore

1. I have heard of a land on the far a-way strand, 'Tis a beau-ti-ful
2. In that beau-ti-ful home where we'll nev-er-more roam, We shall be in that
3. When our work here is done and our life-crown is won, And our troubles and

home of the soul; Built by Je - sus on high, there we nev - er shall die,
sweet by and by; Hap-py praise to the King thru e - ter - ni - ty sing,
tri - als are o'er; All our sor - row will end, and our voic - es will blend,

'Tis a land where we nev - er grow old.
'Tis a land where we nev - er shall die.
With the loved ones who've gone on be - fore,

Refrain

Nev - er grow old, where we'll

nev - er grow old, In a land where we'll nev- er grow old; Nev- er grow

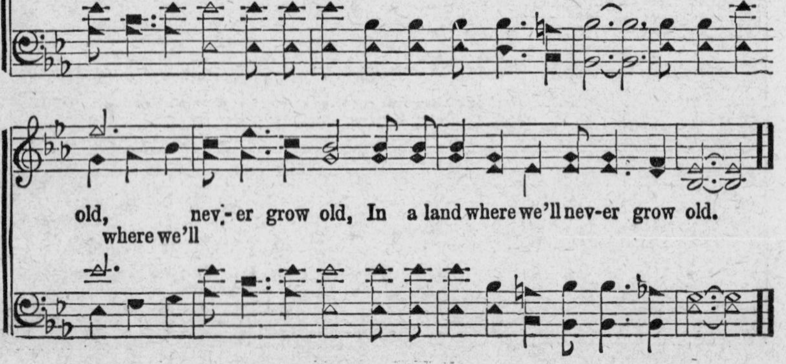
old, nev - er grow old, In a land where we'll nev-er grow old.
where we'll

No. 21
The Royal Telephone
F. M. L.
Copyright, 1919, by F. M. Lehman
F. M. Lehman
1. Cen- tral's nev - er "bus - y," Al-ways on the line; You may hear from
2. There will be no charg-es, Tel - e-phone is free; It was built for
3. Fail to get your ans-wer? Sa-tan's crossed your wire By some strong de-
4. If your line is "ground-ed," And con-nec-tion true Has been lost with
5. Car - nal com - bi - na- tions Can-not get con-trol Of this line to
heav- en Al - most an - y time; 'Tis a roy - al serv-ice, Free for
serv- ice, Just for you and me; There will be no wait-ing On this
lu - sion Or some base de - sire; Take a - way ob-struc-tions—God is
Je - sus, Tell you what to do; Pray'r and faith and prom-ise Mend the
glo - ry, An-chored in the soul; Storm and tri - al can-not Dis-con-
Fine
one and all—When you get in trou-ble, Give this roy - al line a call.
roy - al line— Tel - e-phone to glo - ry, Al -ways answers just in time.
on the throne—And you'll get the answer Thru the roy-al tel - e - phone.
brok - en wire, Till your soul is burn-ing, With the Pen-te- cos- tal fire.
nect the line, Held in constant keeping By the Father's hand di - vine.
D.S.—We may talk to Je - sus Thru this roy - al tel - e - phone.
Chorus
Tel - e-phone to glo-ry, O what joy di-vine! I can feel the cur-rent
mov-ing on the line; Built by God the Fa-ther For His loved and own,
D.S.

No. 22 Since Jesus Came Into My Heart

R. H. McDaniel — Chas. H. Gabriel

M. 80 = ♩
1. What a won-der-ful change in my life has been wrought Since Je-sus came in-to my heart; I have light in my soul for which long I had sought, Since Je-sus came in-to my heart.
2. I have ceased from my wand'ring and go-ing a-stray, Since Je-sus came in-to my heart; And my sins which were man-y are all washed a-way,
3. I'm pos-sessed of a hope that is stead-fast and sure, Since Je-sus came in-to my heart; And no dark clouds of doubt now my path-way ob-scure,
4. There's a light in the val-ley of death now for me, Since Je-sus came in-to my heart; And the gates of the Cit-y be-yond I can see,
5. I shall go there to dwell in that Cit-y I know, Since Je-sus came in-to my heart; And I'm hap-py, so hap-py as on-ward I go,
CHORUS.
Since Je-sus came in-to my heart, Since Je-sus came in-to my heart;
Since Je-sus came in, came in-to my heart, Since Je-sus came in, came in-to my heart;
Floods of joy o'er my soul like the sea bil-lows roll, Since Je-sus came in-to my heart.

No. 23 I Am Resolved

Palmer Hartsough **J. H. Fillmore**

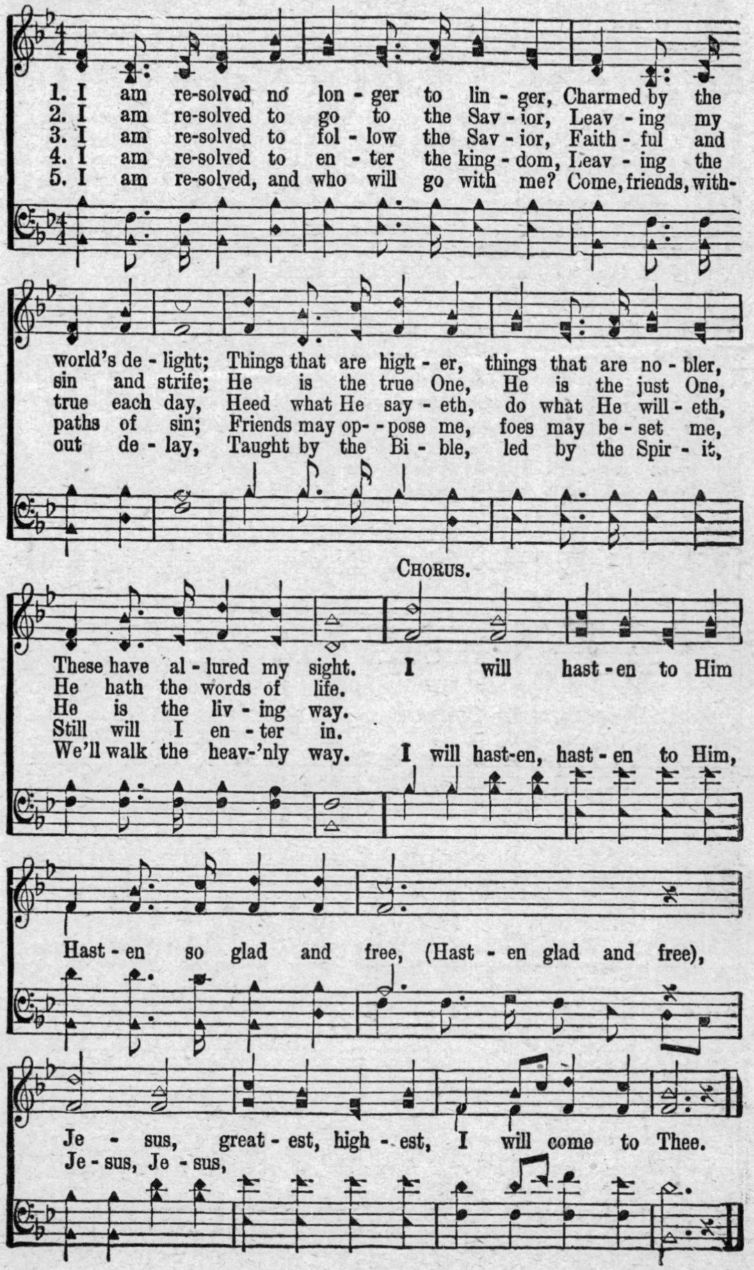

1. I am re-solved no lon - ger to lin - ger, Charmed by the
2. I am re-solved to go to the Sav - ior, Leav - ing my
3. I am re-solved to fol - low the Sav - ior, Faith - ful and
4. I am re-solved to en - ter the king - dom, Leav - ing the
5. I am re-solved, and who will go with me? Come, friends, with-

world's de - light; Things that are high - er, things that are no - bler,
sin and strife; He is the true One, He is the just One,
true each day, Heed what He say - eth, do what He will - eth,
paths of sin; Friends may op - pose me, foes may be - set me,
out de - lay, Taught by the Bi - ble, led by the Spir - it,

These have al - lured my sight.
He hath the words of life.
He is the liv - ing way.
Still will I en - ter in.
We'll walk the heav-'nly way.

CHORUS.

I will hast - en to Him
I will hast-en, hast - en to Him,

Hast - en so glad and free, (Hast - en glad and free),

Je - sus, great - est, high - est, I will come to Thee.
Je - sus, Je - sus,

No. 24

Jesus Believes in You

Laurene Highfield — Samuel W. Beazley

1. Je - sus be - lieves in you, Do you be - lieve in Him? Will you
2. Je - sus be - lieves in you, Do you be - lieve in Him? Will you
3. Je - sus be - lieves in you, Do you be - lieve in Him? Are you
do your ver - y best As He ex-pects you to? Je-sus knows your
jus - ti - fy His faith, Say, will you then prove true? Trust-ing in His
shed-ding forth the light As He bids you to do? Win-ning men to
ef - forts, But He knows your strength as well,
wis-dom, Will you help where there's a place? Do you be-lieve in Je - sus,
praise Him, As your righteousness they see!
Chorus
As He be-lieves in you? Je - sus be-lieves in you, Je - sus be-lieves
in you, Je-sus be-lieves in you, Do you be-lieve in Him?

No. 25 I'll Be List'ning

Arr. by V. O. Stamps

1. When the Sav-ior calls I will an - swer, When He calls for me I will
2. If my heart is right when He calls me, If my heart is right I will
3. If my robe is white when He calls me, If my robe is white I will
hear; When the Sav - ior calls I will an - swer, I'll be some-where
hear; If my heart is right when He calls me, I'll be some-where
hear; If my robe is white when He calls me, I'll be some-where
list'ning for my name.
Chorus
I'll be somewhere list'ning, I'll be somewhere list'ning,
I'll be somewhere list'ning for my name; I'll be somewhere
yes, for my name;
list'ning, I'll be somewhere list'ning, I'll be somewhere list'ning for my name.

No. 26
The Glory-land Way
J. S. T.
J. S. Torbett, owner
J. S. Torbett
1. I'm in the way, the bright and shin-ing way, I'm in the glo-ry-land way;
2. List to the call, the gos-pel call to-day, Get in the glo-ry-land way;
3. On-ward I go, re-joic-ing in His love, I'm in the glo-ry-land way;
glo-ry-land way;
Tell-ing the world that Je-sus saves to-day, Yes, I'm in the glo-ry-land way.
Wan-d'rers, come home, O hast-en to o-bey, For
Soon I shall see Him in that home a-bove, O
glo-ry-land way.
Chorus
I'm in the glo-ry-land way, I'm in the glo-ry-land way;
glo-ry-land way,
glo-ry-land way;
Heav-en is near-er and the way groweth clearer, For I'm in the glo-ry-land way.
glo-ry-land way.

No. 27 Where the Soul Never Dies

W. M. G. — Wm. M. Golden

1. To Ca-naan's land I'm on my way, Where the soul (of man) nev - er dies;
My dark - est night will turn to day, Where the soul (of man) nev - er dies.

2. A rose is bloom-ing there for me, Where the soul (of man) nev - er dies,
And I will spend e - ter - ni - ty, Where the soul (of man) nev - er dies.

3. A love-light beams a-cross the foam, Where the soul (of man) nev - er dies,
It shines to light the shores of home, Where the soul (of man) nev - er dies.

4. My life will end in deathless sleep, Where the soul (of man) nev - er dies;
And ev - er - last - ing joys I'll reap, Where the soul (of man) nev - er dies.

5. I'm on my way to that fair land, Where the soul (of man) nev - er dies;
Where there will be no part-ing hand, And the soul (of man) nev - er dies.

Chorus

No sad fare-wells, No tear - - dimmed eyes,
Dear friends, there'll be no sad fare-wells, There'll be no tear-dimmed eyes,
Where all is love, And the soul nev - er dies.
Where all is peace and joy and love, And the soul of man nev - er dies.

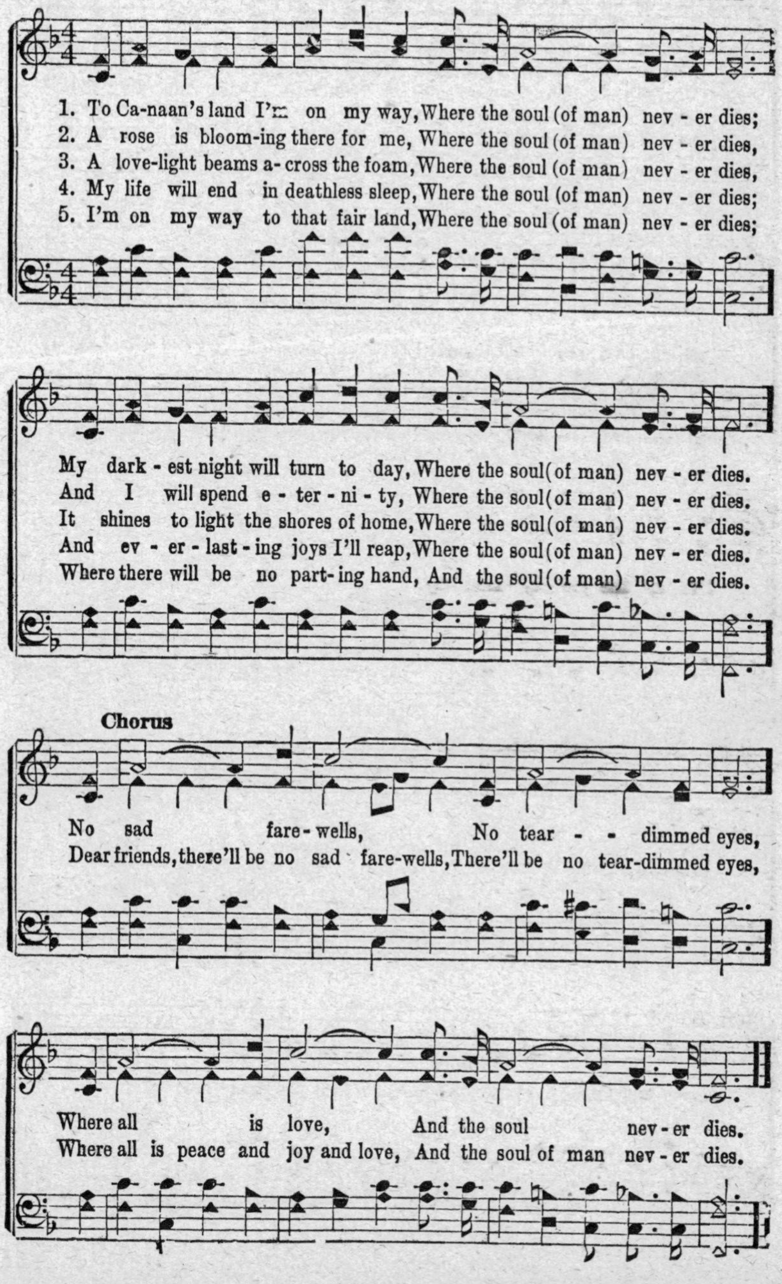

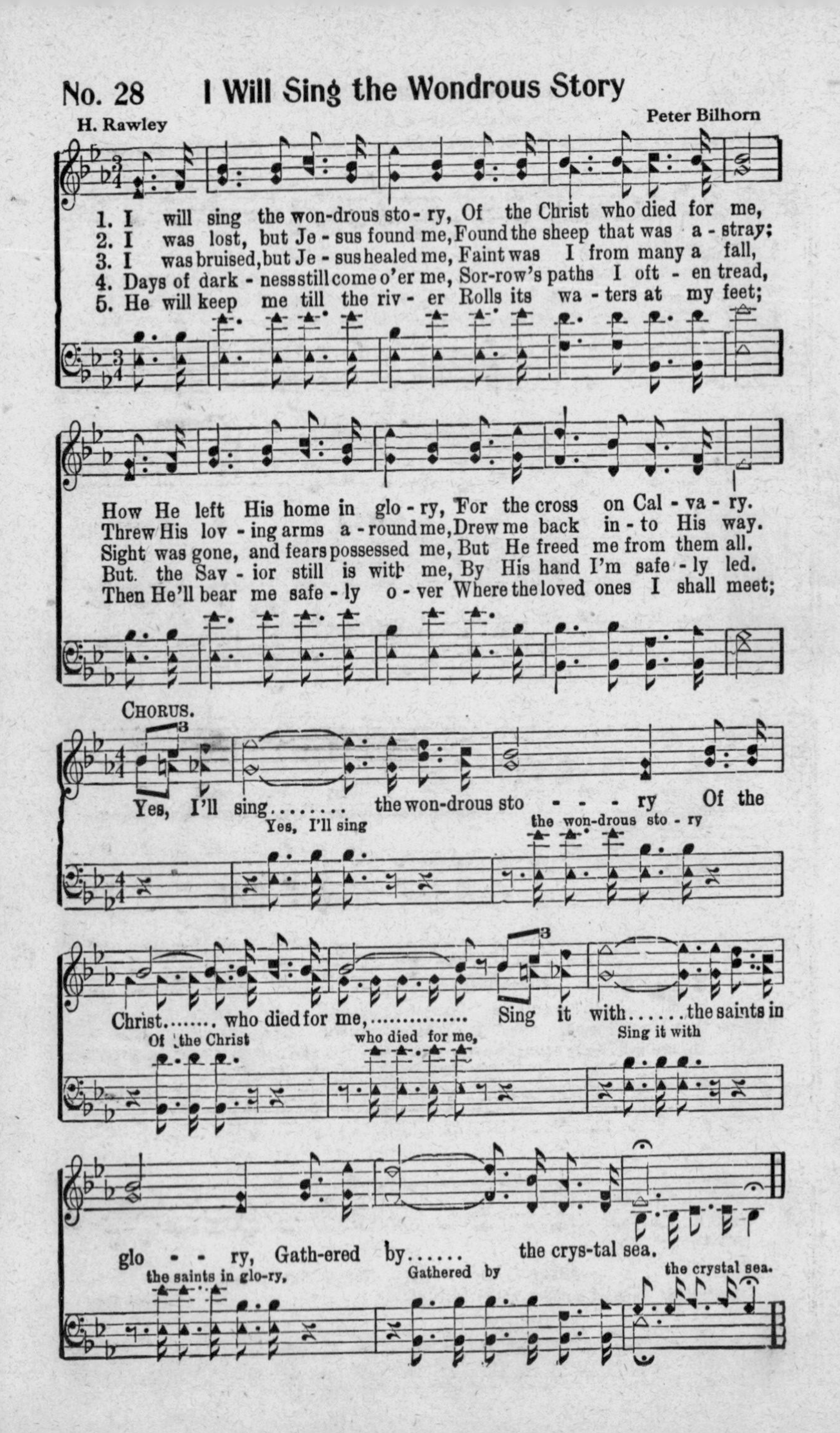
No. 28 I Will Sing the Wondrous Story
H. Rawley
Peter Bilhorn
1. I will sing the won-drous sto-ry, Of the Christ who died for me,
2. I was lost, but Je-sus found me, Found the sheep that was a-stray;
3. I was bruised, but Je-sus healed me, Faint was I from many a fall,
4. Days of dark-ness still come o'er me, Sor-row's paths I oft-en tread,
5. He will keep me till the riv-er Rolls its wa-ters at my feet;
How He left His home in glo-ry, For the cross on Cal-va-ry.
Threw His lov-ing arms a-round me, Drew me back in-to His way.
Sight was gone, and fears possessed me, But He freed me from them all.
But the Sav-ior still is with me, By His hand I'm safe-ly led.
Then He'll bear me safe-ly o-ver Where the loved ones I shall meet;
CHORUS.
Yes, I'll sing........ the won-drous sto---ry Of the
Yes, I'll sing
the won-drous sto-ry
Christ........ who died for me,............... Sing it with......the saints in
Of the Christ
who died for me,
Sing it with
glo--ry, Gath-ered by...... the crys-tal sea.
the saints in glo-ry,
Gathered by
the crystal sea.

No. 29
I Choose Jesus
Copyright, 1941 Renewal
James Rowe
Stamps-Baxter Music & Ptg. Co., owners
Samuel W. Beazley
1. When I need someone in time of grief, Someone my cheer to be, Je- sus I
2. When I need someone to guide my soul, O-ver the stormy sea, Al-ways to
3. When I need help to de-feat the foe, Someone my shield to be, Al-ways to
4. When all my tri-als on earth are o'er, And the dark stream I see, Je- sus shall
choose, for He gives re-lief, He is the best for me.
Je - sus I give control, He is the best for me.
Je - sus in faith I go, He is the best for me.
bear me to yon-der shore, He is the best for me.
Chorus
I choose
Yes, I choose my
Je - sus When I need a friend, What I need I
Sav-ior al-ways helpful friend, What I need I know that sure - ly
Know that He will send; I have proved Him, Good and true is
He to me will freely send; I have proved Him o'er and o'er, And always good and
He; I choose Je - sus, He is the best for me.
true is He; Yes, I choose my Sav-ior dear, of all for me.

No. 30 Joy Unspeakable

1 Pet. 1: 8

B. E. W.
Copyright owned by R. E. Winsett
B. E. Warren
Lively
1. I have found His grace is all complete, He sup-pli-eth ev-'ry need;
2. I have found the pleas-ure I once craved, It is joy and peace with-in;
3. I have found that hope so bright and clear, Liv-ing in the realm of grace;
4. I have found the joy no tongue can tell, How its waves of glo-ry roll!
While I sit and learn at Je-sus' feet, I am free, yes, free in-deed....
What a wondrous blessing! I am saved From the aw-ful gulf of sin.....
Oh, the Savior's presence is so near, I can see His smil-ing face....
It is like a great o'er-flowing well, Springing up with-in my soul....
Chorus
It is joy un-speak-a-ble and full of glo-ry, Full of glo-ry, full of glo-ry; It is joy un-speak-a-ble and full of glo-ry, Oh, the half has nev-er yet been told.

No. 31 Won't It Be Wonderful There?
James Rowe
Copyright, 1930, by Homer F. Morris
Homer F. Morris
1. When with the Sav - ior we en - ter the glo - ry-land, Won't it be wonder-ful there? End - ed the trou-bles and cares of the sto - ry-land,
2. Walk - ing and talk - ing with Christ, the su - per - nal One, Won't it be won-der - ful there? Prais-ing, a - dor-ing the matchless e - ter-nal One,
3. There where the tem-pest will nev - er be sweep-ing us, Won't it be won-der - ful there? Sure that for - ev - er the Lord will be keep-ing us,
Won't it be won-der-ful there?
Refrain
Won't it be won-der-ful there, wonder-ful there,
Hav-ing no bur-dens to bear?....... o - ver there?
Joy - ous - ly sing-ing with heart-bells all ring-ing, O won't it be won-der - ful there? won-der-ful there?

No. 32 In The Shadow of the Cross

in "Guiding Star"

Bernice M. Brostrom — W. H. Daniel

3
1. As we jour-ney on t'ward heaven's shin-ing goal, We may suf - fer
2. On that tree of sor - row Je - sus died for all, Took up - on Him-
3. There are souls to res - cue, there are souls to save, On the sea of
3
pain and loss; Bur-dens on-ly bring us blessings if we live
self our dross; As I see Him there I long to ev - er live
life they toss; May we be a light and teach them how to live
Chorus
In the shad-ow of the cross. Are you liv - ing in the shad - ow
3
of the cross, Where the Sav - ior took your place?
By the cross He'll lead us to that home above, There we'll see Him face to face.

No. 33 An Empty Mansion

Mrs. J. B. Karnes   in "Joyful Songs"   C. A. Luttrell

1. Here I la - bor and toil as I look for a home, Just an hum - ble a-bode a - mong men, While in heav - en a man-sion is wait - ing for me And a gen - tle voice pleading "come in."
2. Ev - er thank-ful am I that my Sav-ior and Lord Prom-ised un - to the wea - ry sweet rest; Noth-ing more could I ask than a man-sion a - bove, There to live with the saved and the blest.
3. When my la - bor and toil-ing have end - ed be - low And my hands shall lie fold - ed in rest, I'll ex-change this old home for a man-sion up there And in -vite the arch an - gel as guest.

Chorus

There's a mansion now emp-ty, just wait-ing for me At the end of life's trou-ble-some way, Man-y friends and dear loved ones will welcome me there Near the door of that man-sion some day.

No. 34 I'm So Tired I Want to Get Home

E. M. B. E. M. Bartlett

1. I am on my way to the land of day, I am go - ing there I know,
2. Long has been my stay and my work for God, He has blest me in the way,
3. I have fought the fight, I have kept the faith, And my course is fin-ished now.

I have jour-neyed long in this pil-grim way, I have suf fered here be-low;
He has kept me straight in the nar-row road, Has been with me ev - 'ry day;
This tired soul of mine longs for rest, sweet rest, To His will I can but bow;

D.S.- Where I'll live with loved ones for - ev-er-more, 'Mid the joys that nev- er cease;

Now my time has come to en - ter in, Soon on earth no more I'll roam,
Now His voice to me is sweet in - deed As He calls for me to come,
Je - sus calls for me and I must go, Soon I'll land in heav-en's dome,

I have come so far on this gos-pel road That I long for heav-en's dome,

Fine

I have come so far on this gos-pel road, I'm so tired, I want to get home.
I am read - y, wait-ing to leave this world, I'm so tired, I want to get home.
These tired feet of mine will find sweet re-lief, I'm so tired, I want to get home.

I have born these years, such a heav-y load, I'm so tired, I want to get home.

Chorus D.S.

I'm so tired, I want to get home To that land of rest and peace,

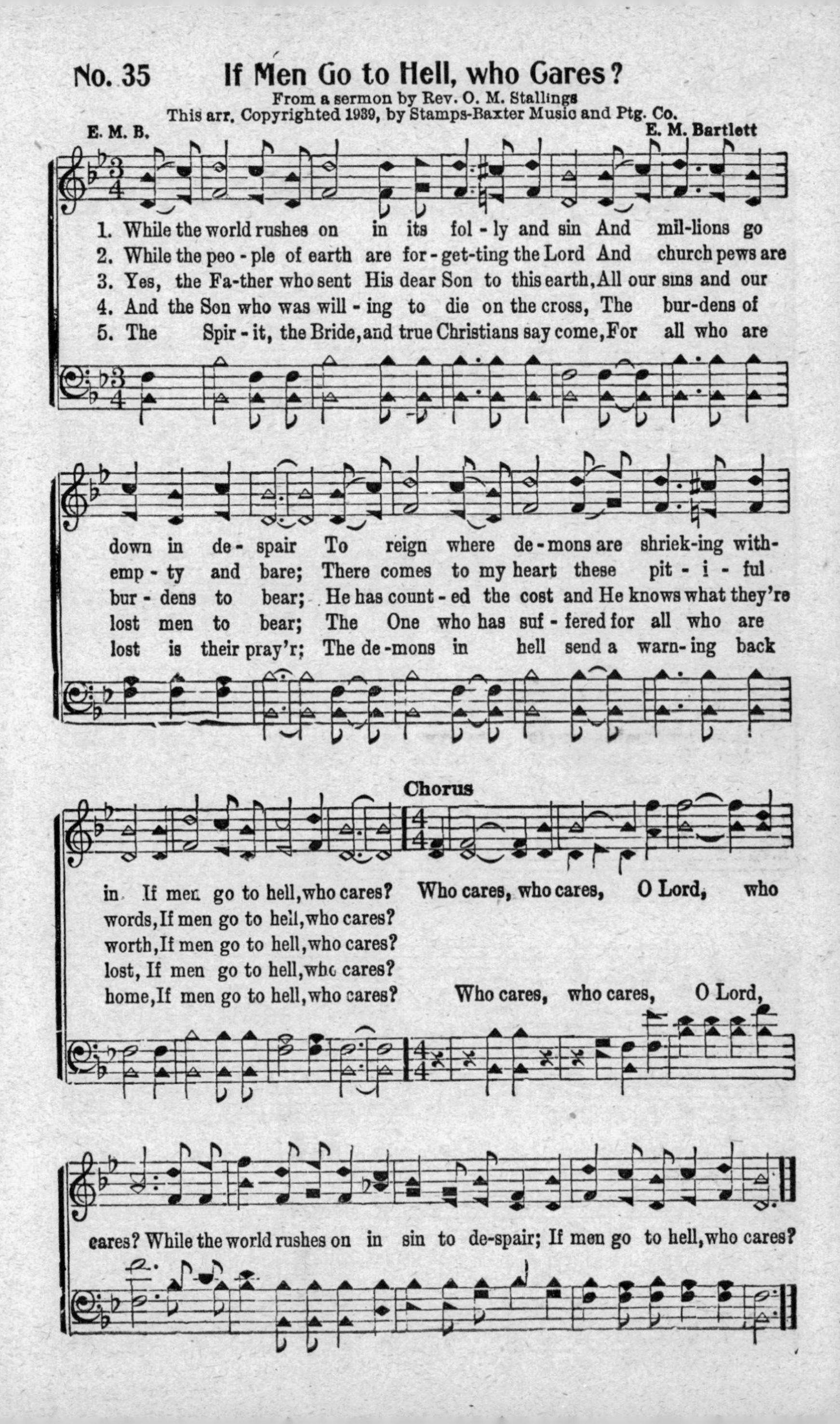
No. 35 If Men Go to Hell, who Cares?
From a sermon by Rev. O. M. Stallings
This arr. Copyrighted 1939, by Stamps-Baxter Music and Ptg. Co.
E. M. B.
E. M. Bartlett
1. While the world rushes on in its fol - ly and sin And mil-lions go
2. While the peo - ple of earth are for - get-ting the Lord And church pews are
3. Yes, the Fa-ther who sent His dear Son to this earth, All our sins and our
4. And the Son who was will - ing to die on the cross, The bur-dens of
5. The Spir - it, the Bride, and true Christians say come, For all who are
down in de - spair To reign where de - mons are shriek-ing with-
emp - ty and bare; There comes to my heart these pit - i - ful
bur - dens to bear; He has count - ed the cost and He knows what they're
lost men to bear; The One who has suf - fered for all who are
lost is their pray'r; The de - mons in hell send a warn - ing back
in. If men go to hell, who cares?
words, If men go to hell, who cares?
worth, If men go to hell, who cares?
lost, If men go to hell, who cares?
home, If men go to hell, who cares?
Chorus
Who cares, who cares, O Lord, who
Who cares, who cares, O Lord,
cares? While the world rushes on in sin to de-spair; If men go to hell, who cares?

No. 36 You Can Shine Where You Are

James Rowe — Homer F. Morris

1. Not up-on some hill-top do you have to live, That your light may send its golden
2. In the val-ley you may spend your earthly days, On your life may sorrow leave its
3. There are many groping in the darkness still, Man-y who from you are nev-er
beams a - far, If you burn it stead - i - ly, Oth- er lives your light will see,
deep - est scar, Yet if you but burn your light, God will guide its rays a-right,
ver - y far, So crave not a high - er place, Giv - ing out the light of day,
Chorus
You can brightly shine for Jesus where you are. You can shine, shine,
Shine for Jesus your Redeemer,
shine where you are, You can shine, shine, shine like a star; O you
Shine as brightly as the morning,
do not have to be, In some land beyond the sea, You can shine, shine where you are,
brightly,

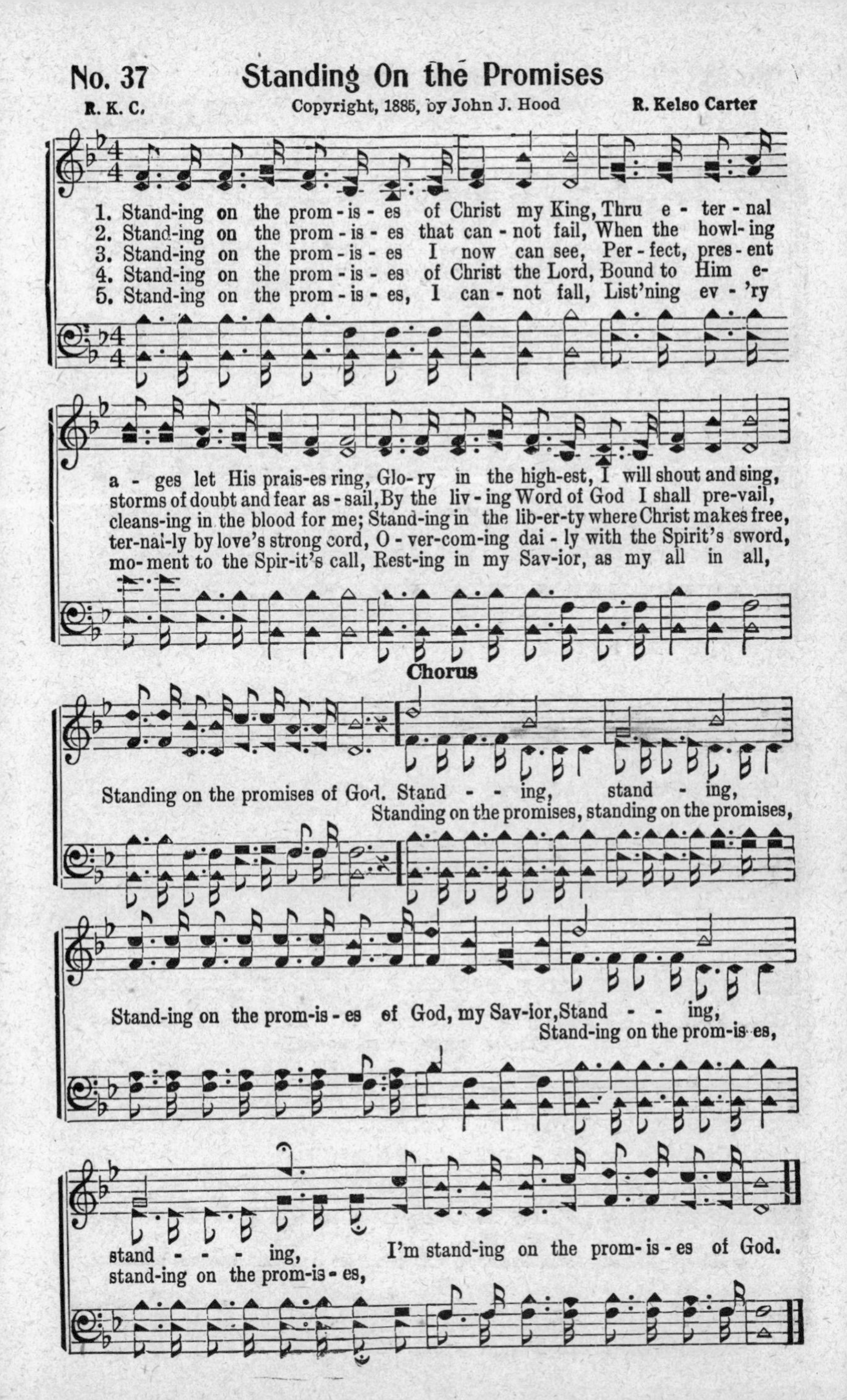
No. 37 Standing On the Promises
R. K. C.
Copyright, 1885, by John J. Hood
R. Kelso Carter
1. Stand-ing on the prom-is-es of Christ my King, Thru e-ter-nal a-ges let His prais-es ring, Glo-ry in the high-est, I will shout and sing,
2. Stand-ing on the prom-is-es that can-not fail, When the howl-ing storms of doubt and fear as-sail, By the liv-ing Word of God I shall pre-vail,
3. Stand-ing on the prom-is-es I now can see, Per-fect, pres-ent cleans-ing in the blood for me; Stand-ing in the lib-er-ty where Christ makes free,
4. Stand-ing on the prom-is-es of Christ the Lord, Bound to Him e-ter-nal-ly by love's strong cord, O-ver-com-ing dai-ly with the Spirit's sword,
5. Stand-ing on the prom-is-es, I can-not fall, List'ning ev-'ry mo-ment to the Spir-it's call, Rest-ing in my Sav-ior, as my all in all,
Standing on the promises of God.
Chorus
Stand-ing, stand-ing,
Standing on the promises, standing on the promises,
Stand-ing on the prom-is-es of God, my Sav-ior, Stand-ing,
Stand-ing on the prom-is-es,
stand-ing, I'm stand-ing on the prom-is-es of God.
stand-ing on the prom-is-es,

No. 38
Farther Along
Copyright, 1937, by The Stamps-Baxter Music Co., in "Starlit Crown"
Rev. W. B. Stevens
W. B. S.
Arr. J. R. Baxter, Jr.
1. Tempt-ed and tried we're oft made to won - der Why it should be thus
2. When death has come and tak - en our loved ones, It leaves our home so
3. Faith - ful till death said our lov - ing Mas - ter, A few more days to
4. When we see Je - sus com - ing in glo - ry, When He comes from His
all the day long, While there are oth - ers liv - ing a - bout us,
lone - ly and drear; Then do we won - der why oth - ers pros - per,
la - bor and wait; Toils of the road will then seem as noth - ing,
home in the sky; Then we shall meet Him in that bright mansion,
Chorus
Nev - er mo - lest - ed tho in the wrong.
Liv - ing so wick - ed year af - ter year.
As we sweep thru the beau - ti - ful gate.
We'll un - der-stand it all by and by.
Far - ther a - long we'll
know all a - bout it, Farther a - long we'll un-derstand why; Cheer up, my
broth-er, live in the sunshine, We'll un-derstand it all by and by.

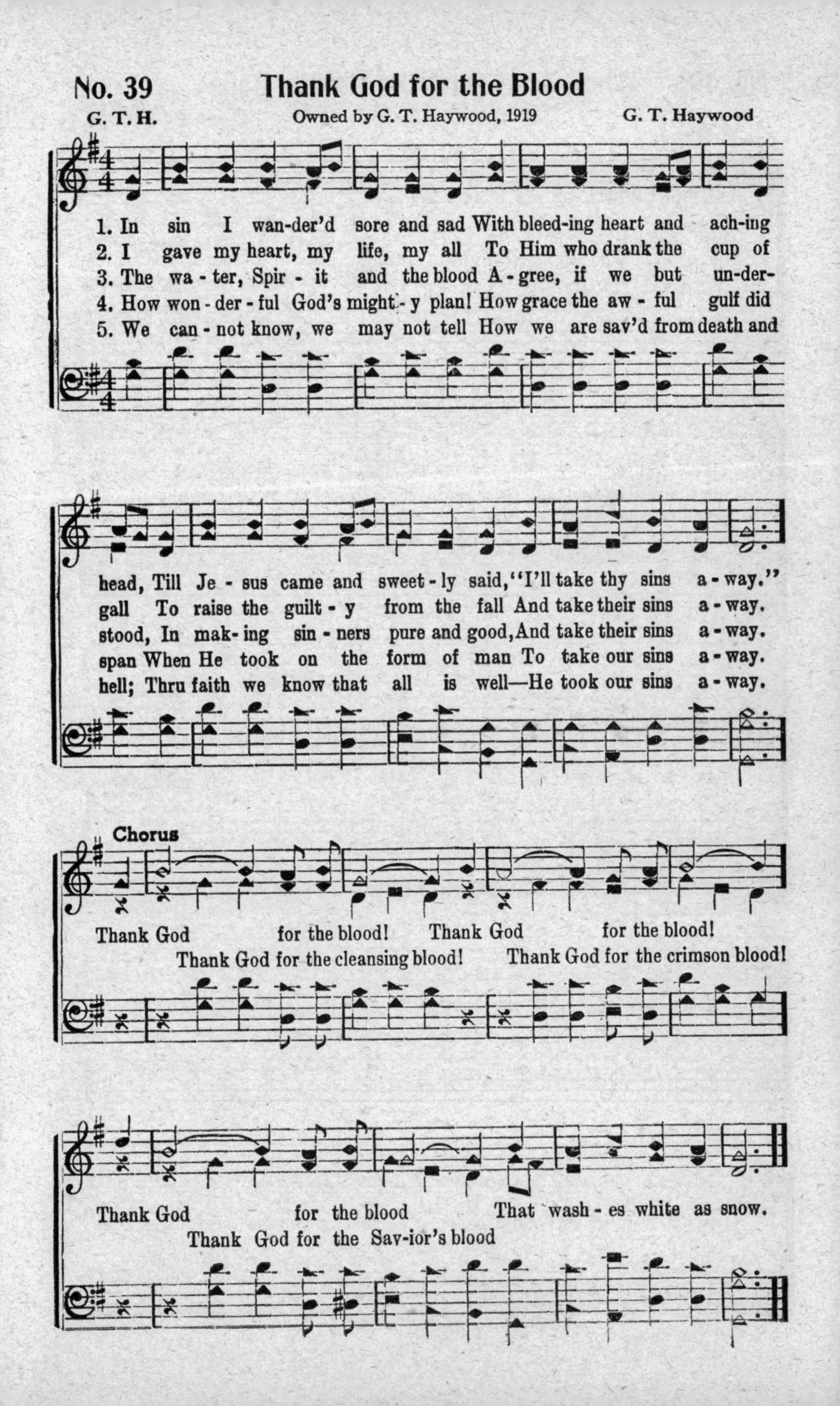
No. 39 Thank God for the Blood
G. T. H.
Owned by G. T. Haywood, 1919
G. T. Haywood
1. In sin I wan-der'd sore and sad With bleed-ing heart and ach-ing
2. I gave my heart, my life, my all To Him who drank the cup of
3. The wa - ter, Spir - it and the blood A - gree, if we but un-der-
4. How won - der - ful God's might - y plan! How grace the aw - ful gulf did
5. We can - not know, we may not tell How we are sav'd from death and
head, Till Je - sus came and sweet - ly said, "I'll take thy sins a - way."
gall To raise the guilt - y from the fall And take their sins a - way.
stood, In mak- ing sin - ners pure and good, And take their sins a - way.
span When He took on the form of man To take our sins a - way.
hell; Thru faith we know that all is well—He took our sins a - way.
Chorus
Thank God for the blood! Thank God for the blood!
Thank God for the cleansing blood! Thank God for the crimson blood!
Thank God for the blood That wash - es white as snow.
Thank God for the Sav-ior's blood

No. 40 When They Ring the Golden Bells

Dion De Marbelle

M. 80
1. There's a land be-yond the riv-er, That we call the sweet for-ev - er, And we
2. We shall know no sin nor sor-row, In that hav - en of to-mor-row, When our
3. When our days shall know their number, When in death we sweet-ly slumber, When the
on - ly reach that shore by faith's decree; One by one we'll gain the portals, There to
barque shall sail beyond the sil-ver sea; We shall on - ly know the blessing Of our
King commands the spir-it to be free; Nev-er-more with anguish la-den, We shall
FINE.
dwell with the immortals, When they ring the golden bells for you and me.
Father's sweet caressing, When they ring the golden bells for you and me.
reach that love-ly ai-den, When they ring the golden bells for you and me.
you and me.
D.S.–yond the shining river, When they ring the golden bells for you and me.
CHORUS.
Don't you hear the bells now ringing? Don't you hear the an-gels sing-ing? 'Tis the
D. S.
glo-ry hal-le-lu-jah Ju - bi - lee. (Ju-bi-lee.) In that far-off sweet forever, Just be-

No. 41 Good Night and Good Morning

Lizzie DeArmond — Homer A. Rodeheaver

M. 85 = ♩
1. When comes to the wea-ry a bless-ed re-lease, When up-ward we pass to His king-dom of peace, When free from the woes that on earth we must bear, We'll say "good-night," here, but "good-morn-ing" up there.
2. When fad-eth the day and dark shad-ows draw nigh, With Christ close at hand, it is not death to die; He'll wipe ev-'ry tear, roll a-way ev-'ry care; We'll say "good-night," here, but "good-morn-ing" up there.
3. When home-lights we see shin-ing bright-ly a-bove, Where we shall be soon, thro' His won-der-ful love, We'll praise Him who called us His heav-en to share, We'll say "good-night," here, but "good-morn-ing" up there.
CHORUS.
Good-morn-ing up there where Christ is the Light, Good-morn-ing up there where cometh no night; When we step from this earth to God's heaven so fair, We'll say "good-night" here, but "good-morn-ing" up there.

No. 42 Let Him In.

Rev. J. B. Atchinson. COPYRIGHT, 1909, BY E. O. EXCELL. RENEWAL E. O. Excell.
1. There's a Stran-ger at the door, Let Him in;
2. O - pen now to Him your heart, Let Him in;
3. Hear you now His lov - ing voice? Let Him in;
4. Now ad-mit the heav'n-ly Guest, Let Him in;
Let the Savior in, Let the Savior in;
He has been there oft be - fore, Let Him in;
If you wait He will de - part, Let Him in;
Now, oh, now make Him your choice, Let Him in;
He will make for you a feast, Let Him in;
Let the Savior in, Let the Savior in;
Let Him in, ere He is gone, Let Him in, the Ho - ly One,
Let Him in, He is your Friend, He your soul will sure de - fend,
He is stand-ing at your door, Joy to you He will re - store,
He will speak your sins for - giv'n, And when earth-ties all are riv'n,
Je - sus Christ, the Fa-ther's Son, Let Him in.
He will keep you to the end, Let Him in.
And His name you will a - dore, Let Him in.
He will take you home to Heav'n, Let Him in.
Let the Savior in, Let the Savior in.

No. 43 We're Marching to Zion
Isaac Watts
Robert Lowry
M 66 =
1. Come, we that love the Lord, And let our joys be known, Join in a song with sweet ac-cord, Join in a song with sweet ac-cord, And thus sur - round the throne, And thus sur-round the throne.
2. Let those re - fuse to sing Who nev - er knew our God; But chil - dren of the heav'n-ly King, But chil - dren of the heav'n-ly King, May speak their joys a - broad, May speak their joys a - broad.
3. The hill of Zi - on yields A thou - sand sa - cred sweets, Be-fore we reach the heav'n-ly fields, Be - fore we reach the heav'n-ly fields, Or walk the gold - en streets, Or walk the gold - en streets.
4. Then let our songs a - bound, And ev - 'ry tear be dry; We're marching thro' Immanuel's ground, We're marching thro' Im-manuel's ground, To fair - er worlds on high, To fair - er worlds on high.
(1) And thus sur-round the throne, And thus sur - round the throne.
CHORUS.
We're march - ing to Zi - on, Beau - ti - ful, beau-ti - ful Zi - on; We're march-ing up-ward to Zi - on, The beau - ti- ful cit - y of God.
We're march-ing on to Zi - on,
Zi - on, Zi-on,

No. 44 The Way of the Cross Leads Home

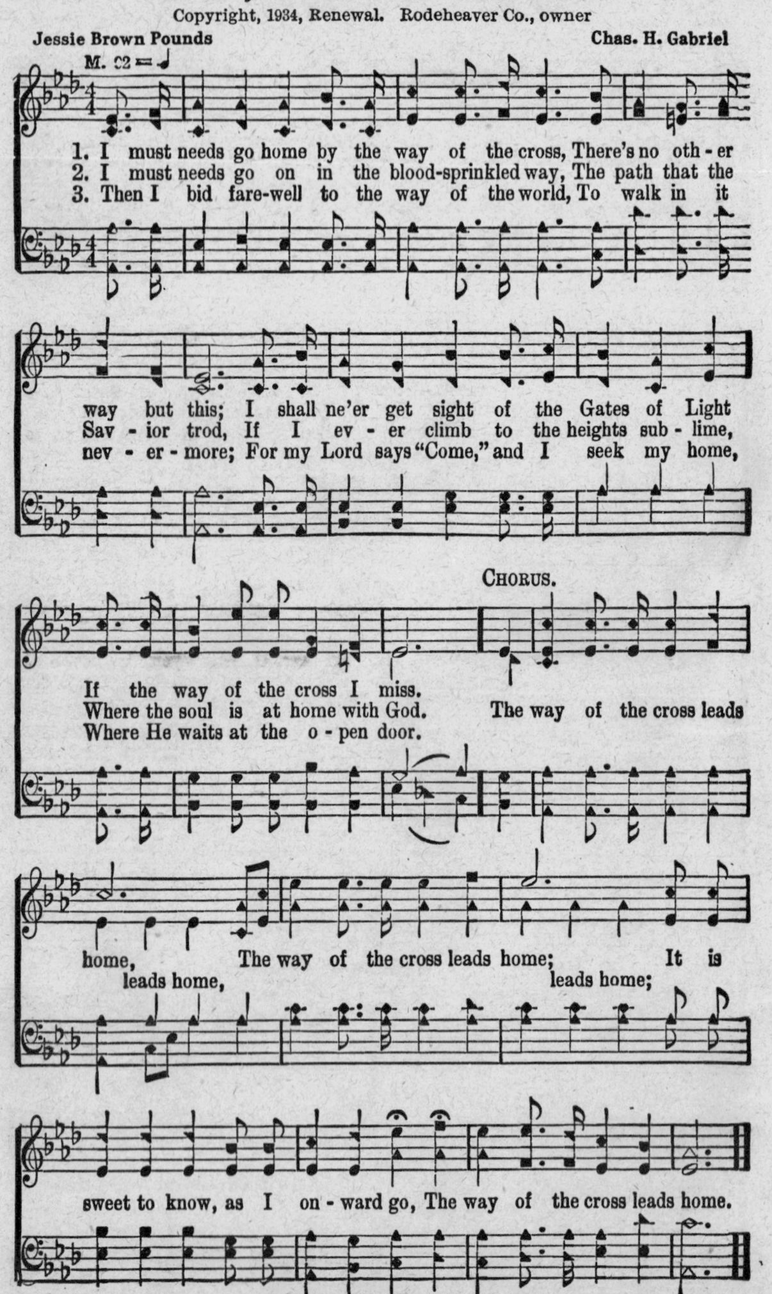
Copyright, 1934, Renewal. Rodeheaver Co., owner
Jessie Brown Pounds
Chas. H. Gabriel
M. 92 = ♩
1. I must needs go home by the way of the cross, There's no oth - er way but this; I shall ne'er get sight of the Gates of Light If the way of the cross I miss.
2. I must needs go on in the blood-sprinkled way, The path that the Sav - ior trod, If I ev - er climb to the heights sub - lime, Where the soul is at home with God.
3. Then I bid fare-well to the way of the world, To walk in it nev - er - more; For my Lord says "Come," and I seek my home, Where He waits at the o - pen door.
CHORUS.
The way of the cross leads home, leads home, The way of the cross leads home; leads home; It is sweet to know, as I on - ward go, The way of the cross leads home.

No. 45 Wonderful Story of Love
J. M. D.
Rev. J. M. Driver
1. Won-der-ful sto-ry of love, Tell it to me a - gain, Wonderful sto-ry of
2. Won-der-ful sto-ry of love, Tho' you are far a - way, Wonderful sto-ry of
3. Won-der-ful sto-ry of love, Je-sus provides a rest, Wonderful sto-ry of
love, Wake the im - mor-tal strain; An - gels with rap-ture announce it,
love, Still He doth call to - day, Call - ing from Cal-va-ry's mountain,
love, For all the pure and blest; Rest in those mansions a-bove us
Shepherds with won-der re - ceive it; Sin - ner, O won't you be-lieve it?
Down from the crys-tal bright foun-tain, E'en from the dawn of cre - a - tion,
With those who've gone on be-fore us, Sing-ing the rap - tur - ous cho - rus,
Chorus
Won-der-ful sto - ry of love. Won - der - ful, Won -
Wonderful sto - ry of love, Won-der-ful
der - ful, Won - der - ful, Wonderful story of love.
sto-ry of love, Wonderful sto-ry of love,

No. 46 Come On, Let's All Go Home
Copyright, 1939, by Stamps-Baxter Music and Ptg. Co.
A. E. B.
Albert E. Brumley
1. There's a bless - ed land of song and sto - ry, Far be - yond the
2. O get read - y for that bright to - mor - row, Cease your wand'rings,
3. Soon the eve - ning shad-ows will be fall - ing And our pil - grim-
dark and surg - ing foam; There is room e - nough for all in glo - ry,
broth-er, do not roam; Come with me and leave your earth-ly sor - row,
age will soon be done, Come, the har - vest Mas-ter now is call - ing,
Come on, let's all go home.
Chorus
Come on, let's all go home,
Come on, let's go to see Je - sus, Come on, why lon - ger
roam? (O wand'ring sisters and brothers?) Come on, O haste a - way,

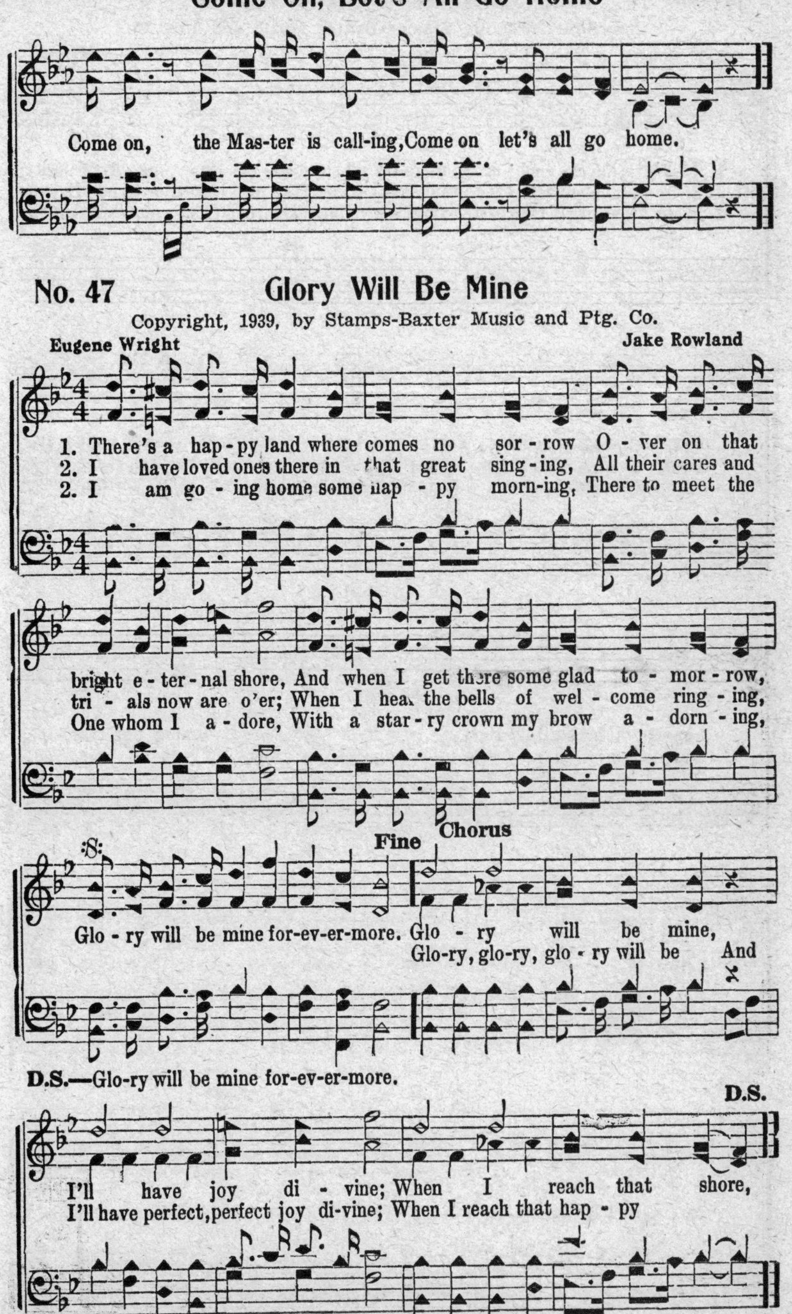
Come On, Let's All Go Home
Come on, the Mas-ter is call-ing, Come on let's all go home.
No. 47
Glory Will Be Mine
Copyright, 1939, by Stamps-Baxter Music and Ptg. Co.
Eugene Wright
Jake Rowland
1. There's a hap-py land where comes no sor-row O-ver on that
2. I have loved ones there in that great sing-ing, All their cares and
2. I am go-ing home some hap-py morn-ing, There to meet the
bright e-ter-nal shore, And when I get there some glad to-mor-row,
tri-als now are o'er; When I hear the bells of wel-come ring-ing,
One whom I a-dore, With a star-ry crown my brow a-dorn-ing,
Fine
Chorus
Glo-ry will be mine for-ev-er-more. Glo-ry will be mine,
Glo-ry, glo-ry, glo-ry will be And
D.S.—Glo-ry will be mine for-ev-er-more.
D.S.
I'll have joy di-vine; When I reach that shore,
I'll have perfect, perfect joy di-vine; When I reach that hap-py

No. 48 A Million Years from Now

E. W. Sug., V. O. S. in "Gospel Tide" Eugene Wright

1. We read a-bout a coun-try Where sin can-not in-vade, A won-der-land of beau-ty Whose splen-dors nev-er fade; There we shall praise the Sav-ior As we be-fore Him bow, All care will be for-got-ten,
2. We all have friends and loved ones Up-on the oth-er shore And if we run with pa-tience The race that's set be-fore, We'll join the throng im-mor-tal And tell the sto-ry how We o-ver-came the temp-ter,
3. In that great res-ur-rec-tion, When Christ shall call His own, We'll shout and sing to-geth-er A-round the shin-ing throne; O what a jub-i-la-tion, When crowns a-dorn our brow, We'll know the joys of heav-en,

Chorus

A mil-lion years from now. A mil-lion years from now, A mil-lion years from now, We'll still be shout-ing vic-t'ry As to our Lord we bow; No one will ev-er die,

A Million Years from Now

No heart will ev-er sigh, We'll just be-gin to live A mil-lion years from now.
No. 49 I'll Go Where He Sendeth Me
James Rowe
W. C. Tinsley, owner
W. C. Tinsley
1. My Sav-ior needs help-ers from day to day, To serve Him on land and sea;
2. So man-y are need-ing the gos-pel light, So man-y made free would be;
3. The way may be drear-y and thorn-y, too, But His bless-ed smile I'll see,
And so I am read-y to speed a-way—I'll go where He send-eth me.
And so, to be use-ful with all my might, I'll go where He send-eth me.
And so, for my Sav-ior my best to do, I'll go where He send-eth me.
Chorus
I'll go, ... I'll go, ... Of help of my Lord to be; ......
I'll will-ing-ly go and glad-ly I'll go, to be;
I'll go, ... I'll go, ... Wher-ev-er He send-eth me. ......
I'll will-ing-ly go and glad-ly I'll go I'll go.

No. 50 The Lily of the Valley

English Melody
1. I have found a friend in Je-sus, He's ev-'ry-thing to me, He's the
2. Oh, He all my griefs has ta-ken, and all my sor-rows borne; In temp-
3. He will nev-er, nev-er leave me, nor yet for-sake me here, While I
fair-est of ten-thousand to my soul; The Lil-y of the Val-ley, in
ta-tion He's my strong and mighty tow'r; I have all for Him for-sa-ken, and
live by faith and do His bless-ed will; A wall of fire a-bout me, I've
D. S.—Lil-y of the Val-ley, the
FINE.
Him a-lone I see All I need to cleanse and make me ful-ly whole.
all my i-dols torn From my heart, and now He keeps me by His pow'r.
nothing now to fear, With His man-na He my hun-gry soul shall fill.
bright and morning star, He's the fair-est of ten thou-sand to my soul.
In sor-row He's my com-fort, in troub-le He's my stay,
Tho' all the world for-sake me, and Sa-tan tempt me sore,
Then sweep-ing up to glo-ry to see His bless-ed face,
D. S.
He tells me ev-'ry care on Him to roll. He's the
Thro' Je-sus I shall safe-ly reach the goal. He's the
Where riv-ers of de-light shall ev-er roll. He's the

No. 51 The Old Rugged Cross

Copyright, 1941. Renewal. Rodeheaver Co., Owner
G. B.
Rev. Geo. Bennard
Solo and Chorus
1. On a hill far a-way stood an old rug-ged cross, The em-blem of
2. Oh, that old rug-ged cross, so de-spised by the world, Has a wondrous at-
3. In the old rug-ged cross, stained with blood so di-vine, A won - drous
4. To the old rug-ged cross I will ev - er be true, Its shame and re-
suf - f'ring and shame, And I love that old cross where the dear-est and best
trac - tion for me, For the dear Lamb of God left His glo - ry a-bove,
beau - ty I see; For 'twas on that old cross Je - sus suf-fered and died,
proach glad-ly bear; Then He'll call me some day to my home far a - way,
For a world of lost sin-ners was slain.
To bear it to dark Cal-va - ry.
To par - don and sanc-ti - fy me.
Where His glo - ry for-ev - er I'll share.
Chorus
So I'll cher-ish the old rug-ged cross,
cross, the
cross, ... Till my tro-phies at last I lay down; I will cling to the
old rug-ged cross,
old rug - ged cross, ... And ex-change it some day for a crown.
cross, the old rug - ged cross,

No. 52 After the Shadows

James Rowe
Copyright, 1915, by Samuel W. Beazley
Stamps-Baxter Music and Ptg. Co., owners
Samuel W. Beazley
1. Af-ter the mid-night, morning will greet us; Af-ter the sad-ness, joy will ap-
2. Af-ter the bat-tle, peace will be giv - en; Af-ter the weeping, song there will
3. Shadows and sunshine all thru the sto - ry, Teardrops and pleasure, day af-ter
pear; Af-ter the temp-est, sun-light will meet us; Af - ter the jeer-ing,
be; Af-ter the jour-ney there will be heav-en, —Burdens will fall and
day; But when we reach the king-dom of glo - ry, Tri - als of earth will
praise we shall hear.
we shall be free.
van - ish a - way.
Chorus
Af - ter the shad - ows, there will be sun - shine;
Af-ter the shad-ows, there will be sunshine;
Rit.
Af-ter the frown, the soul-cheering smile;.... Cling to the Sav - ior,
After the frown, soul-cheering smile; Cling to the Savior,
love Him for - ev - er; All will be well in a lit - tle while.
love Him for-ev-er;

No. 53
The Unclouded Day
J. K. A.
Rev. J. K. Alwood
1. O they tell me of a home far be - yond the skies, O they
2. O they tell me of a home where my friends have gone, O they
3. O they tell me of the King in His beau - ty there, And they
4. O they tell me that He smiles on His chil - dren there, And His
tell me of a home far a - way; O they tell me of a home
tell me of that land far a - way, Where the tree of life
tell me that mine eyes shall be - hold, Where He sits on the throne
smile drives their sor - rows all a - way; And they tell me that no tears
D.S.—O they tell me of a home,
Fine
where no storm - clouds rise, O they tell me of an un - cloud - ed day.
in e - ter - nal bloom Sheds its fragrance thru the un - cloud - ed day.
that is whit - er than snow, In the cit - y that is made of gold.
ev - er come a - gain, In that love - ly land of un - cloud - ed day.
where no storm - clouds rise, O they tell me of an un - cloud - ed day.
Chorus
D.S.
O the land of cloud - less day, O the land of an un - cloud - ed sky;

No. 54
O I Want to See Him
R. H. C.
Copyright, 1916, by R. H. Cornelius
R. H. Cornelius
1. As I jour-ney thru the land sing-ing as I go, Point-ing souls to
2. When in ser-vice for my Lord dark may be the night, But I'll cling more
3. When in valleys low I look tow'rd the mountain height, And be - hold my
4. When be-fore me bil-lows rise from the might-y deep, Then my Lord di-
Cal - va - ry— to the crim-son flow, Man - y ar - rows pierce my soul
close to Him, He will give me light; Sa-tan's snares may vex the soul,
Sav-ior there, lead-ing in the fight, With a ten-der hand outstretched
rects my bark; He doth safe - ly keep, And He leads me gent - ly on
from without, within; But my Lord leads me on, thru Him I must win.
turn my tho'ts a-side; But my Lord goes a-head, leads what-e'er be-tide.
tow'rd the valley low, Guid-ing me, I can see, as I on - ward go.
thru this world be-low; He's a real Friend to me, O I love Him so.
Fine
D.S.—let me lift my voice; Cares all past, home at last, ev - er to re - joice.
Chorus
O I want to see Him, look up-on His face, There to sing for- ev - er
of His sav - ing grace; On the streets of glo - ry
His sav-ing grace;
D.S.

No. 55 The Beautiful Garden of Prayer

Eleanor Allen Schroll
J. H. Fillmore
M. 46 = 𝅗𝅥
1. There's a gar-den where Je-sus is wait-ing, There's a place that is wondrous-ly fair; For it glows with the light of His pres-ence, 'Tis the beau-ti-ful gar-den of prayer.
2. There's a gar-den where Je-sus is wait-ing, And I go with my bur-den and care, Just to learn from His lips words of com-fort, In the beau-ti-ful gar-den of prayer.
3. There's a gar-den where Je-sus is wait-ing, And He bids you to come meet Him there; Just to bow, and re-ceive a new bless-ing, In the beau-ti-ful gar-den of prayer.
REFRAIN.
O the beau-ti-ful gar-den, the gar-den of prayer, O the beau-ti-ful gar-den of prayer; There my Savior a-waits, and He o-pens the gates To the beau-ti-ful gar-den of prayer.

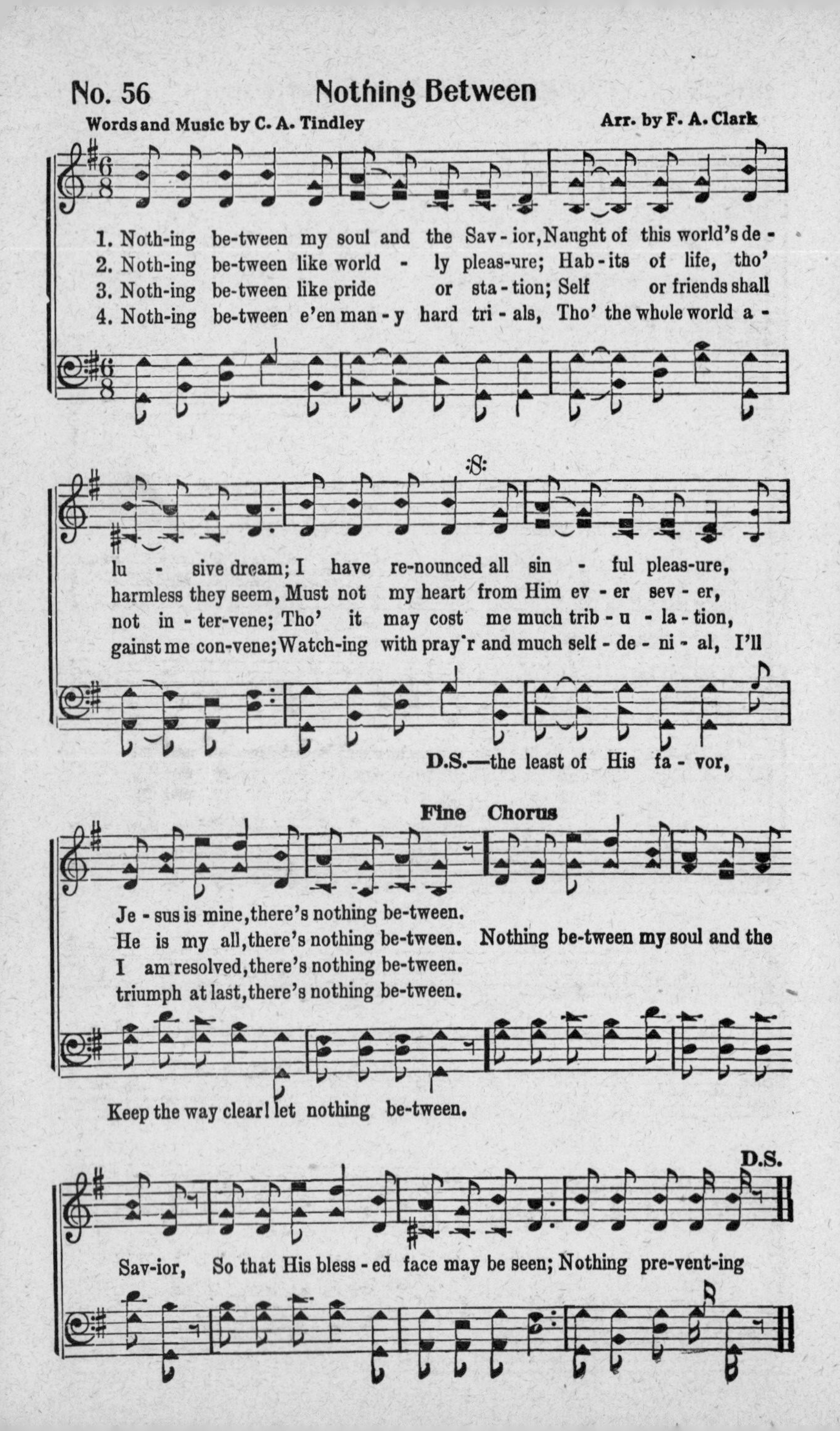
No. 56
Nothing Between
Words and Music by C. A. Tindley
Arr. by F. A. Clark
1. Noth-ing be-tween my soul and the Sav - ior, Naught of this world's de - lu - sive dream; I have re-nounced all sin - ful pleas-ure, Je - sus is mine, there's nothing be-tween.
2. Noth-ing be-tween like world - ly pleas-ure; Hab - its of life, tho' harmless they seem, Must not my heart from Him ev - er sev - er, He is my all, there's nothing be-tween.
3. Noth-ing be-tween like pride or sta - tion; Self or friends shall not in - ter-vene; Tho' it may cost me much trib - u - la - tion, I am resolved, there's nothing be-tween.
4. Noth-ing be-tween e'en man - y hard tri - als, Tho' the whole world a - gainst me con-vene; Watch-ing with pray'r and much self - de - ni - al, I'll triumph at last, there's nothing be-tween.
D.S.—the least of His fa - vor, Keep the way clear! let nothing be-tween.
Fine
Chorus
Nothing be-tween my soul and the Sav-ior, So that His bless - ed face may be seen; Nothing pre-vent-ing
D.S.

No. 57
When Morning Comes
M. 88 = ♩
1. Tri-als dark on ev-'ry hand, and we can-not un - der-stand All the ways that
2. We are oft-en des - ti - tute of the things that life demands, Want of shel-ter
3. Temp - ta-tions, hidden snares, often take us un - a-wares, And our hearts are
God will lead us to that blessed promised land; But He'll guide us with His eye,
and of food, thirst-y hills and bar-ren land; But we're trusting in the Lord,
made to bleed for each thoughtless word or deed; And we won-der why the test,
and we'll fol-low till we die, We will understand it bet-ter by and by.
and ac-cord-ing to His word We will understand it bet-ter by and by.
when we try to do our best, But will understand it bet-ter by and by.
Chorus.
By and by, when the morning comes, All the saints of God are gathering home, We will
tell the sto-ry how we've over-come, We will understand it bet-ter by and by.

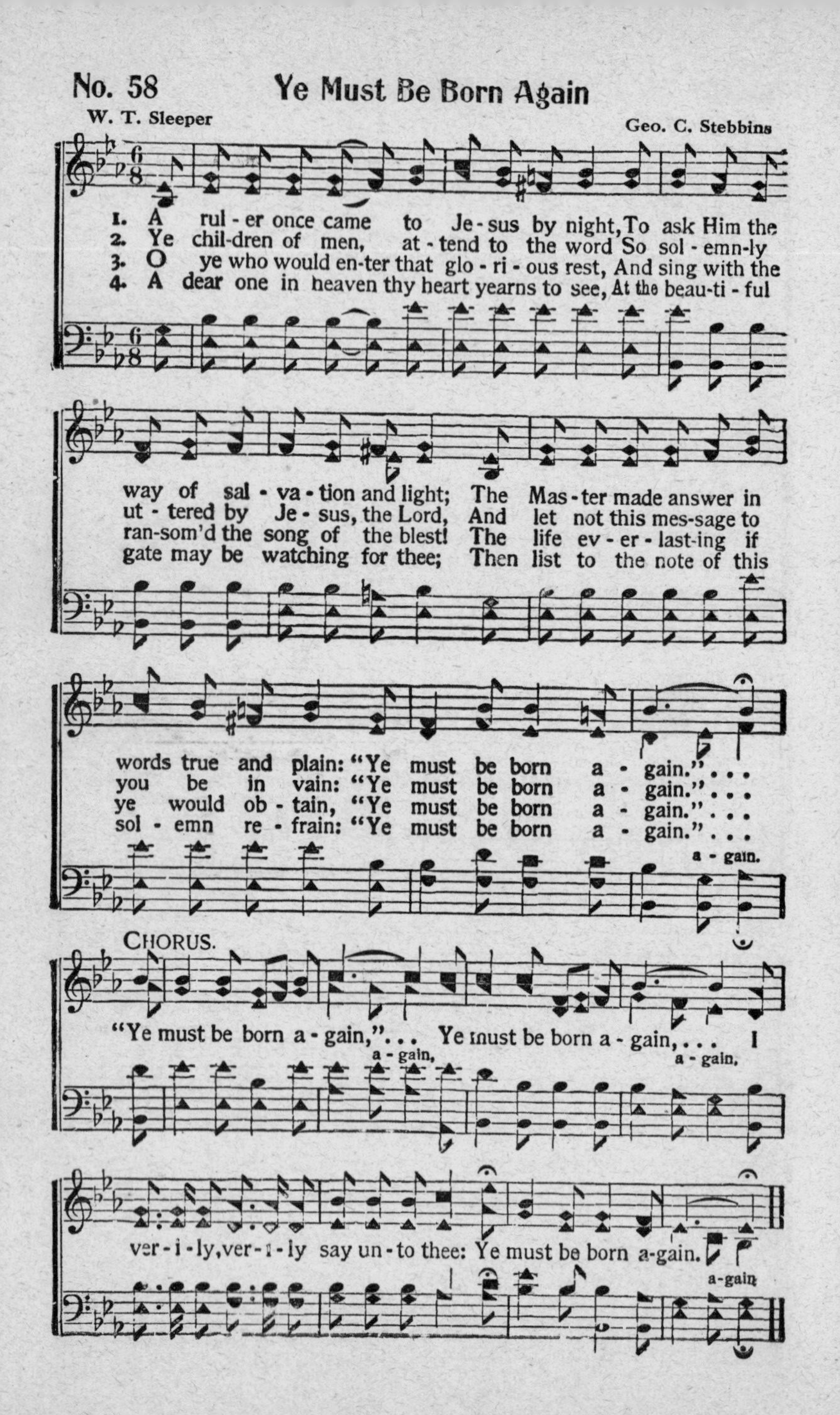
No. 58
Ye Must Be Born Again
W. T. Sleeper
Geo. C. Stebbins
1. A rul - er once came to Je - sus by night, To ask Him the
2. Ye chil-dren of men, at - tend to the word So sol - emn-ly
3. O ye who would en-ter that glo - ri - ous rest, And sing with the
4. A dear one in heaven thy heart yearns to see, At the beau-ti - ful
way of sal - va - tion and light; The Mas - ter made answer in
ut - tered by Je - sus, the Lord, And let not this mes-sage to
ran-som'd the song of the blest! The life ev - er - last-ing if
gate may be watching for thee; Then list to the note of this
words true and plain: "Ye must be born a - gain." . . .
you be in vain: "Ye must be born a - gain." . . .
ye would ob - tain, "Ye must be born a - gain." . . .
sol - emn re - frain: "Ye must be born a - gain." . . .
a - gain.
CHORUS.
"Ye must be born a - gain," . . . Ye must be born a - gain, . . . I
a - gain,
a - gain,
ver - i - ly, ver - i - ly say un - to thee: Ye must be born a-gain.
a-gain

No. 59 Christ Receiveth Sinful Men
Arr. from Neumaster
James McGranahan
M. 88 = ♩
1. Sin - ners Je - sus will re - ceive: Sound this word of grace to all
2. Come, and He will give you rest; Trust Him for His word is plain;
3. Now my heart con - demns me not, Pure be - fore the law I stand;
4. Christ re - ceiv - eth sin - ful men, E - ven me with all my sin;
Who the heav'n-ly path - way leave, All who lin - ger, all who fall.
He will take the sin - ful - est; Christ re - ceiv - eth sin - ful men.
He who cleans'd me from all spot, Sat - is - fied its last de - mand.
Purg'd from ev - 'ry spot and stain, Heav'n with Him I en - ter in.
Refrain. M. 88 = ♩.
Sing it o'er.............. and o'er a - gain;.......... Christ re-
Sing it o'er a - gain, Sing it o'er a - gain:
ceiv - - - eth sin - ful men;......... Make the mes - - - sage
ceiv-eth sin - ful men, Christ re - ceiveth sin-ful men; Make the message plain
clear and plain:.......... Christ re - ceiv - eth sin - ful men.
Make the message plain.

No. 60
The Old Gospel Ship
Copyright, 1939, by Tennessee Music and Printing Co.,
Arr. Alphus LeFevre
1. I have good news to bring and that is why I sing, All my joys with you
2. O I can scarce-ly wait I know I'll not be late, For I'll spend my time
3. If you're ashamed of me you have no cause to be, For with Christ I am
I'll share; I'm going to take a trip in the Old Gos- pel ship
in pray'r; And when my ship comes in I will leave this world of sin
an heir; If too much fault you find you will sure be left be - hind
And go sail-ing thru the air.
And go sail-ing thru the air.
While I go sail-ing thru the air.
Chorus
O I'm "gonna" take a trip, in the
good Old Gospel Ship, I'm go - ing far be - yond the sky; O I'm "gonna"
shout and sing un- til the heavens ring, When I'm bidding this world good-bye.

No. 61 How Wonderful Jesus Is!
T. H. Copyright, 1914, by Thoro Harris Thoro Harris
1. Je - ho-vah's arm is now re-vealed: How won-der - ful Je - sus is!
2. Great Sac - ri - fice or-dained by God, How won-der - ful Je - sus is!
3. The Li - on strong of Ju - dah He, How won-der - ful Je - sus is!
4. He pleads be - fore the courts of heav'n, How won-der - ful Je - sus is!
5. He bears our sor-rows far a - way, How won-der - ful Je - sus is!
6. His death-less love let saints de - clare: How won-der - ful Je - sus is!
7. His per- fect praise let an-gels sing: How won-der - ful Je - sus is!
"For Him hath God the Father sealed:" How won-der-ful Je-sus is!
Pro - claim thru all the earth a-broad How won-der-ful Je-sus is!
The smit- ten Lamb of Cal - va - ry, How won-der-ful Je-sus is!
Thru His a-tone-ment peace is giv'n: How won-der-ful Je-sus is!
In His pre - vail - ing name we pray: How won-der-ful Je-sus is!
And speak His glo - ry ev -'ry-where: How won-der-ful Je-sus is!
And make the bells of heav-en ring: How won-der-ful Je-sus is! di-vine-
Chorus
How won- der - ful Je- sus is! All glo - ry and praise be His,
ly so might-y
Heav'n's fair-est One, God's matchless Son: How won-der- ful Je - sus is!

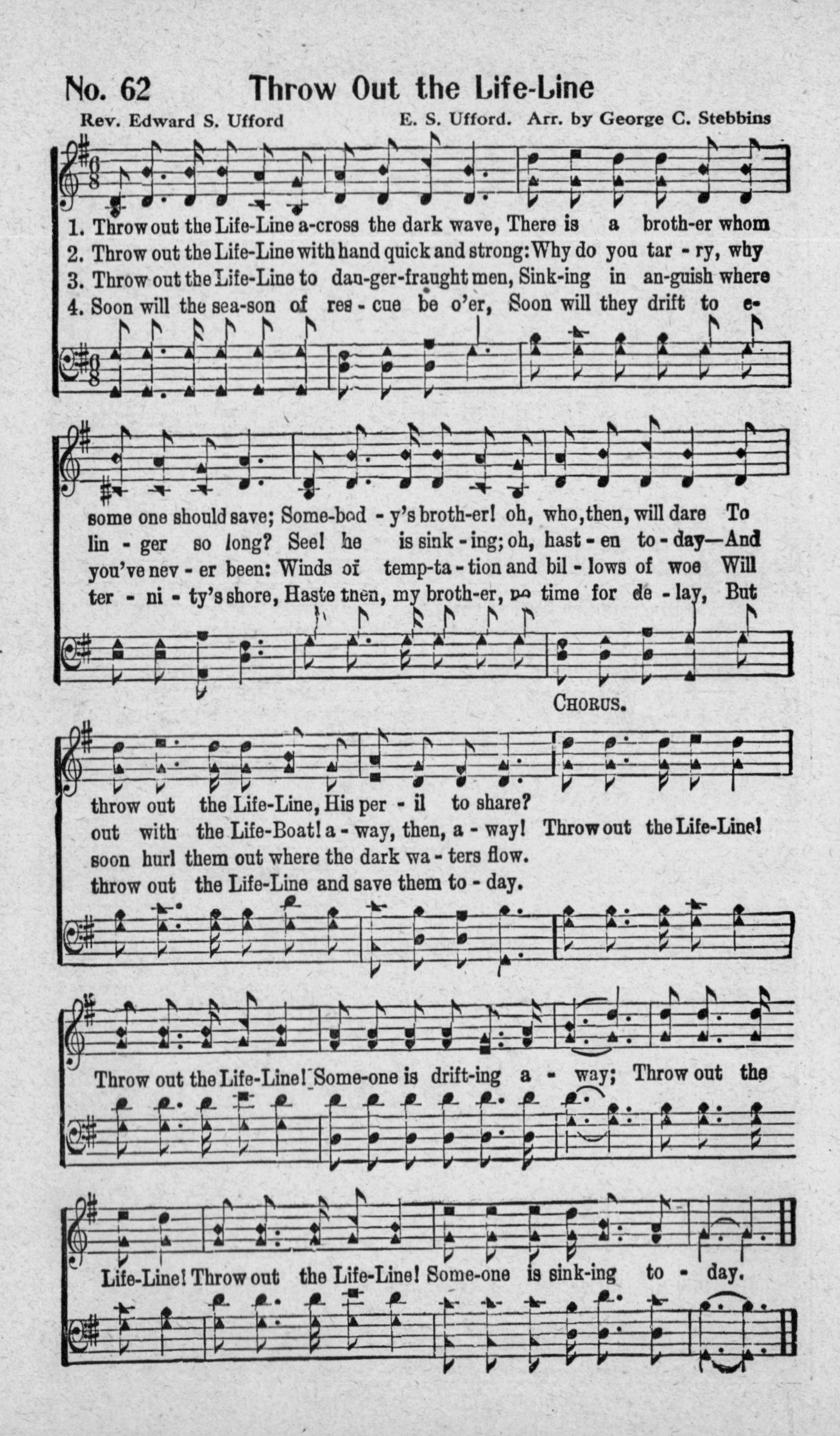
No. 62 Throw Out the Life-Line
Rev. Edward S. Ufford
E. S. Ufford. Arr. by George C. Stebbins
1. Throw out the Life-Line a-cross the dark wave, There is a broth-er whom
2. Throw out the Life-Line with hand quick and strong: Why do you tar - ry, why
3. Throw out the Life-Line to dan-ger-fraught men, Sink-ing in an-guish where
4. Soon will the sea-son of res - cue be o'er, Soon will they drift to e-
some one should save; Some-bod - y's broth-er! oh, who, then, will dare To
lin - ger so long? See! he is sink - ing; oh, hast - en to - day—And
you've nev - er been: Winds of temp-ta - tion and bil - lows of woe Will
ter - ni - ty's shore, Haste then, my broth-er, no time for de - lay, But
throw out the Life-Line, His per - il to share?
out with the Life-Boat! a - way, then, a - way!
soon hurl them out where the dark wa - ters flow.
throw out the Life-Line and save them to - day.
Chorus.
Throw out the Life-Line!
Throw out the Life-Line! Some-one is drift-ing a - way; Throw out the
Life-Line! Throw out the Life-Line! Some-one is sink-ing to - day.

No. 63
Heaven Holds All to Me
T. S. T.
Tillit S. Teddlie
1. Earth holds no treas-ures but per - ish with us - ing, How - ev - er
2. Out on the hills of that won-der - ful coun-try, Hap-py, con-
3. Why should I long for the world and its sor-rows, When in that
pre - cious they be; Yet there's a coun - try to which I am
tent - ed and free, Loved ones are wait - ing and watch-ing my
home o'er the sea Mil - lions are sing - ing the won - der - ful
go - ing, Heav-en holds all to me.
com - ing, Heav-en holds all to me.
sto - ry? Heav-en holds all to me.
Chorus
Heav- en holds all to
me, Bright-er its glo - ry will be; Joy with- out
to me,
p
m
rit.
meas - ure will be my treas-ure, Heav-en holds all to me.

No. 64 Tell Me the Story of Jesus

Fanny J. Crosby Jno. R. Sweney

1. Tell me the sto - ry of Je- sus, Write on my heart ev -'ry word;
2. Fast-ing a - lone in the des-ert, Tell of the days that are passed,
3. Tell of the cross where they nailed Him, Writhing in an- guish and pain;

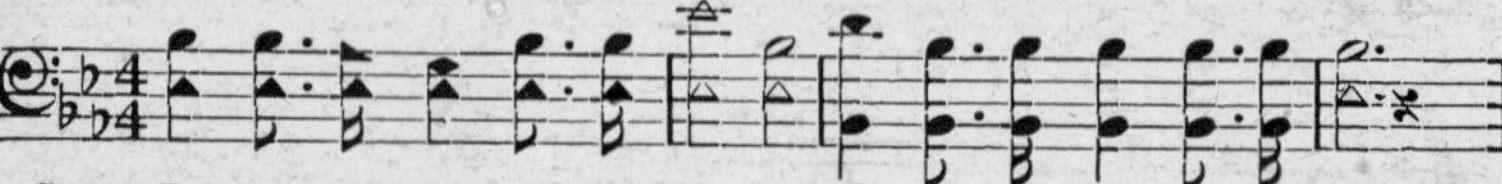

CHO.—Tell me the sto - ry of Je- sus, Write on my heart ev -'ry word;

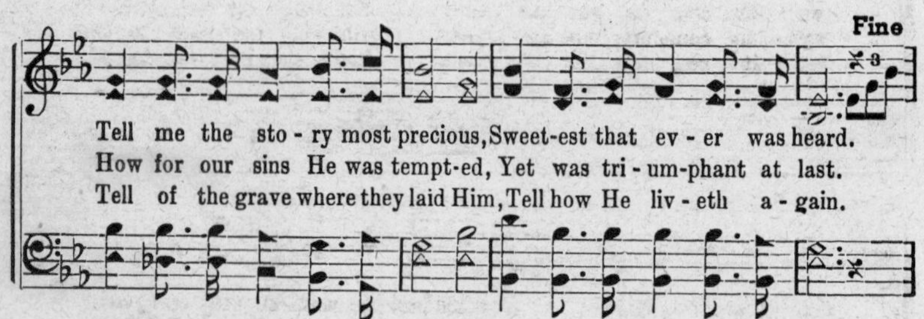
Fine

Tell me the sto - ry most precious, Sweet-est that ev - er was heard.
How for our sins He was tempt-ed, Yet was tri - um-phant at last.
Tell of the grave where they laid Him, Tell how He liv - eth a - gain.

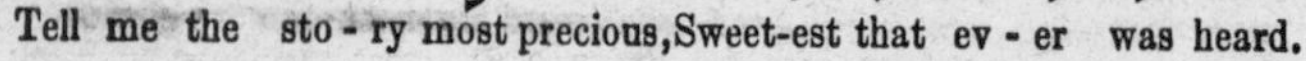

Tell me the sto - ry most precious, Sweet-est that ev - er was heard.

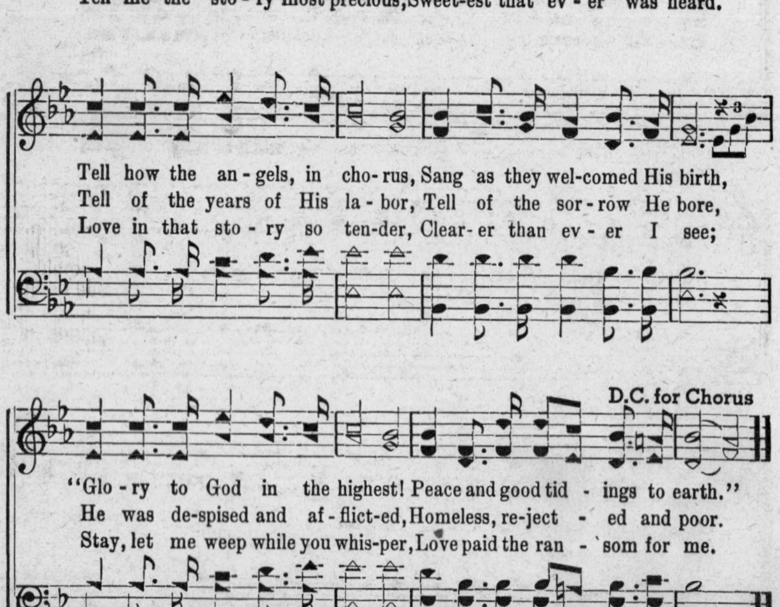
D.C. for Chorus

Tell how the an - gels, in cho- rus, Sang as they wel-comed His birth,
Tell of the years of His la - bor, Tell of the sor - row He bore,
Love in that sto - ry so ten-der, Clear- er than ev - er I see;

"Glo - ry to God in the highest! Peace and good tid - ings to earth."
He was de-spised and af - flict-ed, Homeless, re-ject - ed and poor.
Stay, let me weep while you whis-per, Love paid the ran - som for me.

No. 65 If I Could Hear My Mother Pray Again
James Rowe
J. W. Vaughan, owner
J. W. Vaughan
1. How sweet and hap - py seem those days of which I dream, When mem-o-
2. She used to pray that I on Je - sus would re - ly, And al - ways
3. With - in the old home-place, her pa - tient, smil-ing face Was al - ways
4. Her work on earth is done, the life-crown has been won, And she will
ry re - calls them now and then! And with what rap-ture sweet my
walk the shin - ing gos - pel way; So trust - ing still His love I
spreading com-fort, hope and cheer; And when she used to sing to
be at rest with Him a - bove; And some glad morn-ing, she I
Fine
wea - ry heart would beat, If I could hear my moth-er pray a - gain.
seek that home a-bove, Where I shall meet my moth-er some glad day.
her e - ter - nal King, It was the songs the an - gels loved to hear.
know will wel-come me To that e - ter - nal home of peace and love.
D.S.—so much to me, If I could hear my moth-er pray a - gain.
Chorus
If I could hear my moth-er pray a- gain, If I could
If I could on- ly If I could on- ly
If I could on - ly hear
D.S.
hear her ten- der voice as then! So glad I'd be, 'twould mean
hap- py I should
So hap - py I should be

No. 66 If the Light Has Gone Out
Copyright, 1917, by The Trio Music Co., in "The Guiding Star"
C. J. W.
Used by permission
Curtis J. Williams
Very slowly
1. When the sun of your life has gone down And the clouds in the west turn to gold, (turn to gold,) End-less night then to you will have come, If the light has gone out in your soul.
2. When you come to the end of the way, And life's sto-ry for you has been told, (has been told,) O how sad all to you will ap-pear, If the light has gone out in your soul.
3. When be-fore judgment's bar you shall stand, And the deeds that have here had con-trol, (had con-trol,) Good and e-vil ap-pear, O what then, If the light has gone out in your soul?
Fine
D.S.—still! (how still!) When the light has gone out of your soul.
Chorus
O just think how in death you will feel, you will feel, With the light grow-ing dim in your soul; in your soul; O how lone-ly 'twill be! O how
D.S.

No. 67 More Abundantly.
T. H.
COPYRIGHT, 1914, BY W. B. ROSE, AGENT.
Thoro Harris.
1. Are you trusting Jesus, All a-long the way? Does He grow more precious
2. For His matchless favor Mag-ni - fy the name Of our gra-cious Sav-ior
3. Come to Him believing, Hark-en to His call; All from Him re-ceiv-ing,
To your heart each day? Are you His dis - ci - ple? Test His word and see,
Who from glo-ry came; Let the saints a-dore Him For this wondrous word,
Yield to Him your all; Je - sus will ac-cept you When to Him you flee;
He will give the Spir-it More a - bun-dant - ly.
Sealing our redemption Thro' the crimson flood.
He will grant His blessing More a - bun-dant - ly.
CHORUS.
More a - bun-dant-ly,
More and more a - bun - dant - ly,
more a-bun-dant-ly, "That they might have life, and more abundantly;" More a-
more and more a-bun-dant-ly,
More and more a-
bun-dant-ly, more a-bun-dant-ly, "That they might have life, and more a-bun-dant-ly.
bun-dant-ly, more and more abundantly,

No. 68 How Beautiful Heaven Must Be

Rev. A. S. Bridgewater — A. P. Bland, owner — A. P. Bland

1. We read of a place that's called heaven, It's made for the pure and the free;
2. In heav-en, no drooping nor pin - ing, No wish-ing for else-where to be;
3. Pure wa-ters of life there are flow-ing, And all who will drink may be free;
4. The an-gels so sweet-ly are sing - ing, Up there by the beau-ti - ful sea;
These truths in God's word He has giv - en, How beau-ti-ful heav-en must be.
God's light is for- ev - er there shin - ing, How beau-ti-ful heav-en must be.
Rare jew- els of splen-dor are glow - ing, How beau-ti-ful heav-en must be.
Sweet chords from their gold harps are ring - ing, How beau-ti-ful heav-en must be.
Chorus
How beau-ti- ful heav-en must be,...... Sweet home of the hap-py and free;
must be,
Fair ha -ven of rest for the wea - ry, How beau-ti-ful heav-en must be.

No. 69 When I Walk Up the Streets of Gold

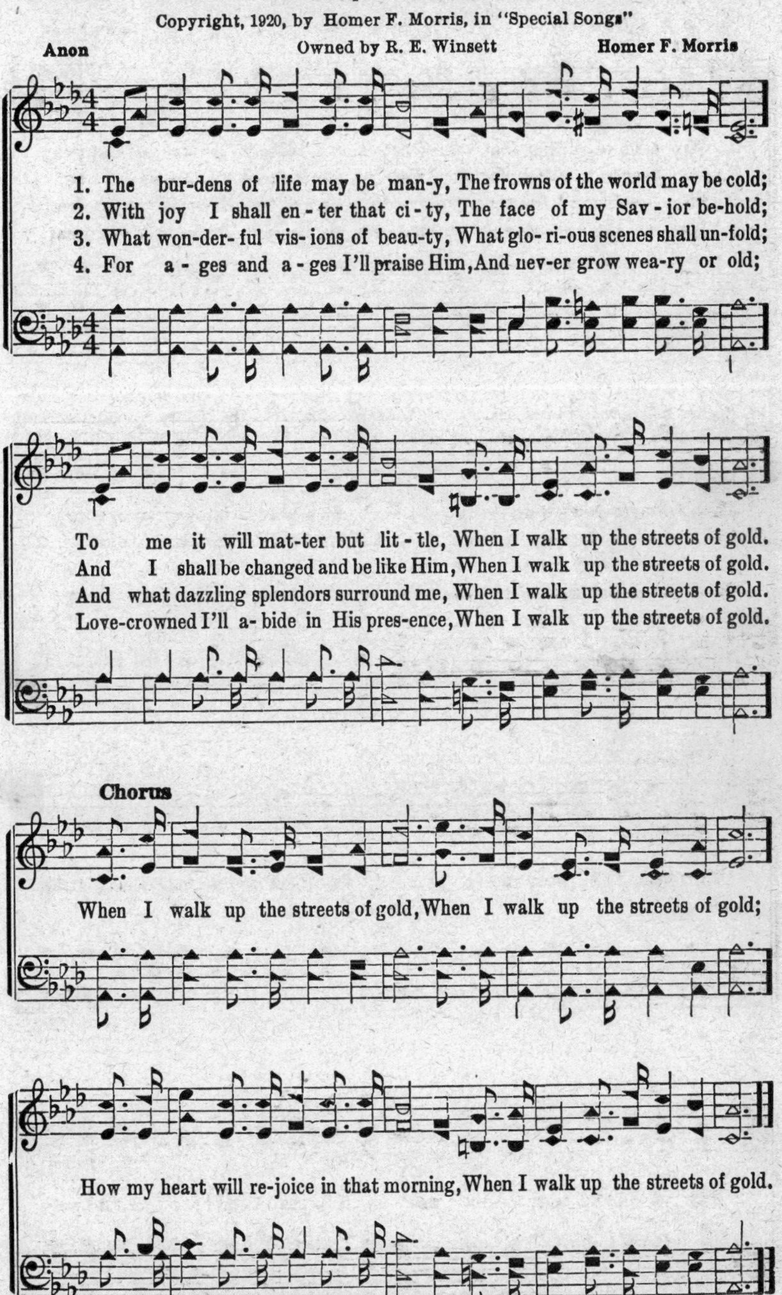
Copyright, 1920, by Homer F. Morris, in "Special Songs"
Anon
Owned by R. E. Winsett
Homer F. Morris
1. The bur-dens of life may be man-y, The frowns of the world may be cold;
2. With joy I shall en-ter that ci-ty, The face of my Sav-ior be-hold;
3. What won-der-ful vis-ions of beau-ty, What glo-ri-ous scenes shall un-fold;
4. For a-ges and a-ges I'll praise Him, And nev-er grow wea-ry or old;
To me it will mat-ter but lit-tle, When I walk up the streets of gold.
And I shall be changed and be like Him, When I walk up the streets of gold.
And what dazzling splendors surround me, When I walk up the streets of gold.
Love-crowned I'll a-bide in His pres-ence, When I walk up the streets of gold.
Chorus
When I walk up the streets of gold, When I walk up the streets of gold;
How my heart will re-joice in that morning, When I walk up the streets of gold.

No. 70

Jesus Paid it All

M. S. Shaffer — Stamps-Baxter Music and Ptg. Co., owners — Samuel W. Beazley

1. Gone is all my debt of sin, A great change is bro't within, And to live I
2. O I hope to please Him now, Light of joy is on my brow, As at His dear
3. Sin - ner, not for me a-lone Did the Son of God a-tone; Your debt, too, He
now be-gin, Ris-en from the fall; Yet the debt I did not pay Some one
feet I bow, Safe with-in His love. Mak-ing His the debt I owed, Free-dom
made His own, On the cru-el tree. Come to Him with all your sin; Be as
died for me one day, Sweeping all the debt a-way, Je-sus paid it all.
true He has bestowed; So I'm sing-ing on the road To my home a-bove.
white as snow with-in; Full sal-va-tion you may win And re-joice with me.
Chorus Bass to predominate in power.
Je-sus died and paid it all, yes, On the cross of Cal-va-ry, O
Je - sus died and paid it On the cross of Cal - va-ry,
And my ston-y heart was melt-ed At His dy-ing, dy-ing call
And my heart was melt - ed At His dy-ing call;

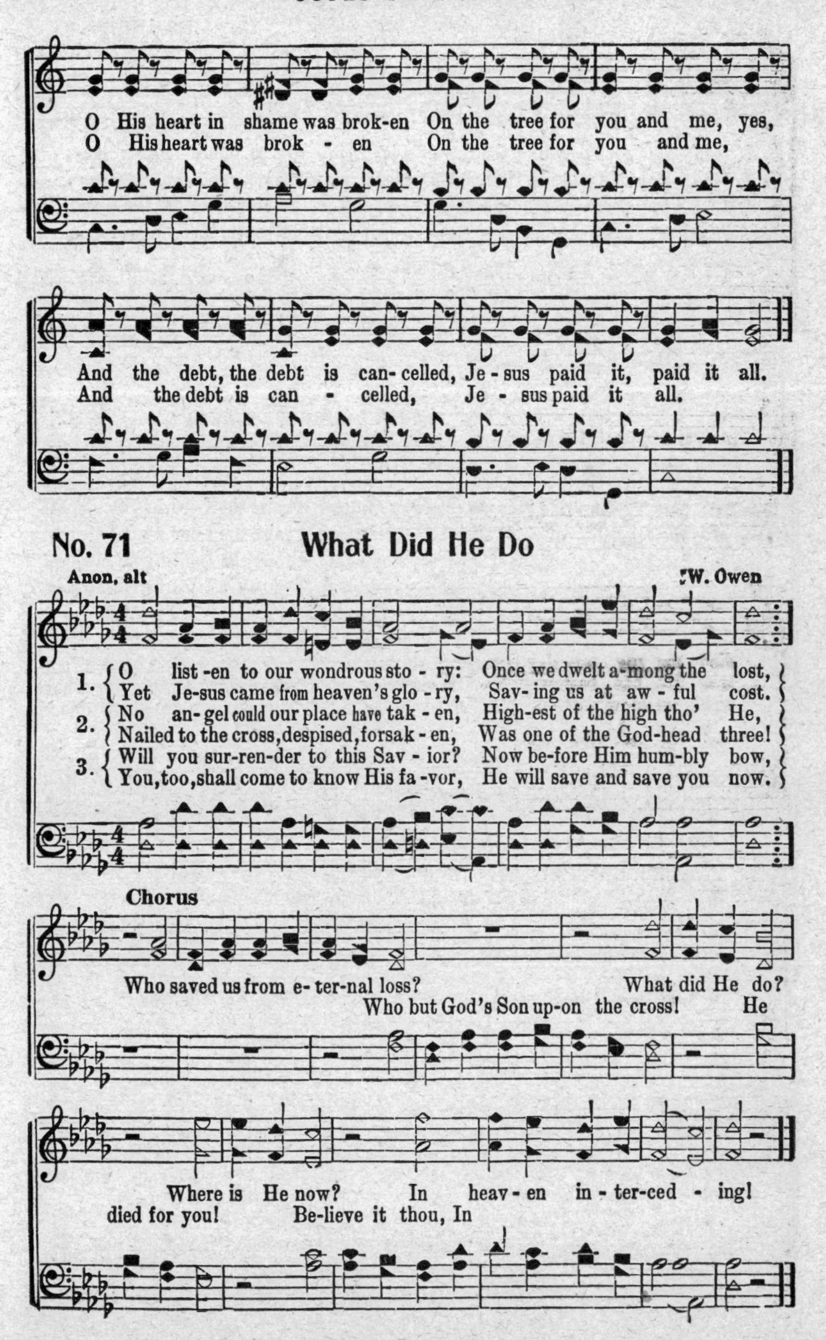
Jesus Paid it All
O His heart in shame was brok-en On the tree for you and me, yes,
O His heart was brok - en On the tree for you and me,
And the debt, the debt is can-celled, Je - sus paid it, paid it all.
And the debt is can - celled, Je - sus paid it all.
No. 71
What Did He Do
Anon. alt
W. Owen
1. O list-en to our wondrous sto - ry: Once we dwelt a-mong the lost,
Yet Je-sus came from heaven's glo - ry, Sav-ing us at aw - ful cost.
2. No an-gel could our place have tak - en, High-est of the high tho' He,
Nailed to the cross, despised, forsak - en, Was one of the God-head three!
3. Will you sur-ren-der to this Sav-ior? Now be-fore Him hum-bly bow,
You, too, shall come to know His fa-vor, He will save and save you now.
Chorus
Who saved us from e- ter-nal loss? What did He do?
Who but God's Son up-on the cross! He
Where is He now? In heav - en in - ter-ced - ing!
died for you! Be-lieve it thou, In

No. 72 By His Stripes We Are Healed.

T. H. COPYRIGHT, 1914, BY THORO HARRIS. Thoro Harris.

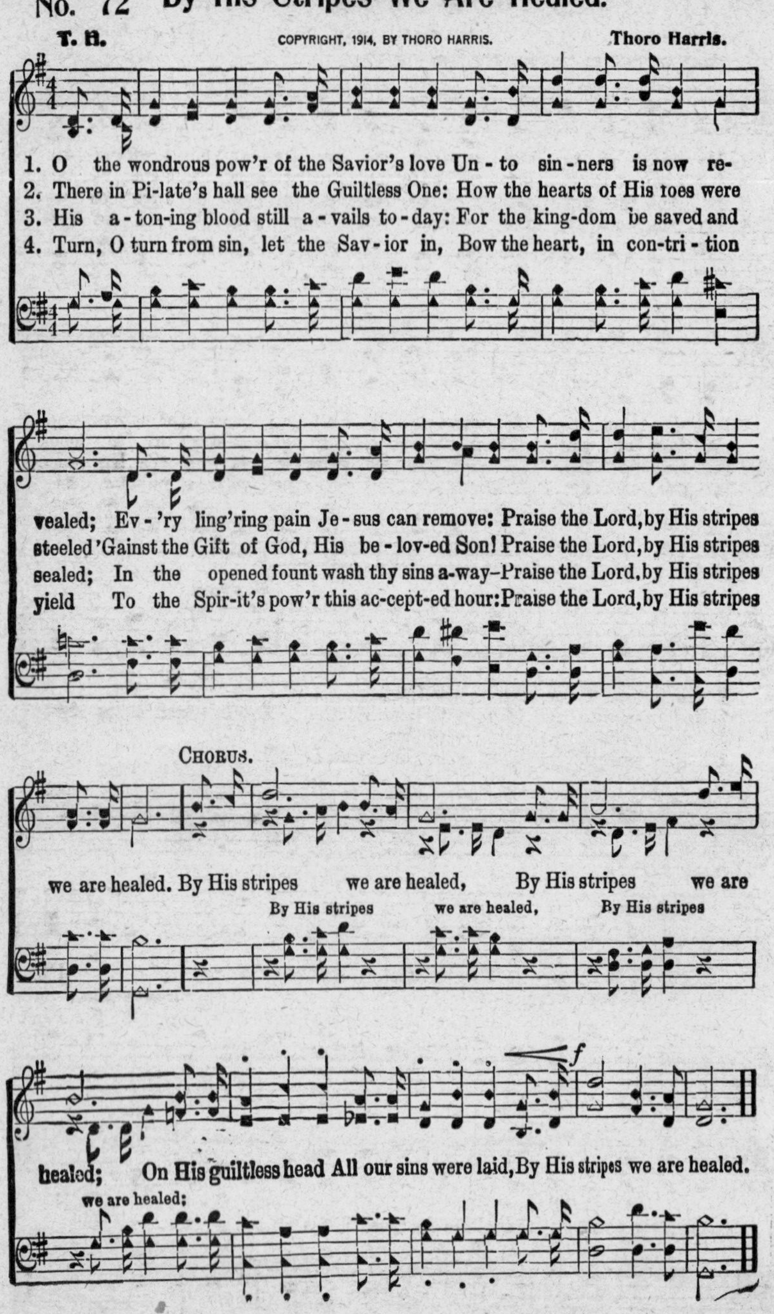
T. H.
COPYRIGHT, 1914, BY THORO HARRIS.
Thoro Harris.
1. O the wondrous pow'r of the Savior's love Un - to sin - ners is now re-
2. There in Pi-late's hall see the Guiltless One: How the hearts of His foes were
3. His a - ton-ing blood still a - vails to - day: For the king-dom be saved and
4. Turn, O turn from sin, let the Sav - ior in, Bow the heart, in con-tri - tion
vealed; Ev - 'ry ling'ring pain Je - sus can remove: Praise the Lord, by His stripes
steeled 'Gainst the Gift of God, His be - lov-ed Son! Praise the Lord, by His stripes
sealed; In the opened fount wash thy sins a-way–Praise the Lord, by His stripes
yield To the Spir-it's pow'r this ac-cept-ed hour: Praise the Lord, by His stripes
CHORUS.
we are healed. By His stripes we are healed, By His stripes we are
By His stripes we are healed, By His stripes
healed; On His guiltless head All our sins were laid, By His stripes we are healed.
we are healed;
f

No. 73 I Intend to Go Through With Him

Herbert Buffum H. F. Morris, owner Homer F. Morris

May be used as Soprano and Tenor Duet.

1. My heart is so hap - py in Je - sus my Lord, No clouds can my
2. I know man - y oth - ers have fall - en a - way, En-snared by the
3. I find His yoke eas - y, His bur - den is light, He bright-ens the
4. My friends may for - sake me and turn from my path, I'll seek not their

faith in Him dim; I've start-ed to walk in the straight narrow way,
pit - falls of sin; The ship-wrecks of faith line the shore all a - long,
shad-ows so dim; I lean on His prom-ise and draw from His grace,
fa - vor to win; His smile is suf - fi - cient and pays me for all,

I in - tend to go thru with Him.........
But I mean to go thru with Him.........
I in - tend to go thru with Him.........
I in - tend to go thru with Him. (with Him.)

Refrain

I in - tend to go thru,

I in-tend to be true Thru sunshine or thru shadows dim;....... I'll
shadows dim;

count all but loss, For Christ and the cross, I in-tend to go thru with Him.

No. 74 The Half Has Never Been Told.

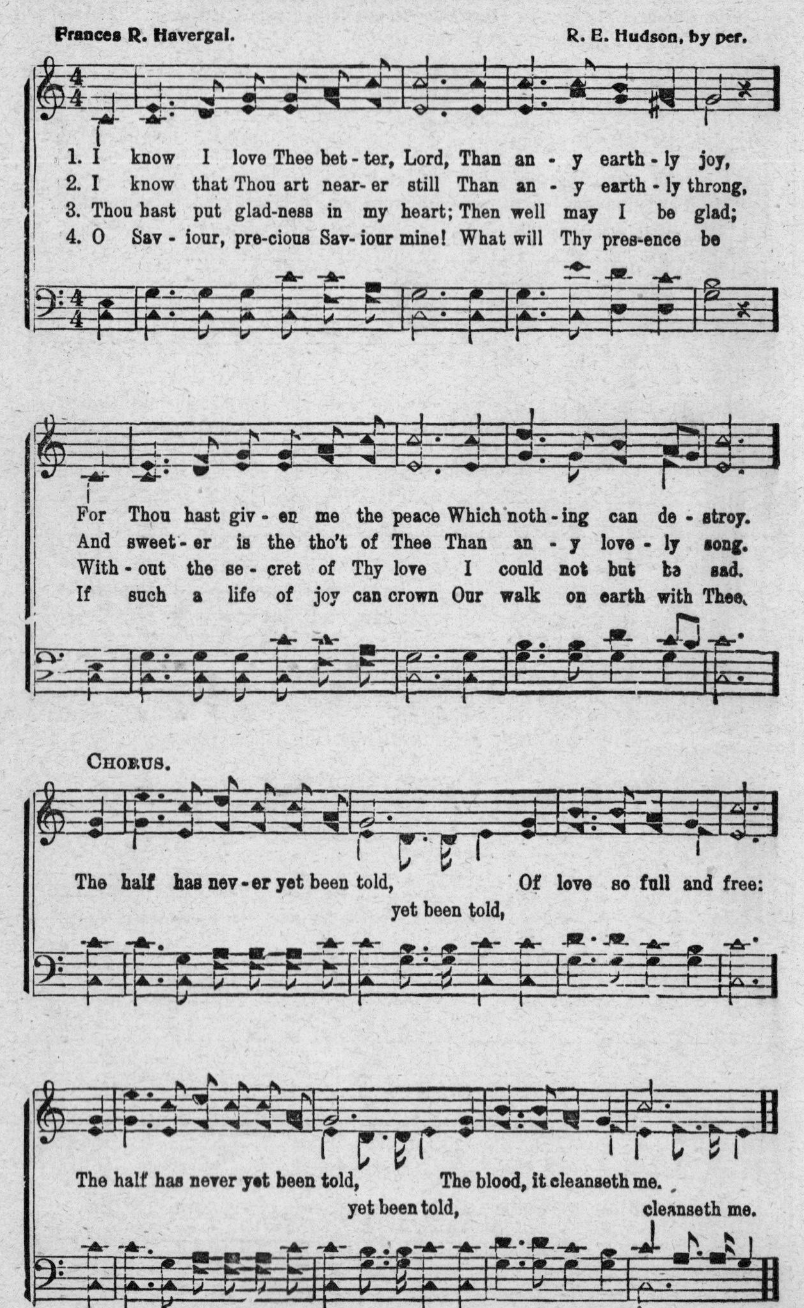

Frances R. Havergal.
R. E. Hudson, by per.
1. I know I love Thee bet-ter, Lord, Than an-y earth-ly joy,
2. I know that Thou art near-er still Than an-y earth-ly throng,
3. Thou hast put glad-ness in my heart; Then well may I be glad;
4. O Sav-iour, pre-cious Sav-iour mine! What will Thy pres-ence be
For Thou hast giv-en me the peace Which noth-ing can de-stroy.
And sweet-er is the tho't of Thee Than an-y love-ly song.
With-out the se-cret of Thy love I could not but be sad.
If such a life of joy can crown Our walk on earth with Thee.
Chorus.
The half has nev-er yet been told, Of love so full and free:
yet been told,
The half has never yet been told, The blood, it cleanseth me.
yet been told,
cleanseth me.

No. 75 Help Somebody To-day

Mrs. Frank A. Breck

Chas. H. Gabriel

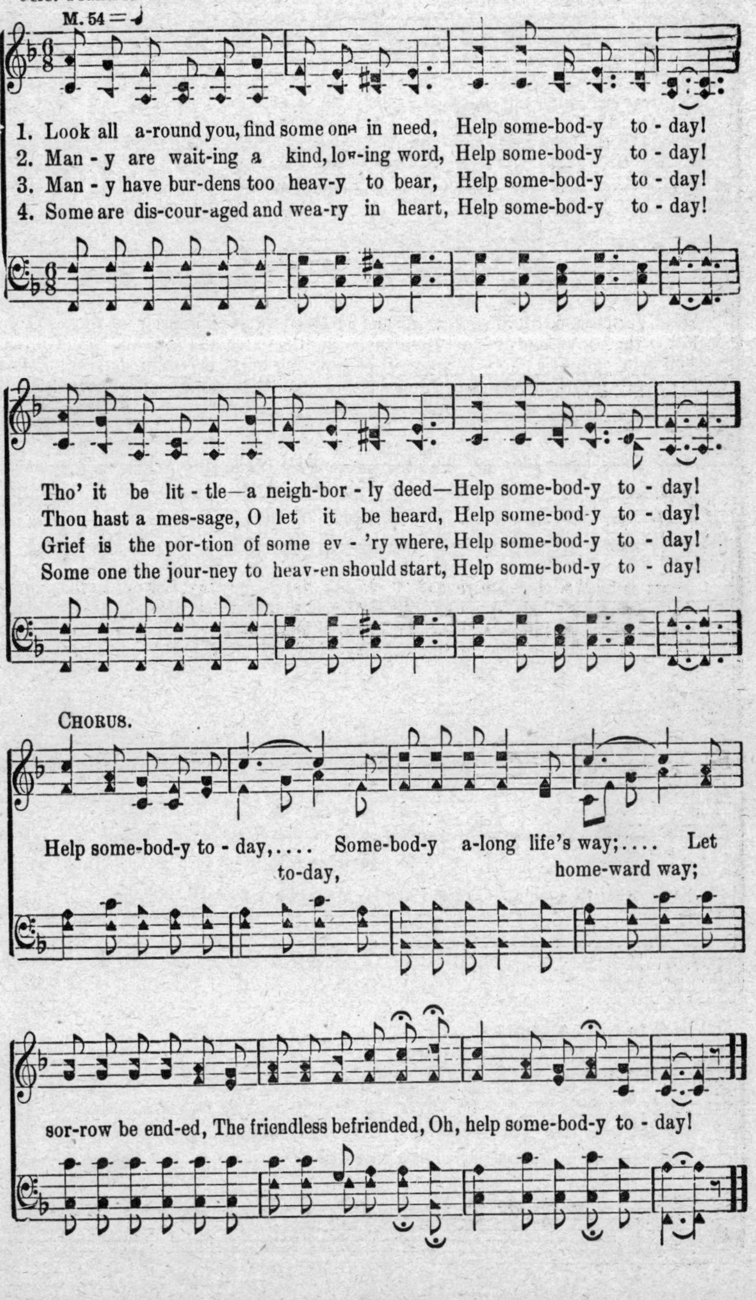

M. 54 = ♩

1. Look all a-round you, find some one in need, Help some-bod-y to - day!
2. Man - y are wait-ing a kind, lov-ing word, Help some-bod-y to - day!
3. Man - y have bur-dens too heav-y to bear, Help some-bod-y to - day!
4. Some are dis-cour-aged and wea-ry in heart, Help some-bod-y to - day!

Tho' it be lit - tle—a neigh-bor - ly deed—Help some-bod-y to - day!
Thou hast a mes-sage, O let it be heard, Help some-bod-y to - day!
Grief is the por-tion of some ev - 'ry where, Help some-bod-y to - day!
Some one the jour-ney to heav-en should start, Help some-bod-y to - day!

CHORUS.

Help some-bod-y to - day,.... Some-bod-y a-long life's way;.... Let
to-day, home-ward way;

sor-row be end-ed, The friendless befriended, Oh, help some-bod-y to - day!

No. 76 Our Lord's Return to Earth
J. M. K.
Copyright, 1904, by Myland & Kirk, R. E. Winsett, owner
J. M. Kirk
1. I am watch-ing for the com-ing of the glad mil-len-nial day,
2. Je-sus' com-ing back will be the an-swer to earth's sorr'wing cry,
3. Yes, the ran-somed of the Lord shall come to Zi-on then with joy,
4. Then the sin and sor-row, pain and death of this dark world shall cease,
When our bless-ed Lord shall come and catch His wait-ing Bride a-way; O my
For the knowledge of the Lord shall fill the earth and sea and sky; God shall
And in all His ho-ly moun-tain noth-ing hurts or shall de-stoy; Per-fect
In a glo-rious reign with Je-sus of a thou-sand years of peace; All the
heart is filled with rap-ture as I la-bor, watch and pray, For our Lord is com-ing
take a-way all sick-ness and the suff'rer's tears will dry, When our Savior shall come
peace shall reign in ev-'ry heart, and love without al-loy, Aft-er Je-sus shall come
earth is groan-ing, cry-ing for that day of sweet re-lease, For our Je-sus to come
D.S.-will be bound a thousand years, we'll have no tempter then, Aft-er Jesus shall come
Fine Chorus
back to earth a-gain. O our Lord is coming back to earth a-gain,
is com-ing back to earth a-gain,
back to earth a-gain.
D.S.
Yes, our Lord is com-ing back to earth a-gain, Sa-tan
is com-ing back to earth a-gain,

No. 77 The Eastern Gate

I. G. M. Arr. I. G. MARTIN.

1. I will meet you in the morn - ing, Just in - side the East-ern Gate,
2. If you has - ten off to glo - ry, Lin - ger near the East-ern Gate,
3. Keep your lamps all trimmed and burning, For the Bridegroom watch and wait,
4. O the joys of that glad meet - ing With the saints who for us wait,
Then be read - y, faith-ful pil - grim, Lest with you it be too late.
For I'm com-ing in the morn - ing, So you'll not have long to wait.
He'll be with us at the meet - ing, Just in - side the East - ern Gate.
What a bless-ed, hap-py meet - ing, Just in - side the East - ern Gate.
CHORUS.
I will meet you in the morning, I will meet you in the morn-ing, Just in
side the Eastern Gate o - ver there; I will meet you in the morning, I will
meet you in the morning, I will meet you in the morning o - ver there.

No. 78 When We All Get to Heaven
Mrs. J. G. W.
Mrs. J. G. Wilson
1. Sing the wondrous love of Je - sus, Sing His mer - cy and His grace;
2. While we walk the pil - grim path-way, Clouds will o - ver - spread the sky;
3. Let us then be true and faith-ful, Trust-ing, serv - ing ev -'ry day;
4. On - ward to the prize be - fore us! Soon His beau - ty we'll be - hold,
In the man-sions, bright and bless-ed, He'll pre-pare for us a place.
But when trav'ling days are o - ver Not a shad-ow, not a sigh.
Just one glimpse of Him in glo - ry Will the toils of life re - pay.
Soon the pearl - y gates will o - pen, We shall tread the streets of gold.
for us a place.
Chorus
When we all get to heav - en, What a day of re-
When we all What a
joic - ing that will be! When we all see
day of re - joic-ing that will be! When we all
Je - sus, We'll sing and shout the vic - to - ry.
and shout the vic - to - ry.

No. 79 **Victory Ahead**

Copyright, 1905, by Rev. William Grum
W. G.
Owned by R. E. Winsett
Rev. William Grum
1. When the hosts of Is - ra - el, led by God, Round the walls of Jer - i - cho
2. Dav - id, with a shepherd's sling and five stones, Met the gi - ant on the field
3. Dan - iel prayed un-to the Lord thrice each day, Then un - to the li-on's den
4. Oft - en with the car-nal mind I was tried, Ask-ing for de - liv - er-ance
5. When like those who've gone before to that land, By death's riv-er cold and dark
soft - ly trod; Trusting in the Lord, they felt the conq'ror's tread, By faith they
all a - lone; Trusting in the Lord, he knew what God had said, By faith he
led the way; Trusting in the Lord, he did not fear or dread, By faith he
oft I cried, Trusting in the Lord, I reck-on'd I was dead, By faith I
I shall stand; Trusting in the Lord, I will not fear or dread, By faith I
Chorus
saw the vic - to - ry a-head.
saw the vic - to - ry a-head.
saw the vic - to - ry a-head. Vic-to - ry a-head! Vic - to - ry a- head!
saw the vic - to - ry a-head.
see the vic - to - ry a-head.
Thru the blood of Je - sus, vic - to - ry a-head; Trusting in the Lord, I
hear the conq'rors tread, By faith I see the vic - to - ry a - head.

No. 80

Go Into the Field

Brown Rowland | Copyright, 1944. Renewal. The Stamps-Baxter Music Co., owners | Samuel W. Beazley

1. Stand no lon-ger i - dle, heed the call; Go to work for Je-sus, one and all;
2. There to shield and help you He will be; Fruitage of your la-bors you shall see;
3. Je - sus will re-ward for what you do, Life's fair crown of glo-ry give to you,

Fields are wait-ing for your hands to-day, Take up your sickles and speed a-way.
His dear voice shall cheer you thru the day; Sing-ing a car - ol, O speed a-way.
Per - fect rest when ends life's lit-tle day; Reap-ers, get read-y and speed a-way.

Chorus

Go in - to the field, gath-er in the yield, La-bor for the Lord,
Go, ... Go, ...
Go in - to the field, gath - er in the yield, La - bor for the Lord,

gain the great re-ward; Reapers, the hours are speeding, Jesus your help is needing,
gain the great reward,

Shall He call in vain? Go in-to the field, reap the golden yield,
in vain? Go, ...
Go in - to the field, reap the golden yield.

Go Into the Field

Heed His lov-ing plea, true to Je - sus be; Love for the
Go, ...
Heed His lov-ing plea, true to Je-sus be;
Master showing, work while the sun is glowing, Gather now the grain. (golden grain.)
No. 81
I'll Be Ready
Copyright, 1936, by Shaw Eiland. Renewal
The Stamps-Baxter Music Co., owners
B. W. Pirtle
F. L. Eiland
1. O 'tis sweet to sing this sto - ry, I'll be read-y when He comes;
2. All I am to Him I'm giv - ing, I'll be read-y when He comes;
3. Striving on, His will o - bey - ing, I'll be read-y when He comes;
4. Sin-ners there in dark-ness stray-ing, O be read-y when He comes;
Fine
It to tell is all my glo - ry, I'll be read - y when He comes.
Day by day for Him I'm liv - ing, I'll be read - y when He comes.
Working, watching, ev - er pray-ing, I'll be read - y when He comes.
Do not far - ther risk de - lay - ing, But be read - y when He comes.
D.S.—O 'tis sweet to tell the sto - ry, I'll be read - y when He comes.
Chorus
D.S.
I'll be read - y when He comes, I'll be read - y when He comes;

No. 82

I'm Not Asnamed

E. M. B. E. M. Bartlett

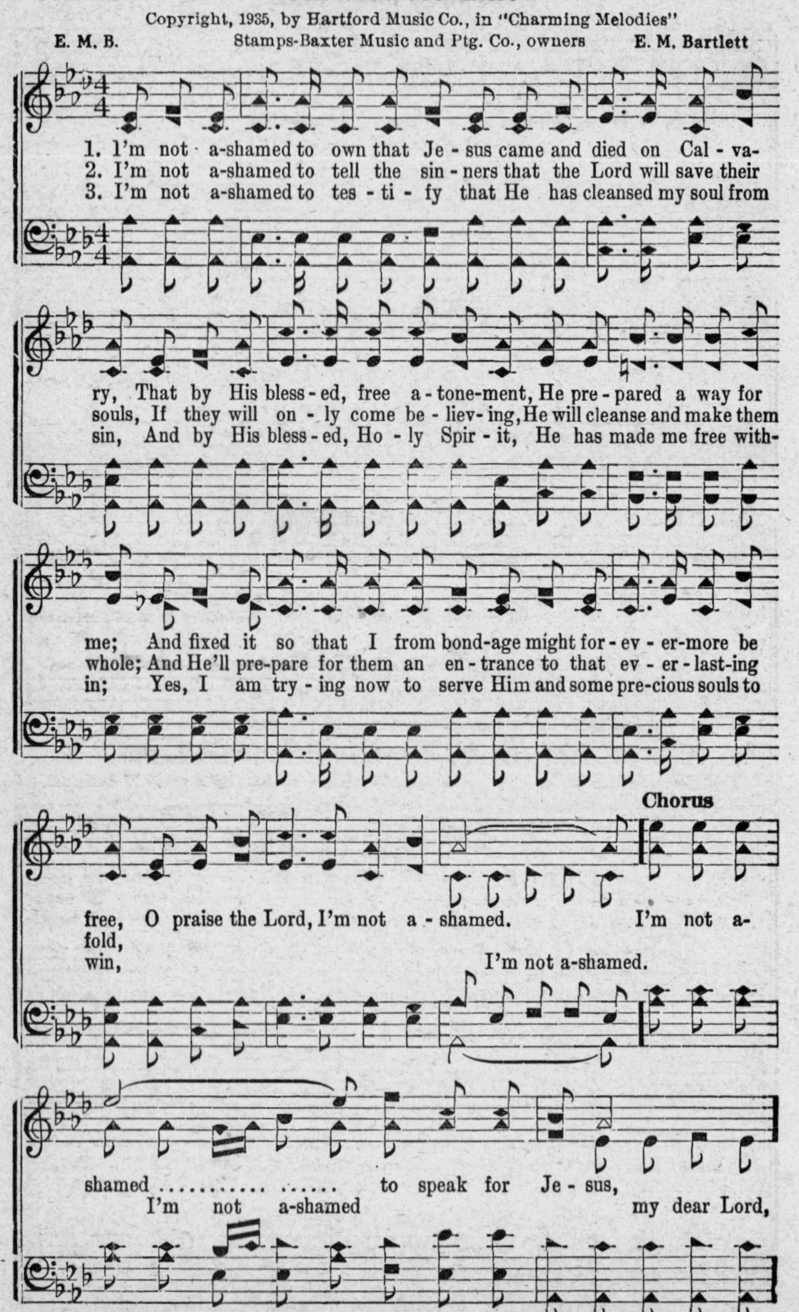
1. I'm not a-shamed to own that Je - sus came and died on Cal - va-
2. I'm not a-shamed to tell the sin - ners that the Lord will save their
3. I'm not a-shamed to tes - ti - fy that He has cleansed my soul from
ry, That by His bless - ed, free a - tone-ment, He pre - pared a way for
souls, If they will on - ly come be - liev - ing, He will cleanse and make them
sin, And by His bless - ed, Ho - ly Spir - it, He has made me free with-
me; And fixed it so that I from bond-age might for - ev - er-more be
whole; And He'll pre-pare for them an en - trance to that ev - er - last-ing
in; Yes, I am try - ing now to serve Him and some pre-cious souls to
free, O praise the Lord, I'm not a - shamed.
fold,
win,
I'm not a-shamed.
Chorus
I'm not a-
shamed .... to speak for Je - sus,
I'm not a-shamed
my dear Lord,

I'm Not Ashamed
I'm not a-shamed .... to praise His name; ....
I'm not a-shamed to praise His name, to praise His name;
I'm not a - shamed.......... to own His bless-ings,
I'm not a-shamed to own His blessings, praise His name,
O praise the Lord,...... ..... I'm not a - shamed. ....
O praise the Lord, I'm not a-shamed, I'm not ashamed.
No. 83 I Am Bound For the Promised Land
Rev. Samuel Stennet
Rev. 21 : 2.
Arr. by Rev. E. M. Parnum
1. On Jordan's storm - y banks I stand, And cast a wish - ful eye,
2. O'er all those wide ex - tended plains Shines one e - ter - nal day;
3. When shall I reach that hap - py place, And be for - ev - er blest!
Cho.—I am bound for the promised land, I am bound for the promised land;
'Tward Ca - naan's fair and hap - py land, Where my pos - ses - sions lie.
There God the Son for - ev - er reigns, And scat - ters night a - way.
When shall I see my Fa - ther's face, And in His bos - om rest?
O . who will come and go with me, I am bound for the prom-ised land.

No. 84
Sweeping Through the Gates
Copyright, 1890, by E. T. Pound, J. L. Moore, owner
Arr. by R. E. W.
J. L. Moore
1. I am now a child of God, I've been wash'd in Je - sus' blood, I am
2. Oh, the bless - ed Lord of light Now up - holds me by His might, And His
3. I'll go sweeping thru the gate, Where the bless - ed for me wait, Where the
4. Christ will burst my pris - on bars, And I'll soar be-yond the stars, To my
watching and I'm longing while I wait; Soon on wings of love I'll fly, To a
arms en - fold and comfort while I wait; I am lean - ing on His breast; O the
wea - ry workers rest for - ev-er-more, When the strife on earth is done, And the
Father's house, the bright and blest estate; When the morn e-ter-nal breaks, And the
D.S.—In the blood of Calv'ry's Lamb, Saved from
Fine
home be-yond the sky, To my wel-come, I'll go sweeping thru the gates.
sweetness of this rest! Hal - le - lu - jah! I'll go sweeping thru the gates.
crown of life is won, Oh, the glo - ry of that cit - y just be - fore!
song immortal wakes, Wash'd in Je - sus' blood, I'll sweep on thru the gates.
ev - 'ry stain I am, Hal - le - lu jah! I'll go sweeping thru the gates.
Chorus
Sweep - - ing thru the gates,
Sweep - ing thru the gates; I'll go sweep-ing thru the gates;
D.S.
Sweep - - ing thru the gates.
Sweep-ing thru the gates; I'll go sweep - ing thru the gates.

No. 85 All Alone

G. T. B. G. T. Byrd

1. On Mount Ol - ive's sa - cred brow Je - sus spent the night in pray'r,
2. There are days I'd like to be with the sanc - ti - fied and blest,
3. There are days to fast and pray for the pil - grims in his way,
4. Where a heart is brok - en up with the bit - ter, woe - ful cup,
He's the pat-tern for us all, all a - lone, If we'll on - ly steal a- way,
There are days I like to be all a - lone, These can nev - er grace im-part,
There are days to be with Christ all a - lone, We can tell Him all our grief,
There's the time to go to Christ all a - lone, In our bless-ed Lord di - vine,
in some por-tion of the day, We will find it al-ways pays to be a - lone.
to my wea-ry, sin-toss'd heart, There are days I'd like to be just all a - lone.
He will give us quick re-lief, There are days I'd like to be just all a - lone.
there is peace and joy sublime, When we take our sor-rows all to Him a - lone.
Chorus
There are days I'd like to be all a - lone with Christ my Lord,
3
3
3
1
2
I can tell Him of my trou- bles all a - lone; all a - lone.

No. 86 Talk It Over With Jesus

Thomas Ramsey — Virgil O. Stamps

1. O broth - er strug-gling on-ward 'neath a bur - den of de - spair,
2. If you are per - se - cut - ed by some mem-bers of your church,
3. When you are grow-ing fee - ble from the man - y years of pain,
Your bod - y grow-ing weak-er with your trou - ble and your care;
When friends have turned a - gainst you and your good name would be - smirch;
When age has wrecked your bod - y and your health you can't re - gain;
When your en - e - mies ap-proach you, do not fal - ter in the fight,
If it seems your soul is sink - ing and your way is dark as night,
If it seems the way is dark - er from the dim-ness of your sight,
Chorus
Talk it o - ver with Je - sus, He will make it right. Talk it o - ver with
Je - sus and com-fort will be found, Tell Him all of your trou-bles,
joy there will be found,

Talk It Over With Jesus
wheth-er day or night; Get your knees acquainted with the cold and rock-y
cold and
ground, Talk it o - ver with Je - sus, He will make it right.
rock- y ground,
No. 87 Sitting At the Feet of Jesus
Rev. K. C. Minter
Minter and Davis, owners
J. W. Davis
1. Sit - ting at the feet of Je - sus, Watching, waiting ev -'ry day; Trust-ing
2. List'ning at the feet of Je - sus, His com-mand to go or stay; Trust-ing
3. Seek-ing still the feet of Je - sus, I would seek no oth- er place; For 'tis
4. When the toils of life are o - ver, When my race on earth is run; May the
Fine
Chorus
in His grace and pow-er, Safe to keep me all the way.
al - ways in His wisdom, Safe to guide when I o - bey. Sit-ting at the feet of
there I claim the prom-ise Of the full-ness of His grace.
eve'ning shadows gath'ring Find me there when day is done.
D.S.—Drive the shadows from my way.
D.S.
Je - sus, Where I love to kneel and pray, Till His good-ness and His glo - ry,

No. 88 Everybody Will Be Happy Over There.
E. M. B.
COPYRIGHT BY E. M. BARTLETT. USED BY PERMISSION.
E. M. Bartlett.
1. There's a hap-py land of prom-ise o-ver in the great be-yond, Where the saved of earth shall soon the glo-ry share; Where the souls of men shall enter and live on for-ev-er-more, Ev-'ry-bod-y will be hap-py o-ver there.
2. Moth-ers, fa-thers, sis-ters, brothers will be singing 'round the throne, In that land where no one ev-er knows a care; And the Christians of all a-ges will join in the tri-umph song, Ev-'ry-bod-y will be hap-py o-ver there.
3. We will hear no-bod-y pray-ing and no mourning in that land, For no bur-dens there will be for us to bear; All the peo-ple will be singing "Glo-ry, glo-ry to the Lamb," Ev-'ry-bod-y will be hap-py o-ver there.
4. There we'll meet the One who saved us and who kept us by His grace, And who brought us to that land so bright and fair; We will praise His name for-ev-er as we look up-on His face, Ev-'ry-bod-y will be hap-py o-ver there.
Refrain.
Ev-'ry-bod-y will be hap-py, will be hap-py o-ver there; We will shout and
Ev-'ry-bod-y will be hap-py o-ver there, o-ver there,....
We will shout and sing His prais-es thro' the

Everybody Will Be Happy Over There
Sing His praise, Ev-'ry-bod-y will be hap-py o-ver there,
nev-er end-ing a-ges,
No. 89
Christ Arose
Copyright, 1916, by Mary Runyon Lowry. Renewal
Used by permission
R. L.
Robert Lowry
1. Low in the grave He lay—Je-sus, my Sav-ior! Wait-ing the com-ing day—
2. Vain-ly they watch His bed—Je-sus, my Sav-ior! Vain-ly they seal the dead—
3. Death can-not keep His prey—Je-sus, my Sav-ior! He tore the bars a-way—
Chorus
Je-sus, my Lord! Up from the grave He arose, With a mighty triumph o'er His
He arose,
foes; He a-rose a victor from the dark domain, And He lives forever with His
He a-rose
saints to reign; He a-rose! He a-rose! Hal-le-lu-jah! Christ arose!
He a-rose! He a-rose!

No. 90
I'll Live In Glory
Copyright, 1936, in "Songs of Praise No. 5"
Owned by J. M. Henson
J. M. H.
J. M. Henson
1. I'd like to stay here long-er than man's al-lot-ted days And watch the fleeting
2. I want to be of serv-ice a-long this pil-grim way, And lead the lost to
3. The end I know is near-ing -- by faith I look a-way To yon-der home su-
chang-es of life's un-e-ven ways, But if my Sav-ior calls me to
Je-sus as fer-vent-ly I pray; As day by day I trav-el I'll
per-nal—the land of end-less day; I'll cling to Him for-ev-er, and
that sweet home on high, I'll live with Him for-ev-er in Glo-ry by and by.
keep Him ev-er nigh, And live with Him for-ev-er in Glo-ry by and by.
look be-yond the sky, And spend the end-less a-ges in Glo-ry by and by.
Chorus
O yes, I'll live in Glo-ry by and by, I'll tell and sing love's
live in Glo-ry by and by,
sto-ry there on high; There with my dear Redeemer no
tell loves's sto-ry there on high; there no

I'll Live in Glory
more to die, O yes, I'll live in glo-ry by and by.
no more to die, glo-ry by and by.
No. 91
Some Day
J. Graydon Hall
James D. Vaughan and H. E. Barnett, owners
H. E. Barnett
1. My tri-als here on earth will cease, Some day,..... some day;
2. No more in dark-ness I will roam,
3. Those gone be-fore me I shall meet,
4. My lov-ing Sav-ior I shall see,
Some day, some hap-py day;
And I will have un-end-ing peace, Some day,..... some day.
But rest e-ter-nal-ly at home,
My loved ones will my spir-it greet,
With Him in glo-ry I shall be,
Some day, some hap-py day.
Chorus
Some day, some hap-py day, From sin..... set free;
Some day,
From sin my soul is free;
I'll live with Christ for aye, Some day,..... some day.
I'll live
Some day, some hap-py day.

No. 92 The Cross of Calvary
Copyright, 1917. by Hildebrand-Burnett Co.
Stamps-Baxter Music Co., owners
E. G. Coleman
Howard E. Smith
1. Up - on the rug-ged moun-tain side, Our Sav-ior trudged a-long, Sur-round-ed
2. The sun re-fused to shine up - on that scene on Cal - va - ry, Where Je - sus
3. This ten - der, lov-ing Sav - ior, still in - vit- ing us to come, Is call - ing
by the an - gry mob, and crowd-ed by the throng; But pa-tient - ly He
died in ag - o - ny to set the sin - ner free; Our Sav - ior, brok - en
from His throne a-bove, O wand'ring child, come home; Be-lieve on Him, He
bore the cross to ran-som you and me, He went to pay the price up-
heart - ed, died that we might look and live, And in His dy - ing breath He
paid the price on rug - ged Cal - va - ry, He bore the cross, He gave His
D.S.—He paid the price up - on the
Fine Chorus
on the cross of Cal - va - ry.
cried, "oh, Father please forgive." Up-on the cross of Cal - va - ry, He died, And
life to ran-som you and me.
lone - ly cross of Cal-va-ry.
D.S.
heav-en's pearly gates were opened wide; He gave His life to ransom you and me—

No, 93
Sometime
Copyright, 1925, by Jas. C. Moore
Mrs. J. M. Hunter
Morris-Henson, Moore, owners
Jas. C. Moore
Good as Soprano and Alto Duet
1. Some-time the shad-ows will be gone, Sometime will come the gold-en dawn,
2. Some-time I'll meet my friends a-gain, For - ev - er safe from death and pain,
3. O grace di - vine! O love un - told! O crowns of life! O harps of gold!
Some-time I'll lift mine eyes and see The man-sions He's pre-
With my dear Sav - ior I shall be In man-sions He's pre-
My wel - come will be glad and free In man-sions He's pre-
pared for me.
Chorus
O gold - en time, ... O hap - py
O gold - en time,
day, ... O pre-cious home not far a - way; What
O hap-py day, not far a - way;
wondrous joy when I shall see The man-sion He's pre-pared for me.

No. 94 On the Jericho Road

D. S. McC. — Donald S. McCrossan
Arr. by Luther G. Presley

Not too fast

1. As you trav-el a - long .... on the Jer - i - cho road,.... ....
2. On the Jer - i - cho road .... blind Bar-tim-ae - us sat,..........
3. O broth-er to you .... this mes-sage I bring,........
Does the world seem all wrong......... and heav - y your load ?..........
His life was a void,.......... so emp - ty and flat; ....
Tho hope may be gone,.......... He'll cause you to sing; ....
Just bring it to Christ,........... your sins all con - fess,............ .
But Je-sus ap-peared, ... one word bro't him sight,...........
At Je-sus' com-mand,.......... sin's shack-les must fall,..........
On the Jer - i - cho road .... your heart He will bless ....
On the Jer - i - cho road........... Christ banished his night ....
On the Jer - i - cho road .... will you answer His call?...........
Chorus
On the Jer-i-cho road there's room for just two,
On the Jer-i - cho road .... there's room for just two, ...

On the Jericho Road
No more and no less, Just Je-sus and you;
No more and no less.................. just Je- sus and you; . . ..
Each bur-den He'll bear, . . each sorrow He'll share, ...
Each burden He'll bear each sorrow He'll share,
There's never a care for Je - sus is there.
There's never a care .... for Je-sus is there.... ....
No. 95
His Broken Body
(FOR COMMUNION)
Homer F. Morris
1. 'Twas on that dark, that dole - ful night, When pow'rs of earth and hell a- rose
2. Be - fore the mourn-ful scene be- gan He took the bread, and blessed, and break;
3. "This is my bod - y, broke for sin; Re-ceive and eat the liv - ing food;"
4. "Do this," He cried, "till time shall end In mem'ry of your dy - ing Friend;
5. Je - sus, Thy feast we cel - e-brate; We show Thy death, we sing Thy name,
A - gainst the Son of God's de-light, And friends betrayed Him to His foes.
What love thru all His ac-tions ran! What wondrous words of grace He spake:
Then took the cup, and blessed the wine; "'Tis the new covenant in my blood."
Meet at my ta - ble, and re - cord The love of your de - part - ed Lord."
Till Thou re-turn, and we shall eat The mar-riage sup-per of the Lamb.

No. 96 My Redeemer

James McGranahan
1. I will sing of my Re-deem-er, And His won-drous love to me;
2. I will tell the won-drous sto-ry, How my lost es-tate to save,
3. I will praise my dear Re-deem-er, His tri-um-phant pow'r I'll tell,
4. I will sing of my Re-deem-er, And His heav'n-ly love to me;
On the cru-el cross He suf-fered, From the curse to set me free.
In His boundless love and mer-cy, He the ran-som free-ly gave.
How the vic-to-ry He giv-eth O-ver sin, and death, and hell.
He from death to life hath brought me, Son of God with Him to be.
Chorus.
Sing, oh, sing.......... of my Re-deem-er, With His
Sing, oh, sing of my Re-deem-er, Sing, oh, sing of my Re-deem-er,
blood........ He purchased me,....... On the cross..... He sealed my
He purchased me, With His blood He purchased me, He sealed my pardon, On the
Repeat pp after last verse.
par-don, Paid the debt........ and made me free.........
cross He sealed my pardon, Paid the debt and made me free, and made me free.

No. 97
The Haven of Rest
H. L. Gilmour
Geo. D. Moore
1. My soul in sad ex - ile was out on life's sea, So bur-dened with
2. I yield - ed my - self to His ten - der em-brace, And faith tak - ing
3. The song of my soul, since the Lord made me whole, Has been the old
4. How pre - cious the tho't that we all may re - cline, Like John the be-
5. O come to the Sav - ior, He pa - tient-ly waits To save by His
sin and dis-tressed, Till I heard a sweet voice saying, "Make me your choice;"
hold of the Word, My fet-ters fell off, and I anchored my soul;
sto - ry so blest, Of Je - sus, who'll save who-so-ev - er will have
lov - ed and blest, On Je-sus' strong arm, where no tempest can harm,-
pow - er di - vine; Come, an-chor your soul in the "Ha-ven of Rest,"
D.S.—The tempest may sweep o'er the wild stormy deep;
Fine
Chorus.
And I en-tered the Ha - ven of Rest.
The "Ha - ven of Rest" is my Lord.
A home in the "Ha - ven of Rest." I've an - chored my
Se - cure in the "Ha - ven of Rest."
And say, "My be - lov - ed is mine,"
In Je - sus I'm safe ev - er - more.
D.S.
soul in the "Ha - ven of rest," I'll sail the wide seas no more;

No. 98 It Won't Be Very Long

Rev. Morgan Williams E. M. Bartlett

1. It won't be ver-y long till this short life shall end. It won't be ver-y long till Je-sus shall de-scend; And then the dead in Christ from beds of clay shall rise To meet the Lord and King up yon-der in the skies.
2. It won't be ver-y long till here we cease to roam, It won't be ver-y long till all the saints get home; And then with smil-ing face we'll walk the streets of gold, And sing the Savior's praise where saints are nev-er old.
3. It won't be ver-y long till bur-dens we lay down, It won't be ver-y long till we'll re-ceive a crown; And then we'll shout and sing with an-gels round the throne, And when we meet up there, we'll know as we are known.
4. It won't be ver-y long till earth shall pass a-way, It won't be ver-y long till works of men de-cay; But Je-sus has pre-pared a hap-py dwell-ing place, For all who look a-bove and trust His matchless grace.
Refrain
It won't be ver-y long, It won't be ver-y long Till Je-sus shall ap-pear, That day is draw-ing near; Will
It won't be ver-y long, It won't be ver-y long, Till Je-sus shall ap-pear; That day is draw-ing near; Will

It Won't Be Very Long
you be read-y then To meet the ransomed throng? Get
you be read-y then To meet the ransomed throng? Get
read-y for that day, It won't be ver-y long.
read-y for that day, It won't be ver-y long.
No. 99 After Death,—What Then?
Copyright, 1928, by E. M. Bartlett
E. M. B.
Stamps-Baxter Music and Ptg. Co., owners
E. M. Bartlett
1. This life will end some fu-ture day, An-oth-er life will then be-gin;
2. The saved will have e-ter-nal life, And they will safe-ly en-ter in
3. The lost will go in-to de-spair, Their tor-ment there will then be-gin;
Fine
Are you pre-pared for that e-vent, Just af-ter death,—what then?
To share the glo-ries of the Lord, Just af-ter death,—what then?
They'll cry for mer-cy from the Lord, Just af-ter death,—what then?
D.S.—When time on earth shall cease to be, Just af-ter death,—what then?
Chorus
D.S.
Just af-ter death,—O! an-swer me, Where will you spend e-ter-ni-ty?

No. 100

Our King Immanuel

James Rowe
Samuel W. Beazley
1. See! the Mon - arch of mon - archs Come in maj - es - ty!
2. Like the waves of the o - cean Rolls His praise to - day,
3. O the joy that will thrill us Some glad day on high,
Let us bow down and wor - ship Him Who do - eth all things well;
For His won - der - ful love has helped So man - y to ex - cel;
When we see Him in glo - ry, where Ce - les - tial prais - es swell;
He leads the na - tions out of sin And caus - es foes to flee:
He sends the cap - tives, free from chains, All sing - ing on their way:
Where cher - u - bim and ser - a - phim All join us when we cry:
All hail, ... Our King Im - man - u - el!
All hail our King Im - man - u - el!
Chorus
O hon - or His name for - ev - - - er For what His grace has done;
O hon - or His name For - ev - er for

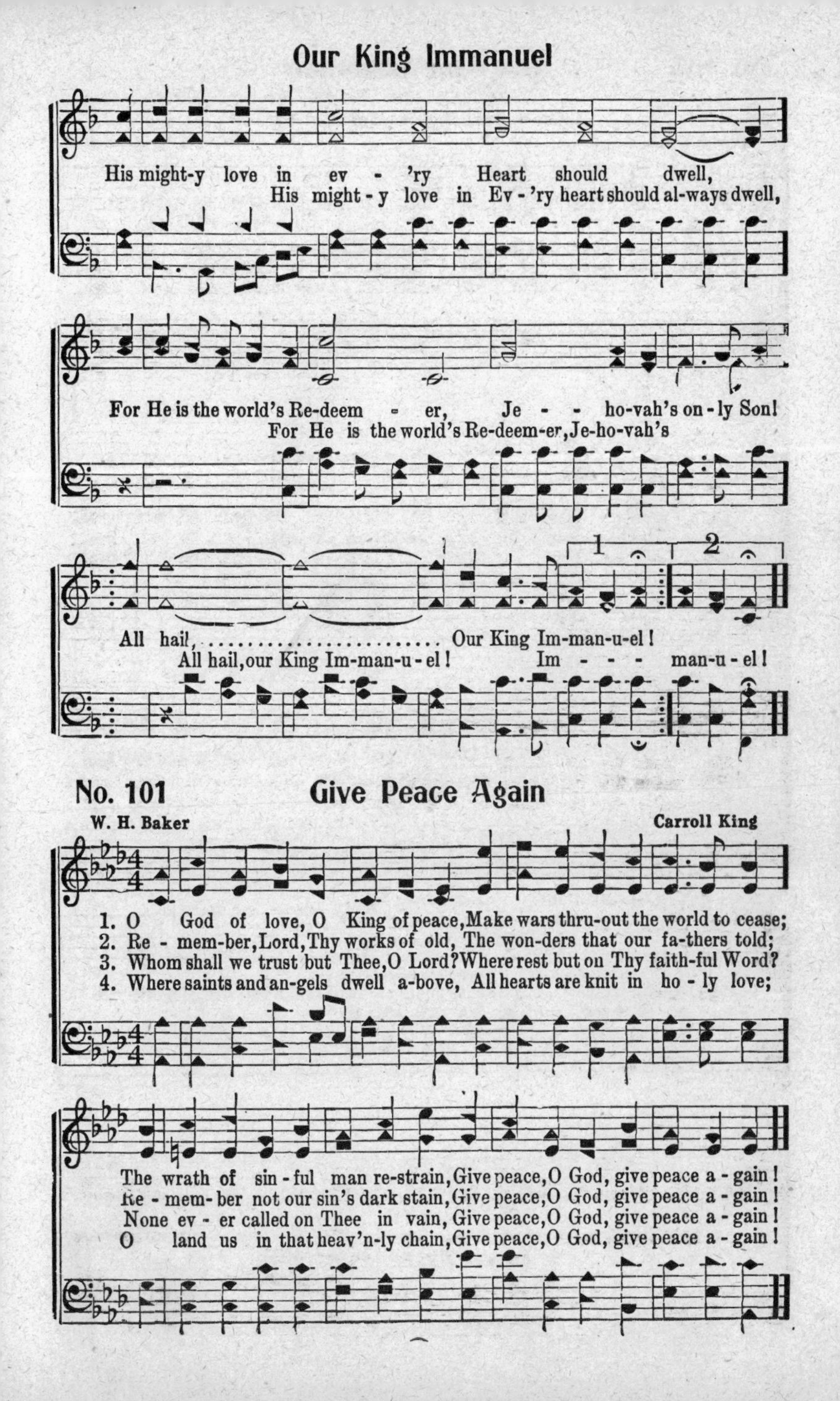
Our King Immanuel
His might-y love in ev - 'ry Heart should dwell,
His might - y love in Ev - 'ry heart should al-ways dwell,
For He is the world's Re-deem - er, Je - - ho-vah's on - ly Son!
For He is the world's Re-deem-er, Je-ho-vah's
All hail, ... Our King Im-man-u-el!
All hail, our King Im-man-u - el! Im - - - man-u - el!
No. 101 Give Peace Again
W. H. Baker
Carroll King
1. O God of love, O King of peace, Make wars thru-out the world to cease;
2. Re - mem-ber, Lord, Thy works of old, The won-ders that our fa-thers told;
3. Whom shall we trust but Thee, O Lord? Where rest but on Thy faith-ful Word?
4. Where saints and an-gels dwell a-bove, All hearts are knit in ho - ly love;
The wrath of sin - ful man re-strain, Give peace, O God, give peace a - gain!
Re - mem- ber not our sin's dark stain, Give peace, O God, give peace a - gain!
None ev - er called on Thee in vain, Give peace, O God, give peace a - gain!
O land us in that heav'n-ly chain, Give peace, O God, give peace a - gain!

No. 102
His Way With Thee
C. S. N.
Rev. Cyrus S. Nusbaum
1. Would you live for Je-sus, and be always pure and good? Would you walk with Him with-in the nar-row road? Would you have Him bear your bur-den, car-ry all your load? Let Him have His way with thee.
2. Would you have Him make you free, and fol-low at His call? Would you know the peace that comes by giv-ing all? Would you have Him save you, so that you need never fall? Let Him have His way with thee.
3. Would you in His kingdom find a place of constant rest? Would you prove Him true each prov-i-den-tial test? Would you in His serv-ice la-bor always at your best? Let Him have His way with thee.
Chorus.
His pow'r can what you ought to be; His blood can cleanse your heart and make you free; His love can fill your soul, and you will see 'Twas best for Him to have His way with thee.
rit.

No. 103
No Tears in Heaven
Copyright, 1935, by The Stamps-Baxter Music Co.,
in "Harbor Bells No. 4"
R. S. A.
Robert S. Arnold
1. No tears in heav-en, no sor-rows giv-en, All will be glo-ry in that
2. Glo-ry is wait-ing, wait-ing up yon-der, Where we shall spend an end-less
3. Some morning yon-der, we'll cease to pon-der O'er things this life has bro't to
land;... There'll be no sad-ness, all will be gladness, When we shall join that
day;.... There with our Sav-ior, we'll be for-ev-er, Where no more sor-row
view;... All will be clear-er, loved ones be dear-er, In heav'n where all will
Chorus
hap-py band.... No tears,............ no tears, no tears up there,
can dis-may....
be made new.... in heav-en fair,
Sor-row and pain will all have flown;.... No tears, ...
in heav-en fair,
no tears, no tears up there, No tears in heav-en will be known.

No. 104 Rescue the Perishing

Fannie J. Crosby   William H. Doane

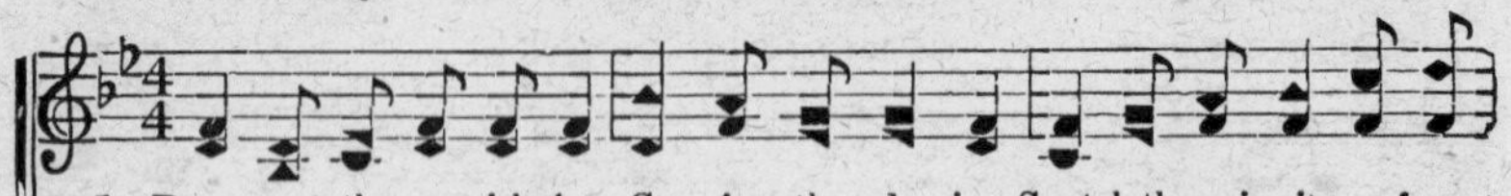

1. Res - cue the per - ish - ing, Care for the dy - ing, Snatch them in pit - y from
2. Tho they are slighting Him, Still He is wait - ing, Wait - ing the pen - i - tent
3. Down in the hu - man heart, Crushed by the temp - ter, Feel - ings lie bur - ied that
4. Res - cue the per - ish - ing, Du - ty de - mands it; Strength for thy la - bor the

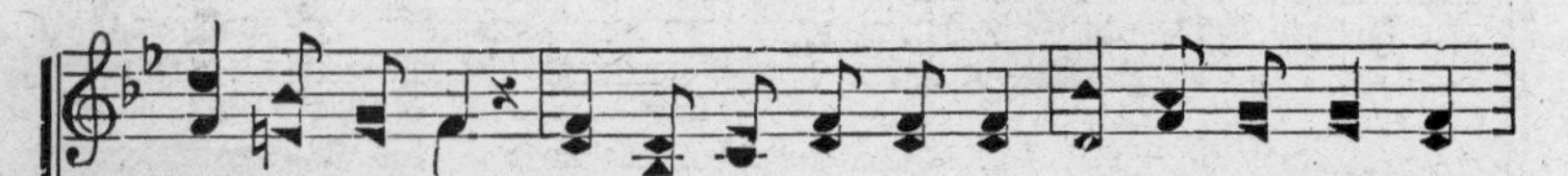

sin and the grave; Weep o'er the err - ing one, Lift up the fall - en
child to re - ceive; Plead with them ear - nest - ly, Plead with them gent - ly,
grace can re - store; Touched by a lov - ing heart, Wakened by kind - ness,
Lord will pro - vide; Back to the nar - row way Pa - tient - ly win them;

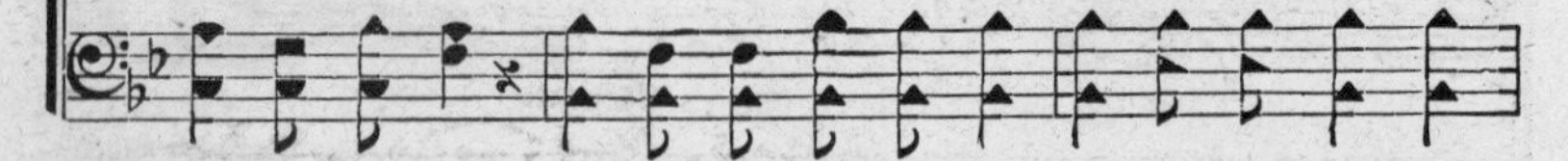

Chorus

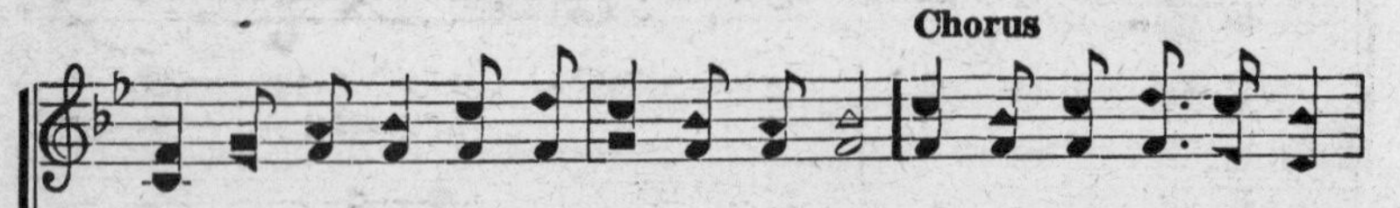

Tell them of Je - sus the might - y to save.
He will for - give if they on - ly be - lieve. Res - cue the per - ish - ing,
Chords that are brok - en will vi - brate once more.
Tell the poor wan - d'rer a Sav - ior has died.

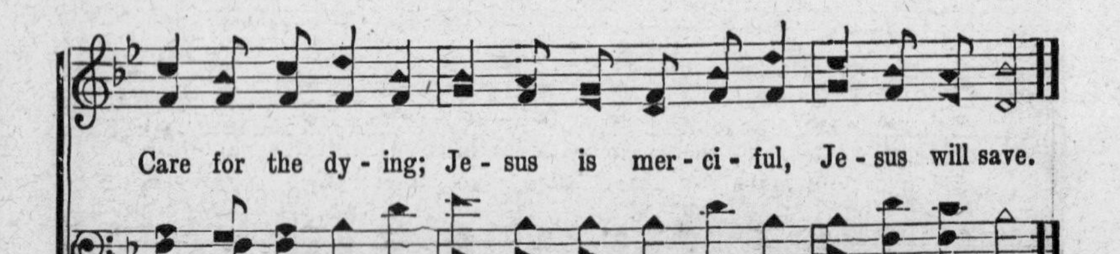
Care for the dy - ing; Je - sus is mer - ci - ful, Je - sus will save.

No. 105 O Why Not Surrender Tonight?

Herbert Buffum in "Buffum Songs Special" R. E. Winsett

1. O wan-d'rer a - far from the dear Shep-herd's fold, Re - ject - ing its
2. So long you have wan-dered your own stub - born way, And sure - ly not
3. The doors of the sheep-fold are o - pened so wide, And O what a
4. Some day you will find it too late to come in, The sheep-fold will
shel - ter, its light; You've long heard the voice that is bid - ding come back,
know-ing your plight; You still are but turn- ing a deaf ear to Him,
won - der - ful sight; When ev - er a poor wand'ring sin - ner re - turns,
then be closed tight; So come while the of - fer of mer - cy holds good,
Chorus
O why not sur - ren - der to - night? To - night, to - night,
To - night, to-night,
O why not sur - ren - der to - night? To - mor-row may nev - er a-
gain greet thy sight, O why not ac - cept Him to - night?

No. 106
An Old Account Settled
F. M. G.
F. M. Graham
1. There was a time on earth when in the book of heav'n An old account was
2. The old account was large, and growing ev-'ry day, For I was al-ways
3. When at the judgment bar I stand be-fore my King, And He the book will
4. O sin-ner, seek the Lord, re-pent of all your sin, For thus He has com-
stand-ing for sins yet un-for-giv'n; My name was at the top, and
sin-ning, and nev-er tried to pay; But when I looked a-head and
o-pen, He can-not find a thing; Then will my heart be glad, while
mand-ed, if you would en-ter in; And then if you should live a
man-y things be-low, I went un-to the Keep-er, and set-tled long a-go.
saw such pain and woe, I said that I would set-tle, and set-tled long a-go.
tears of joy will flow Be-cause I had it set-tled, and set-tled long a-go.
hun-dred years be-low, E'en here you'll not re-gret it, you set-tled long a-go.
Chorus
Long a-go, long a-go, Yes, the old account was
Down on my knees, I set-tled it all,
set-tled long a-go; And the record's clear to-day, for He
hal-le-lu-jah!

An Old Account Settled
washed my sins a - way, When the old ac-count was set-tled long a - go.
No. 107 Are You Washed in the Blood?
E. A. H.
Rev. E. A. Hoffman
1. Have you been to Je - sus for the cleansing pow'r? Are you washed in the
2. Are you walk - ing dai - ly by the Sav-ior's side? Are you washed in the
3. When the Bride-groom cometh will your robes be white? Pure and white in the
4. Lay a - side the garments that are stained with sin, And be washed in the
blood of the Lamb? Are you ful - ly trust-ing in His grace this hour? Are you
blood of the Lamb? Do you rest each moment in the Cru - ci - fied? Are you
blood of the Lamb? Will your soul be read - y for the mansion bright? And be
blood of the Lamb; There's a fountain flow-ing for the soul un-clean, O be
D.S.—Are your garments spotless? Are they white as snow? Are you
Fine
Chorus
washed in the blood of the Lamb? Are you washed in the
Are you washed
washed in the blood of the Lamb?
D.S.
blood, In the soul-cleans-ing blood of the Lamb?
in the blood, of the Lamb?

No. 108 When All of God's Singers Get Home
Luther G. Presley Copyright, 1937, by Stamps-Baxter Music Co.,
Cho. V. O. S. in "Starlit Crown" Virgil O. Stamps
1. What a song of de-light in that ci-ty so bright Will be waft-ed 'neath
2. As we sing here on earth, songs of sad-ness or mirth, 'Tis a fore-taste of
3. Hav-ing o-ver-come sin, "hal-le-lu-jah a-men" Will be heard in that
heav-en's fair dome, How the ransomed will raise hap-py songs in His praise,
rap-ture to come; But our joy can't com-pare with the glo-ry up there,
land o'er the foam, Ev-'ry heart will be light and each face will be bright,
Chorus
When all of God's singers get home. When all of God's singers get home,
When all of God's singers get home,
Where nev-er a sor-row will come; There'll be "no
or heart-aches will come; There'll be no
place like home," When all of God's sing-ers get home.
place like heav-en my home, God's singers get home.

No. 109 God Put a Rainbow In the Cloud

Copyright, 1931
Owned by Morris & Henson
Rev. Andrew Jenkins
Rev. A. J.
Arr. by Mrs. M. L. Spain
1. When God shut No-ah in the grand old ark, He put a rain-bow in the cloud; When the thunders rolled and the sky was dark, God put a rain-bow in the cloud.
2. A - way down yon-der in E-gypt's sand, God put a rain-bow in the cloud; Just to lead His children to the promised land, God put a
3. When they put old Dan-iel in the li - on's den, God put a rain-bow in the cloud; Just to prove His promise to the sons of men, God put a
4. As a sign by day and a sign by night, God put a rain-bow in the cloud; Just to guide His peo-ple and to keep them right, God put a
5. O Jor - dan deep and Jor - dan wide, God put a rain-bow in the cloud; To lead His peo-ple to the oth - er side, God put a
Chorus
God put a rain-bow in the cloud, (yes, in the cloud,)
God put a rain-bow in the cloud, (in the cloud,) When it looked like the sun wouldn't
Rit.
shine an - y more,
Rit.
God put a rain-bow in the cloud.

No. 110 Swing Out On the Promises

E. M. B. — E. M. Bartlett

1. Swing out on the prom - is - es, the nev - er fail - ing prom - is - es;
2. Swing out on the prom - is - es, Je - ho - vah's bless - ed prom - is - es;
3. Swing out on the prom - is - es, the ho - ly Mas-ter's prom - is - es;

Prom - is - es of Christ, the Lord, di - vine; Cross the line of Ca - naan on His
Trust-ing in His pow'r to make you whole; He will not for-sake the ones who
Give your life com-plete - ly to the Lord; He will not for-sake the soul who

ev - er - last - ing prom-is - es, He will make your path to glo - ry shine.
trust His sa - cred prom-is - es, Cast on Him the bur-dens of your soul.
trusts in His great prom-is - es, Swing out on the prom-ise of His word.

Chorus

Swing out on the prom - is - es, the nev - er - fail - ing prom - is - es;

Swing out on the prom - is - es, the Sav-ior's pre-cious prom - is - es,

Swing Out On the Promises
Trust the Savior's ev - er - last - ing word; Swing out on the prom-is - es, the
all suf - fi - cient prom - is - es; Swing out on the prom - is -es, the
Sav-ior's ho - ly prom - is - es, Swing out on the prom - is - es of God.
No. 111 Jesus Will Save
S. J. P.
S. J. Perry
1. I'm a way-worn pil-grim here, but Je - sus will save; Filled with many a
2. Let us walk by faith each day, for Je - sus will save; And be hap - py
3. There are souls for us to win that Je - sus will save; There are sheaves to
4. When this toilsome life is o'er dear Je - sus will save All His loved ones
D.S.—Come to Him by
Fine Chorus
D.S.
doubt and fear, but Je - sus will save.
on the way, for Je - sus will save. Je - sus will save, yes, Je - sus will save;
gar - ner in that Je - sus will save.
ev - er-more, yes, Je - sus will save.
faith and live, for Je - sus will save.

No. 112
Come to Jesus Today
E. R. Latta
Used by per.
J. H. Tenney
1. Come to Je-sus! He will save you, Tho your sins as crim-son glow;
2. Come to Je-sus! do not tar-ry, En-ter in at mer-cy's gate;
3. Come to Je-sus, dy-ing sin-ner! Oth-er Sav-ior there is none;
If you give your hearts to Je-sus, He will make them white as snow.
O de-lay not till the mor-row, Lest thy com-ing be too late.
He will share with you His glo-ry, When your pil-grim-age is done.
Chorus
Come to Je - - - sus! Come to Je - - - sus! Come to
Come, come to-day! Come, come to-day!
Je-sus! come to-day, Come to Je - - - sus!
yes, come, come to-day! Come, come to-day!
Repeat pp
Come to Je - - - sus! Come to Je-sus! come, come to-day!
Come, come to-day!

No. 113 Be a Light for Jesus
B. F. S.
Morris & Sims, owners
B. F. Sims
1. O ye Chris-tian sol-diers, as you march a-long, Be a light for
2. Keep your lamps trimmed, burning so that all may see, Be a light for
3. Thousands grope in dark-ness that can nev-er see, Be a light for
4. Keep the light bright, shin-ing all the world a-round, Be a light for
Je-sus ev-'ry day; Keep His ban-ner hoist-ed all the whole day long,
Je-sus ev-'ry day; Let the world see Je-sus and from sin be free,
Je-sus ev-'ry day; Un-til we point them up to Mount Cal-va-ry,
Je-sus ev-'ry day; Till, re-leased from dark-ness, all the Lord have found,
Be a light for Je-sus ev-'ry day.
Chorus
Be a light, be a
Bright, shining light,
light, Be a light for Je-sus ev-'ry day, Be a
bright, shin-ing light ev-'ry day,
light, be a light, Be a light for Je-sus ev-'ry day.
Bright, shining light, be a shin-ing light,

No. 114

Lift Him Up

Rev. Johnson Oatman, Jr. | B. B. Beall

1. How to reach the mas-ses, men of ev - 'ry birth? For an an-swer
2. O the world is hun- gry for the liv - ing bread, Lift the Sav-ior
3. Don't ex - alt the preacher, don't ex - alt the pew. Preach the gos pel
4. Lift him up by liv - ing as a Chris-tian ought, Let the world in

Je - sus gave a key, "And I, if I be lift- ed up from the earth, Will
up for them to see, Trust Him, and do not doubt the words that He said, "I'll
sim - ple, full and free, Prove Him and you will find that prom-ise is true, "I'll
you the Sav-ior see, Then men will glad - ly follow Him who once taught, "I'll

draw all men un - to me."

Chorus

Lift Him up, lift Him up,
Lift the pre-cious Sav - ior up, lift the precious Sav-ior up,
Still He speaks from e - ter - ni - ty, "And I, if I be lift - ed up from the earth, Will draw all men un - to me."

No. 115 What the Old World Needs
Copyright, 1917, by Samuel W. Beazley, in "Hosannas"
Rev. C. R. Piety
Stamps-Baxter Music and Ptg. Co., owners
Samuel W. Beazley
1. There are man - y hearts ach-ing 'neath loads that they bear, And all drear-y their days are and long; But the love of a friend would re - lieve toil and care, And fill life with a joy - ous new song.
2. There are souls that are bur-dened 'neath pov-er-ty's sting, Who con-sid- er each man as his foe; They need friend-ship and kind-ness to cause them to sing, And the love of a Sav - ior to know.
3. There are those who might buy an - y rich thing of earth, But their hearts are now ach - ing and cold; They are wast-ing their time seek-ing pleas-ure and mirth, While true love would bring glad-ness un- told.
4. There are man- y to- night that are wound-ed by sin, And they think no one cares for their pain; They are per - ish - ing now, whom the Christ died to win, And they're long-ing for love all in vain.
Chorus
What the old world needs is love, sweet love, Like the Christ bro't from a - bove, from a-bove, Love that reach-es out, around, where the weary ones are found, What the world needs is love.

No. 116 When I See the Blood

Foote Bros., not copyrighted. Let no one do so. May this song ever be free to be published for the glory of God

John J. G. F.

1. Christ, our Re - deem - er, died on the cross, Died for the sin - ner,
2. Chief - est of sin - ners, Je - sus can save, As He has prom - ised,
3. Judg - ment is com - ing, all will be there, Who have re - ject - ed,
4. O what com - pas - sion, O bound - less love! Je - sus hath pow - er,
paid all His due; All who re - ceive Him need nev - er fear,
so will He do; O sin - ner, hear Him, trust in His word,
who have re - fused? O sin - ner, hast - en, let Je - sus in,
Je - sus is true; All who be - lieve are safe from the storm,
Chorus
Yes, He will pass, will pass o - ver you. When I see the
Then He will pass, will pass o - ver you.
Then God will pass, will pass o - ver you.
O He will pass, will pass o - ver you. When I
blood, When I see the blood, When I see the
see the blood, When I see the blood, When I
blood, I will pass, I will pass o - ver you.
see the blood, o - ver you.
rit.

No. 117 From the Garden to the Cross

E. R. Latta, Sug. by J. E. T. Used by permission J. E. Thomas

With feeling

1. In the Gar-den, sore op-pressed, Je-sus ut-tered this re-quest:
2. Ju-das, now, with trait-or kiss, Gives Him to His en-e-mies!
3. Now, the Jew-ish coun-cil try, And re-solve that He shall die!
4. Robe and crown, in mock-er-y, And the taunt-ing sol-diers, see!
5. View Him, now, up-on the cross, Us to save from end-less loss!

Fa-ther if it so may be. Let this cup de-part from me!
See that wild and nois-y crowd, They will kill the Son of God!
He, of wit-ness false, the prey, Is, to Pi-late, led a-way!
See Him, now, on Cal-v'ry's road, Sink-ing 'neath His heav-y load!
Dy-ing, there, up-on the tree—Dy-ing, there for you and me!

Chorus

In the gar-den, how He moan'd, Weeping, there, so bit-ter-ly!
Yet, the aw-ful cup, would drink, For you and me!

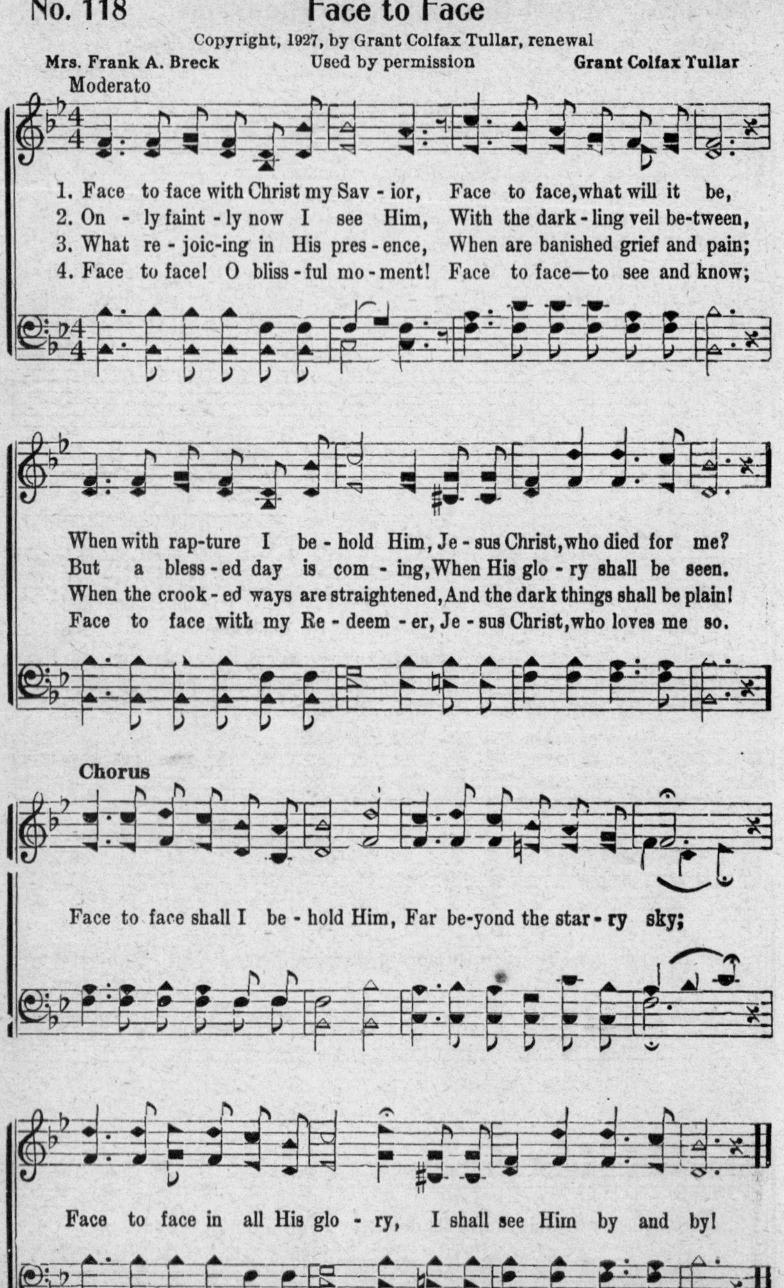
No. 118
Face to Face
Copyright, 1927, by Grant Colfax Tullar, renewal
Mrs. Frank A. Breck
Used by permission
Grant Colfax Tullar
Moderato
1. Face to face with Christ my Sav - ior, Face to face, what will it be,
2. On - ly faint - ly now I see Him, With the dark - ling veil be-tween,
3. What re - joic-ing in His pres - ence, When are banished grief and pain;
4. Face to face! O bliss - ful mo - ment! Face to face—to see and know;
When with rap-ture I be - hold Him, Je - sus Christ, who died for me?
But a bless - ed day is com - ing, When His glo - ry shall be seen.
When the crook - ed ways are straightened, And the dark things shall be plain!
Face to face with my Re - deem - er, Je - sus Christ, who loves me so.
Chorus
Face to face shall I be - hold Him, Far be-yond the star - ry sky;
Face to face in all His glo - ry, I shall see Him by and by!

No. 119 Give Me Your Hand

Author Unknown
Arr. by Albert E. Brumley

1. As an arm - y we're marching t'ward heav-en, So 'tis best that
2. You may not come to our great Ca - the - dral, But be - long to
3. If to - day you are look - ing t'ward Cal-v'ry Where the Sav - ior
4. We are bound for that beau - ti - ful ci - ty, Where be - fore the
to - geth - er we stand, We may not have the same rank or ti - tle,
some small pray - ing band; But if you love my Christ, our Re-deem-er,
paid ev - 'ry de-mand, If you trust in His death for a - tone- ment,
white throne we shall stand, And we'll all be as one there to - geth - er,
But we're sol-diers, so give me your hand.
You're a Chris-tian, so give me your hand.
We're not strang-ers, so give me your hand.
Hal - le - lu - jah, so give me your hand.
Chorus
O I care not what church
you be - long to, Just as long as for God you may stand, But if
your heart to-day is as my heart, You're my broth-er, so give me your hand.

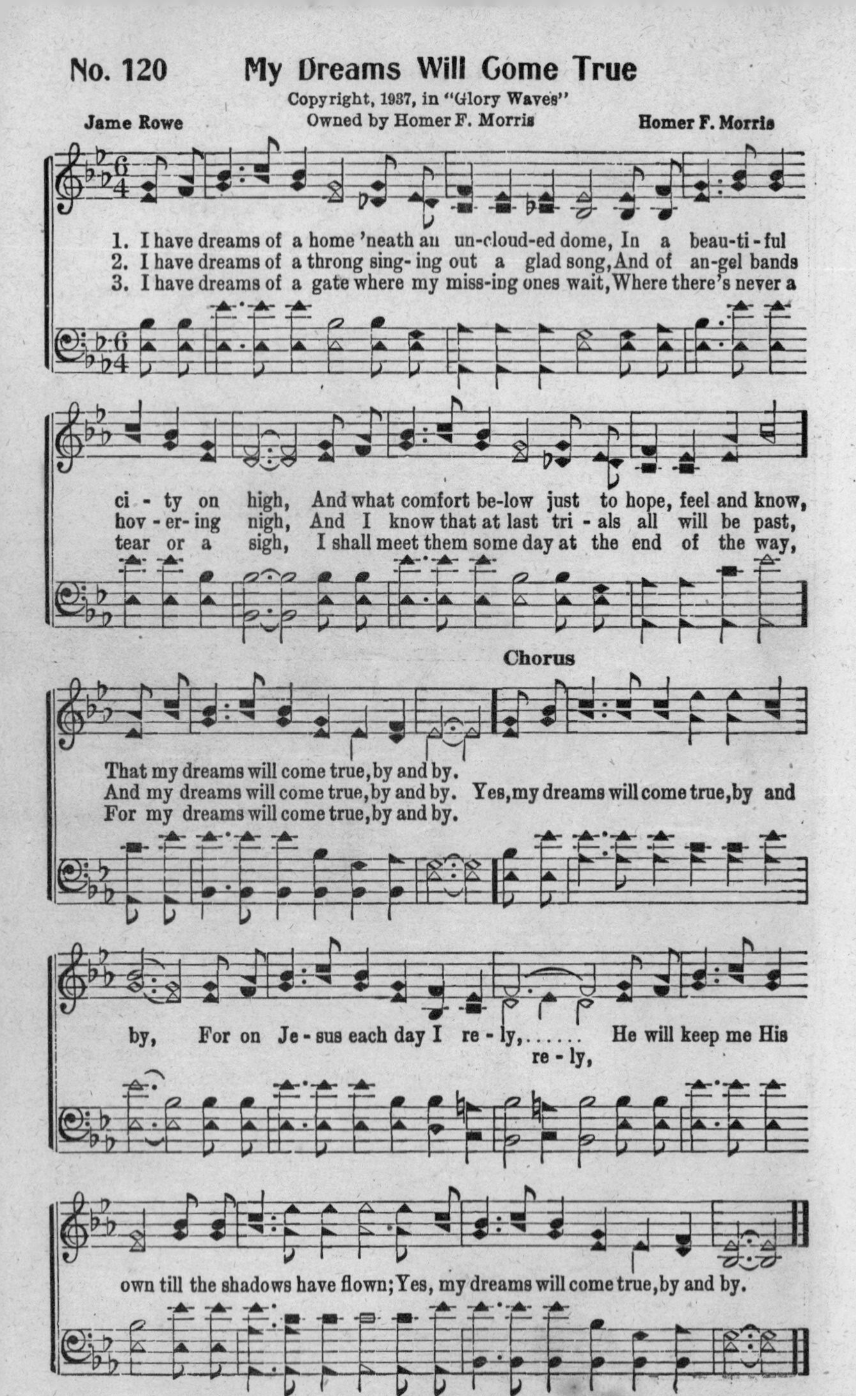
No. 120
My Dreams Will Come True
Copyright, 1937, in "Glory Waves"
Owned by Homer F. Morris
Jame Rowe
Homer F. Morris
1. I have dreams of a home 'neath an un-cloud-ed dome, In a beau-ti-ful
2. I have dreams of a throng sing-ing out a glad song, And of an-gel bands
3. I have dreams of a gate where my miss-ing ones wait, Where there's never a
ci-ty on high, And what comfort be-low just to hope, feel and know,
hov-er-ing nigh, And I know that at last tri-als all will be past,
tear or a sigh, I shall meet them some day at the end of the way,
That my dreams will come true, by and by.
And my dreams will come true, by and by.
For my dreams will come true, by and by.
Chorus
Yes, my dreams will come true, by and
by, For on Je-sus each day I re-ly,...... He will keep me His
re-ly,
own till the shadows have flown; Yes, my dreams will come true, by and by.

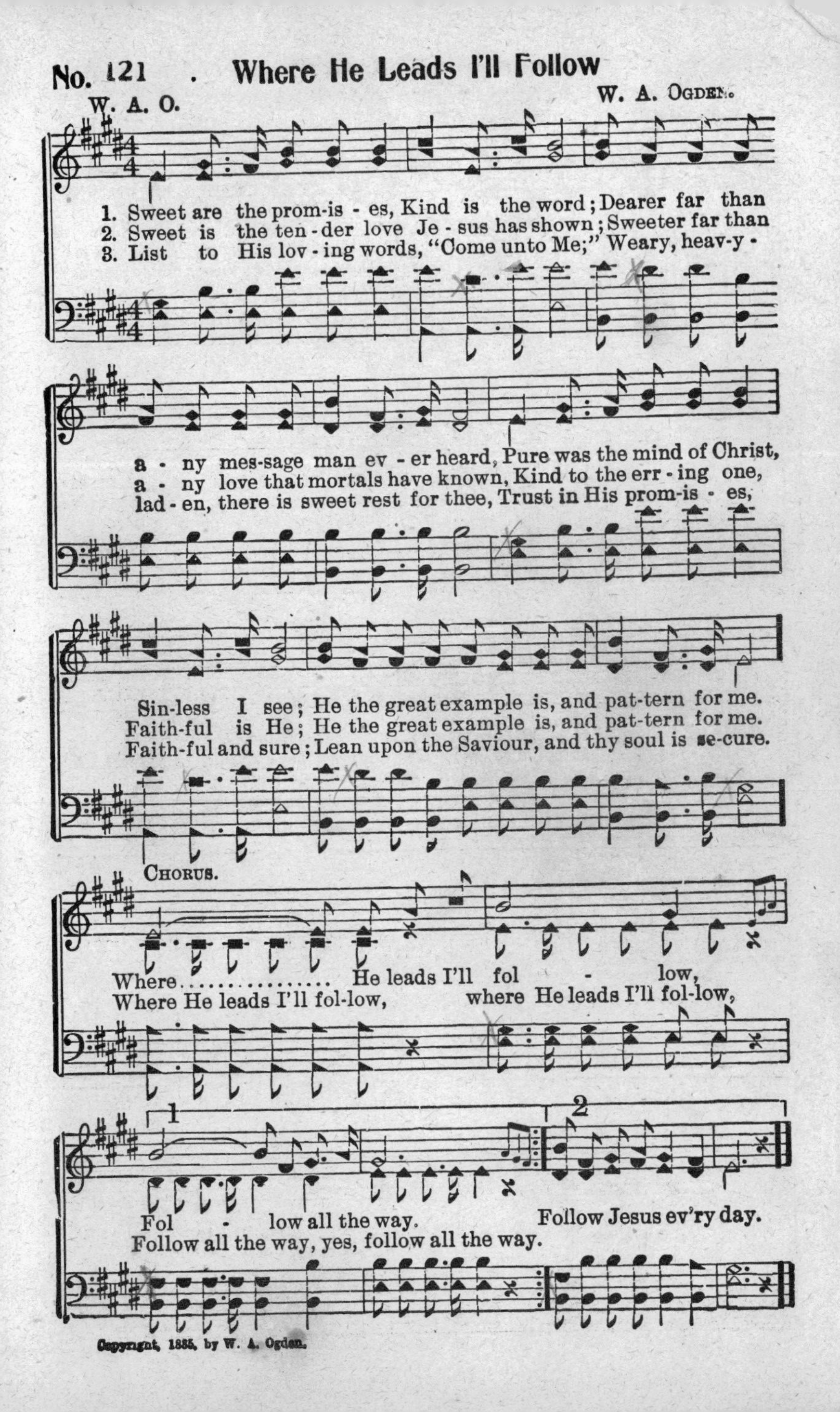
No. 121 . Where He Leads I'll Follow
W. A. O.
W. A. Ogden.
1. Sweet are the prom-is - es, Kind is the word; Dearer far than
2. Sweet is the ten - der love Je - sus has shown; Sweeter far than
3. List to His lov - ing words, "Come unto Me;" Weary, heav-y -
a - ny mes-sage man ev - er heard, Pure was the mind of Christ,
a - ny love that mortals have known, Kind to the err - ing one,
lad - en, there is sweet rest for thee, Trust in His prom-is - es,
Sin-less I see; He the great example is, and pat-tern for me.
Faith-ful is He; He the great example is, and pat-tern for me.
Faith-ful and sure; Lean upon the Saviour, and thy soul is se-cure.
Chorus.
Where................ He leads I'll fol - low,
Where He leads I'll fol-low, where He leads I'll fol-low,
1
2
Fol - low all the way. Follow Jesus ev'ry day.
Follow all the way, yes, follow all the way.
Copyright, 1885, by W. A. Ogden.

No. 122 Camping in Canaan's Land

E. M. Bartlett — Albert E. Brumley

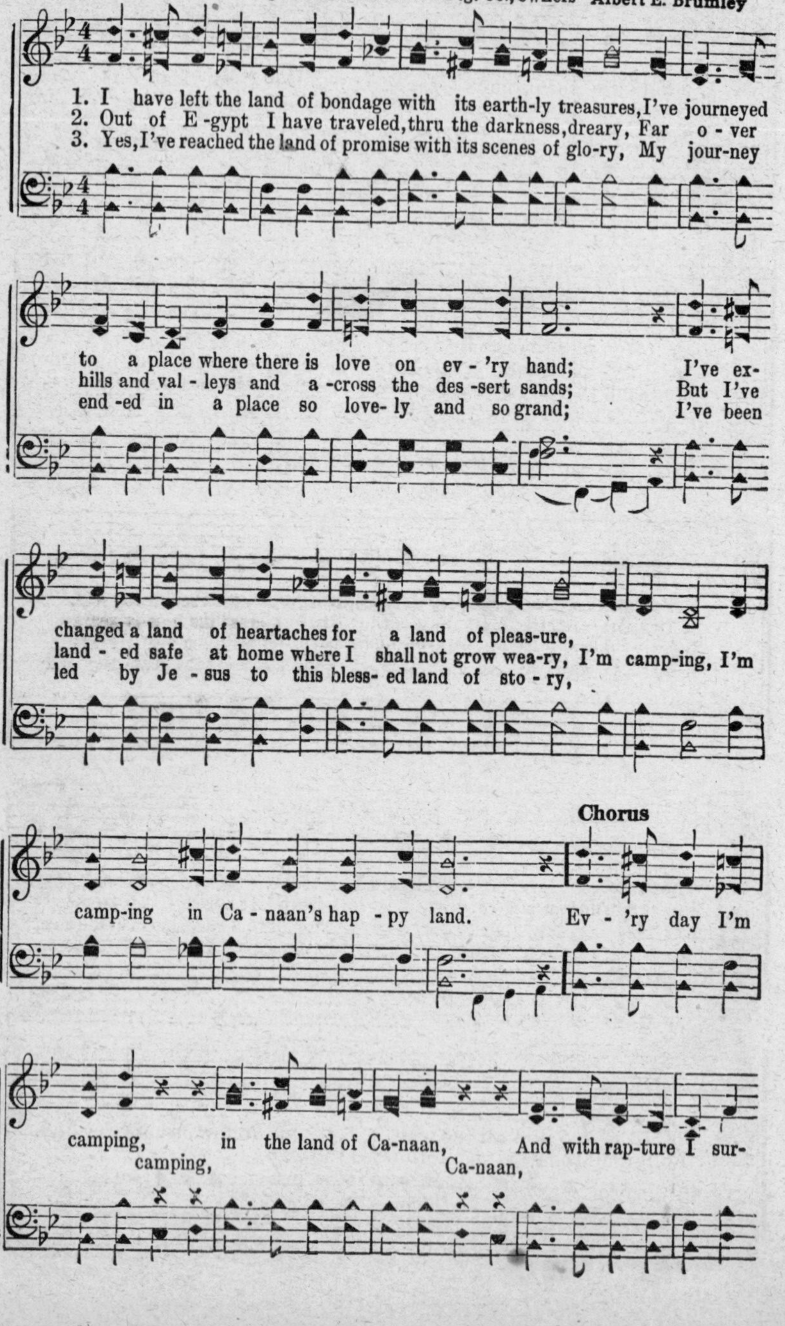

1. I have left the land of bondage with its earth-ly treasures, I've journeyed
2. Out of E-gypt I have traveled, thru the darkness, dreary, Far o-ver
3. Yes, I've reached the land of promise with its scenes of glo-ry, My jour-ney

to a place where there is love on ev-'ry hand; I've ex-
hills and val-leys and a-cross the des-sert sands; But I've
end-ed in a place so love-ly and so grand; I've been

changed a land of heartaches for a land of pleas-ure,
land-ed safe at home where I shall not grow wea-ry, I'm camp-ing, I'm
led by Je-sus to this bless-ed land of sto-ry,

camp-ing in Ca-naan's hap-py land.

Chorus

Ev-'ry day I'm

camping, in the land of Ca-naan, And with rap-ture I sur-
camping, Ca-naan,

Camping in Canaan's Land
vey its won-drous beauties grand, Glo - ry, hal- le - lu-jah,
O glo- ry, I have
found the land of promise, I'm camping, I'm camping in Canaan's happy land.
and
No. 123
Precious Memories
Stamps-Baxter Music Co., Owners
J. B. F. Wright
1. Pre-cious mem'ries, un -seen an-gels, Sent from somewhere to my soul;
2. Pre-cious fa-ther, lov - ing moth-er, Fly a-cross the lone-ly years;
3. In the still-ness of the midnight, Ech - oes from the past I hear;
4. As I trav- el on life's pathway, Know not what the years may hold;
Fine
How they lin- ger, ev - er near me, And the sa-cred past un-fold.
And old home scenes of my childhood, In fond mem-o - ry ap-pears.
Old time sing-ing, glad-ness bringing, From that love-ly land somewhere;
As I pon- der, hope grows fon-der, Pre-cious mem'ries flood my soul;
D.S.— In the still-ness of the mid-night, Pre-cious, sa-cred scenes un-fold.
Chorus
D.S.
Pre-cious mem'ries, how they lin-ger, How they ev- er flood my soul,

No. 124
He Bore It All
J. R. Baxter, Jr.
Copyright, 1926, by V. O. Stamps
Virgil O. Stamps
1. My pre-cious Sav-ior suf-fered pain and ag-o-ny, He bore it
2. They placed a crown of thorns up-on my Sav-ior's head,
3. Up Cal-v'ry's hill in shame the bless-ed Sav-ior trod,
all.............. that I might live;............ He broke the bonds of
By cru-el man with
Free-ly bore it all
I with Him might live; Between two thieves they
sin and set the cap-tive free,
All that I might
spear His side was pierced and bled,
cru-ci-fied the Son of God He bore it all that I might
Fine Chorus
in His pres-ence live. He bore it all that I might see His
live..................
Je-sus bore it all,
shin-ing face,
Free-ly bore it all,
see His shin-ing face, He bore it all.................. that I might

He Bore It All

D.S.
I with Him might live; I stood condemned to die but Je-sus took my place,
live; . . . . Stood condemned to die, free-ly took my place,
No. 125 Old Time Power
"They were all filled with the Holy Ghost."—Acts 2:4
C. D. T. Copyright, 1895, by Charlie D. Tillman Charlie D. Tillman
1. They were in an up - per cham-ber, They were all with one ac-cord,
2. Yes, this pow'r from heav'n de-scend-ed With the sound of rush - ing wind;
3. Yes, this "old time" pow'r was giv - en To our fa-thers who were true;
When the Ho - ly Ghost de-scend - ed, As was prom-ised by our Lord.
Tongues of fire came down up - on them, As the Lord said He would send.
This is prom-ised to be - liev - ers, And we all may have it too.
Chorus
O Lord, send the pow'r just now, O Lord, send the pow'r just now;
O Lord, send the pow'r just now, And bap - tize ev - 'ry one.

No. 126
To The Work
Copyright, 1899, by W. H. Doane. Renewal
Used by permission
Fanny J. Crosby
Wm. H. Doane
1. To the work! to the work! we are serv - ants of God, Let us fol - low the
2. To the work! to the work! let the hun - gry be fed; To the foun-tain of
3. To the work! to the work! there is la - bor for all, For the king-dom of
4. To the work! to the work! in the strength of the Lord, And a robe and a
path that our Mas- ter has trod; With the balm of His counsel our strength to renew,
Life let the wea - ry be led; In the cross and its ban-ner our glo-ry shall be,
dark-ness and er - ror shall fall, And the name of Je-ho-vah ex-alt-ed shall be
crown shall our la - bor re-ward; When the home of the faithful our dwelling shall be,
Let us do with our might what our hands find to do.
While we her - ald the ti-dings, "Sal-va-tion is free!"
In the loud swell-ing cho-rus "Sal-va-tion is free!"
And we shout with the ransomed, "Sal-va-tion is free!"
Chorus
Toil - ing on,
Toil-ing on,
toil - ing on,
toil- ing on,
Toil - ing on,
Toil-ing on,
toil - ing on,
toil - ing on,
Let us hope,
and trust,
let us watch,
and pray,
And la - bor till the Mas-ter comes.

No. 127
I Am Praying for You
S. O'Maley Cluff
Ira D. Sankey
1. I have a Sav-ior, He's plead - ing in glo - ry, A dear, 'ov-ing Sav-ior,
2. I have a Fa-ther, To me He has giv - en A hope for e - ter - ni-
3. I have a robe, 'tis Re-splend - ent in whiteness, A-wait-ing in glo-ry,
4. When Christ has found you, Tell oth - ers the sto - ry, That my lov - ing Sav-ior
Tho' earth-friends be few; And now He is watch-ing In ten - der-ness o'er me,
ty, Bless-ed and true; And soon will He call me To meet Him in heav - en,
My won-der-ing view; O when I re-ceive it All shin - ing in brightness,
Is your Sav-ior too; Then pray that your Savior May bring them to glo - ry,
And, O that my Sav-ior Were your Sav-ior too.
But, O that He'd let me Bring you with me too!
Dear friend could I see you Re - ceiv-ing one too!
And pray'r will be answered—'Twas answered for you!
f Chorus
For you I am pray-ing,
p
f
pp
rall.
For you I am pray-ing, For you I am pray-ing, I'm pray - ing for you.

No. 128

There'll Be Shouting

E. M. B. E. M. Bartlett

1. What a hap - py time is com - ing When we reach our home in heav - en
2. When the saints be - gin to gath - er Round the throne in that blest ci - ty
3. On that bless-ed hap - py morn-ing When old friends are re - u - nit - ed
And the burdens which we've borne, we'll bear no more; When the an - gel sounds the
And the an - gel-choir the songs of praise out-pour; Harps of gold will then be
And when all our loved ones we will see a-gain; In that hap-py land e-
trum-pet, Call-ing us to those bright mansions, There'll be shout-ing on the ev-
ring - ing, Saints of all the a - ges sing-ing; Such a meet - ing as we nev-
ter - nal, We will live in joy su - per - nal And with Je - sus and His an-
er - last - ing shore.
er saw be-fore. There'll be shouting on the hills of glo - ry, Shout-ing
gels ev - er reign.
Chorus
(on the hills,) yes, shout-ing (on the hills,) When we reach that land of

There'll Be Shouting

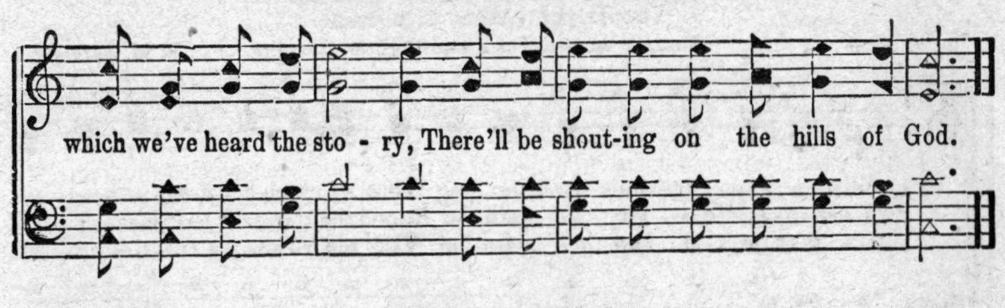

which we've heard the sto - ry, There'll be shout-ing on the hills of God.

No. 129 Who Is That?

Copyright, 1922, by E. M. Bartlett
Stamps-Baxter Music and Ptg. Co., owners

E. M. B. — E. M. Bartlett

1. Who is that call-ing for me to come, Come and be saved from sin?
2. Who is that fol-low - ing af - ter me, Troub'ling my sleep at night?
3. Who is that seek-ing my soul to save, Save from the bondage of sin?
Who is that knocking at my heart's door, Wanting to be let in?
Who is that ask-ing for my poor heart, Say-ing "Come in-to the light?"
Who is that draw-ing by love's strong cord, Break-ing my heart with-in?
Chorus
Who is that knocking, call-ing, seeking, Who is that troub'ling my soul?
my soul?
Sure-ly 'tis Je-sus, ask-ing, plead-ing, Want-ing to make me whole.

No. 130
Coming
J. R. Baxter, Jr.
V. O. Stamps, owner
Virgil O. Stamps
1. Je - sus is com - ing from heav - en Back to the earth some day,
2. Some day the clouds will be lad - en With a most pre - cious King,
3. E - ven the an - gels in heav - en Know not the day nor hour,
Will you be found where faith-ful are crowned, Or be turned a - way from His
He will de-scend, our glo - ri - ous friend, While na - ture shall sing of His
But thru the maze on one of these days We'll see Him in pow'r bro't from
jew - els? O He will come back in His glo - ry O - ver the earth to
glo - ry and In - to sub - jec-tion all na - tions Low at His feet shall
heav - en, for He will be giv - en do - min - ion O - ver the land and
reign, Hast - en, my broth-er, get read - y, Gath - er in the grain.
lie, He will be crowned with true glo-ry, Lord and King most high.
sea, O what a glo - ri - ous rul - er Will our Sav - ior be.
Chorus
He is com - - ing Back to the earth a - gain,
Com-ing, com-ing, com-ing, com-ing,

Coming
Com-ing in love from heav-en a-bove, To reign o - ver men; He is
Com-ing, com-ing, com-ing, com-ing, To reign o ver men;
Com - ing to reign o - ver men;
com-ing in pow - er, glo - ry, O what a sight 'twill be!
Com-ing, com-ing, com-ing, com-ing,
Saints on the earth will greet Him with mirth, The King is He.
com-ing, com-ing, com-ing, com-ing, com-ing, com-ing, King is He.
Saints will greet Him, King is He......
No. 131
Arlington
Rev. Isaac Watts 1720
Thos. A. Arne, 1744
1. Am I a sol - dier of the cross, A fol-lower of the Lamb,
2. Must I be car - ried to the skies. On flow - ery beds of ease;
3. Are there no foes for me to face? Must I not stem the flood?
And shall I fear to own His cause, Or blush to speak His name?
While oth - ers fought to win the prize, And sailed thro' blood - y seas?
Is this vile world a friend to grace, To help me on to God?

No. 132
I'm Going That Way
James Rowe
L. B. Register, Greenville, Fla., owner. By per.
L. B. Register
1. I've heard of a land of joy and peace and wonderful light, (and wonderful light,)
2. The glo - ri-ous news I tell and sing, as on-ward I go, (as on-ward I go,)
3. I know I shall meet Him at the gate, when trials are past, (when trials are past,)
A beau-ti-ful place of mansions fair and skies ev-er bright, (and skies ever bright;)
That those who are still astray in sin my Sav-ior may know, (my Savior may know,)
I know I shall meet Him face to face in glo - ry at last, (in glo - ry at last;)
Where all who be-lieve the Sav-ior dear, for - ev - er shall stay, (forever shall stay,)
I want them to sing His praise a-bove, some beau-ti-ful day, (some beautiful day,)
And O I believe that when we meet "well done" He will say, ("well done" He will say,)
And hav-ing been saved by grace di - vine, I'm go - ing that way.
For glo - ry to Him who died for me, I'm go - ing that way.
For trust-ing His soul - re- deem- ing love, I'm go - ing that way.
Chorus
I'm go-ing that way, (I'm on that way,) I'm going that way, (I'm going that way,)
I'm clinging to Him, (I cling to Him,) and nev-er to stray, (and never to stray,)

I'm Going That Way

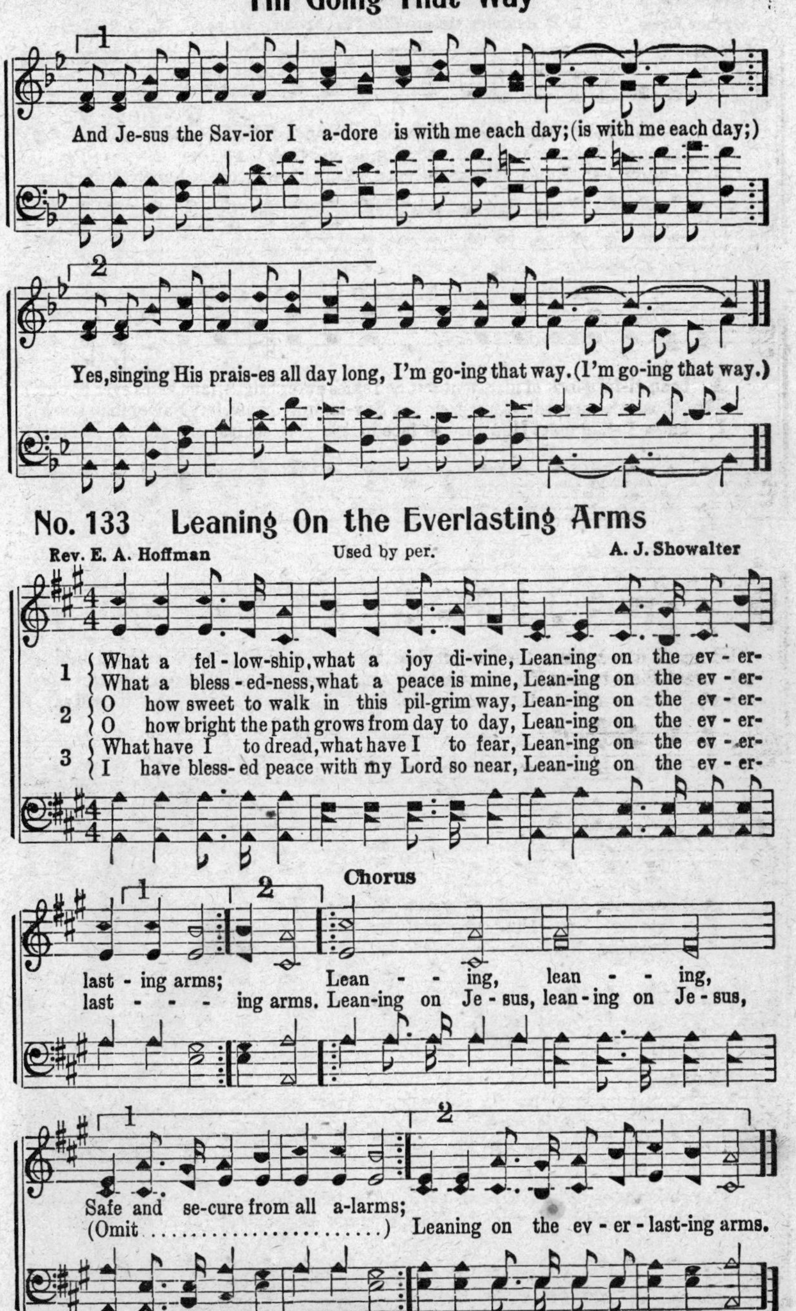
1
And Je-sus the Sav-ior I a-dore is with me each day;(is with me each day;)
2
Yes,singing His prais-es all day long, I'm go-ing that way.(I'm go-ing that way.)
No. 133 Leaning On the Everlasting Arms
Rev. E. A. Hoffman
Used by per.
A. J. Showalter
1 What a fel-low-ship,what a joy di-vine, Lean-ing on the ev-er-
What a bless-ed-ness,what a peace is mine, Lean-ing on the ev-er-
2 O how sweet to walk in this pil-grim way, Lean-ing on the ev-er-
O how bright the path grows from day to day, Lean-ing on the ev-er-
3 What have I to dread,what have I to fear, Lean-ing on the ev-er-
I have bless-ed peace with my Lord so near, Lean-ing on the ev-er-
Chorus
last-ing arms; Lean-ing, lean-ing,
last-ing arms. Lean-ing on Je-sus, lean-ing on Je-sus,
Safe and se-cure from all a-larms;
(Omit ....) Leaning on the ev-er-last-ing arms.

No. 134 Love Took It Away

James Rowe — J. M. Henson

1. Once I bore a bur-den great, Was wea-ry and sad; But no more I bear its weight, I'm pardoned and glad; Love di-vine at last I know, No long-er I stray; On without a stain I go—
2. Once a crav-ing great had I For pleas-ures that stain; Now I pass those pleasures by, They tempt me in vain; I am un-der His con-trol, Re-joic-ing each day; Gone the burden from my soul—Love took it a-way.
3. Once my rec-ord was un-clean, My spir-it was worn; Now my name on high is seen As fair as the morn; O what hap-pi-ness is mine, With Je-sus I stay; Sin no more makes me repine—
Chorus
Love took it a-way, ... One wonderful day, ...
Love took it a-way, ... One won-der-ful day,
Made me free and lift-ed me, In the light to stay; ..... Love
of God to stay;

Love Took It Away
took it a-way, ... One won-der-ful day, ...
Love took it a-way, ... One won-der - ful day,
Gone at last my sin - ful past—Love took it a - way.
No. 135 Shake Hands With Mother Again
W. A. B.
W. A. Berry
1. If I should be liv-ing when Je-sus comes, And know the day and the hour,
2. I'd like to say "Mother, this is your boy, You left when you went a - way;
3. There's com-ing a time when I can go home To meet my loved ones there;
4. There'll be no more sorrow or pain to bear In that home be - yond the sky;
I'd like to be standing at moth-er's tomb When Je-sus comes in His pow'r.
And now my dear mother it gives me great joy To see you a-gain to - day."
There I can see Je-sus up - on His throne In that bright ci - ty so fair.
A glo- ri - ous tho't when we all get there, We nev- er will say "good-by."
Fine
D.S.—When I can hear Je-sus my Sav - ior say, "Shake hands with mother a-gain."
Chorus
D.S.
'Twill be a won-der-ful hap - py day, Up there on the gold-en strand,

No. 136 Wondrous Saving Power

By per. Alva F. Jones, owner of copyright. R. E. Winsett, owner

G. T. B. Rev. G. T. Byrd

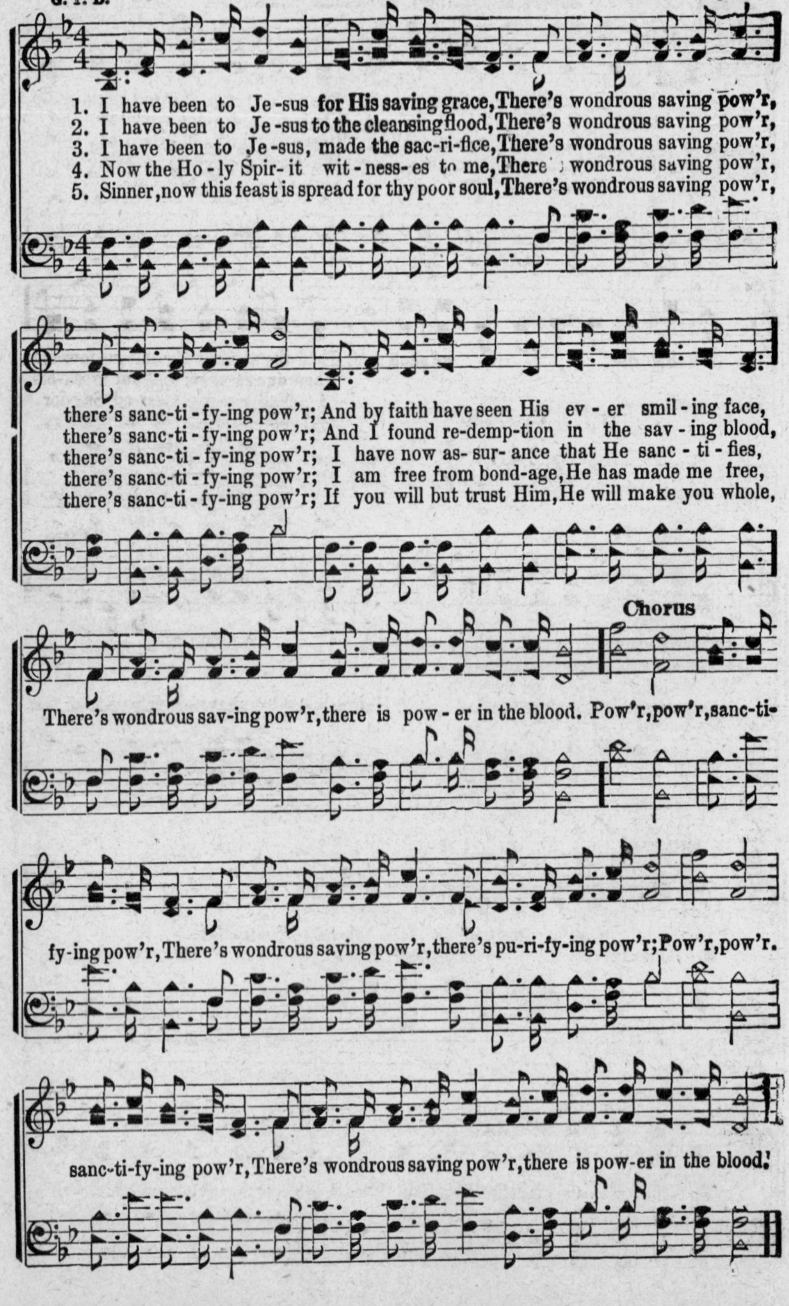

1. I have been to Je-sus for His saving grace, There's wondrous saving pow'r, there's sanc-ti-fy-ing pow'r; And by faith have seen His ev-er smil-ing face,
2. I have been to Je-sus to the cleansing flood, There's wondrous saving pow'r, there's sanc-ti-fy-ing pow'r; And I found re-demp-tion in the sav-ing blood,
3. I have been to Je-sus, made the sac-ri-fice, There's wondrous saving pow'r, there's sanc-ti-fy-ing pow'r; I have now as-sur-ance that He sanc-ti-fies,
4. Now the Ho-ly Spir-it wit-ness-es to me, There's wondrous saving pow'r, there's sanc-ti-fy-ing pow'r; I am free from bond-age, He has made me free,
5. Sinner, now this feast is spread for thy poor soul, There's wondrous saving pow'r, there's sanc-ti-fy-ing pow'r; If you will but trust Him, He will make you whole,

There's wondrous sav-ing pow'r, there is pow-er in the blood.

Chorus

Pow'r, pow'r, sanc-ti-fy-ing pow'r, There's wondrous saving pow'r, there's pu-ri-fy-ing pow'r; Pow'r, pow'r. sanc-ti-fy-ing pow'r, There's wondrous saving pow'r, there is pow-er in the blood.

No. 137 Hallelujah! We Shall Rise
"But if there be no resurrection of the dead, then is Christ not risen."—1 Cor. 15 : 12
J. E. T.
Copyright, 1932, by J. E. Thomas, renewal
J. E. Thomas
1. In the res - ur - rec - tion morn - ing, When the trump of God shall sound,
2. In the res - ur - rec - tion morn - ing, What a meet - ing it will be,
3. In the res - ur - rec - tion morn - ing, Bless - ed tho't it is to me,
4. In the res - ur - rec - tion morn - ing, We shall meet Him in the air,
We shall rise, we shall rise! Then the saints will come re-joic-ing,
When our fa-thers and our moth-ers,
I shall see my bless-ed Sav-ior,
Hal - le - lu - jah! And be car-ried up to glo - ry,
Fine
And no tears will e'er be found, We shall rise, we shall rise.
And our loved ones we shall see,
Who so free- ly died for me,
To our home so bright and fair, Hal-le-lu-jah! in that morning we shall rise.
Chorus
Hal - le - lu - jah! A-men! We shall rise!
We shall rise! we shall rise! Hal - le - lu - jah!
D.S.
In the res - ur - rec-tion morning, When death's prison bars are brok- en,

No. 138 When the Roll Is Called Up Yonder

James M. Black
James M. Black
1. When the trump-et of the Lord shall sound, and time shall be no more, And the
2. On that bright and cloudless morning when the dead in Christ shall rise, And the
4. Let us la - bor for the Mas-ter from the dawn till set-ting sun, Let us
morn-ing breaks, e - ter-nal, bright and fair; When the saved of earth shall gather
glo - ry of His res - ur- rec-tion share; When His chos-en ones shall gather
talk of all His wondrous love and care; Then when all of life is o - ver
o - ver on the oth - er shore, And the roll is called up yon-der, I'll be there.
to their home be-yond the skies, And the roll is called up yon-der, I'll be there.
and our work on earth is done, And the roll is called up yon-der, I'll be there.
Chorus
When the roll.......... is called up yon - - - - der, When the
When the roll is called up yon-der, I'll be there,
roll..... is called up yon - - der, When the roll ..... is called up
When the roll is called up yonder, I'll be there, When the roll is called up

When the Roll Is Called Up Yonder
yon - der, When the roll is called up yon - der, I'll be there.
No. 139 I'm Getting Ready to Go Home
Copyright, 1924, by E. M. Bartlett
E. M. B. Stamps-Baxter Music and Ptg. Co., owners E. M. Bartlett
1. My soul is washed in Je- sus' blood, And I am saved to- day; I'm ful - ly
2. I've put my trust in Christ a- lone, He is my Sav - ior now; He prom-ised
3. A place He is pre - par- ing now, Just as He said He'd do, A man-sion
4. Al - read - y friends are wait-ing there To wel-come you and me; To man-sions
5. O won't that be a hap - py home With all our tri - als o'er; As-sem-bled
trust - ing in His word, He washed my sins a- way.
me a heav'nly home If I would to Him bow.
He'll pre-pare for me And there is one for you. I'm get - ting read -y,
that are bright and fair In lands be-yond death's sea.
round the great white throne, We'll live for-ev - er-more.
Chorus
I'm get-ting read-y, I'm getting read-y to go home;
hal-le - lu- jah I am
I'm get-ting read-y, I'm get-ting read-y, I'm get-ting read-y to go home.
now

No. 140 Just Over In the Glory-Land

James W. Acuff — Emmett S. Dean

1. I've a home pre-pared where the saints a - bide, Just o - ver in the
2. I am on my way to those man-sions fair, Just o - ver in the
3. What a joy - ful tho't, that my Lord I'll see, Just o - ver in the
4. With the blood-washed throng I will shout and sing, Just o - ver in the
glo - ry - land; And I long to be by my Sav - ior's side, Just
glo - ry - land; There to sing God's praise, and His glo - ry share, Just
glo - ry - land; And with kin - dred saved, there for - ev - er be, Just
glo - ry - land; Glad ho- san - nas to Christ, the Lord and King, Just
Chorus
o - ver in the glo - ry-land. Just o - - ver in the glo - ry-land,
o - ver, o - ver
I'll join the hap- py an - gel band, Just o - ver in the
yes, join
glo - ry- land; Just o - - - ver in the glo - ry - land, There
o - ver, o - ver

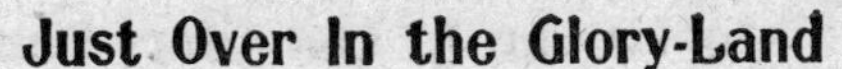
Just Over In the Glory-Land

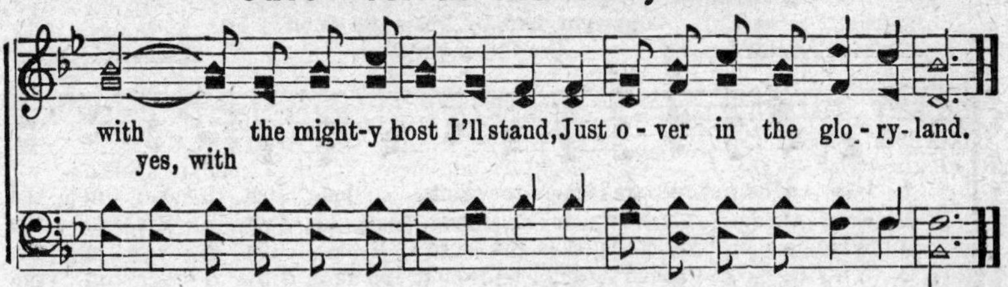
with the might-y host I'll stand, Just o - ver in the glo - ry- land.
yes, with

No. 141 Hold to God's Unchanging Hand

Jennie Wilson
F. L. Eiland

1. Time is filled with swift tran-si-tion, Naught of earth unmoved can stand,
2. Trust in Him who will not leave you, What- so - ev - er years may bring,
3. Cov - et not this world's vain rich-es, That so rap - id - ly de - cay,
4. When your jour-ney is com-plet-ed, If to God you have been true,
Rit.
Build your hopes on things e - ter - nal, Hold to God's un-chang-ing hand!
If by earth- ly friends for-sak - en, Still more close-ly to Him cling!
Seek to gain the heav'nly treasures, They will nev - er pass a - way!
Fair and bright the home in glo - ry, Your en - rap-tured soul will view!
Chorus
Hold to God's unchanging hand! Hold to God's unchanging hand!
to His hand, to His hand,
Rit. Repeat chorus softly
Build your hopes on things e- ter - nal, Hold to God's un-chang-ing hand!

No 142 The Son Hath Made Me Free

Miriam E. Oatman.
COPYRIGHT, 1916, BY W. A. STEWART
W. A. Stewart
1. I was once........ in E-gypt's bon-dage, (Egypt's bondage,) But de-
2. I was once........ a slave to Sa-tan, (slave to Sa-tan,) And He
3. Worldly pleas - ures can-not charm me, (can-not charm me,) No de-
4. All my fear,........ all con-dem - na - tion, (con-dem-na-tion,) All that
liv - 'rance came to me, (came to me,) And I'm liv - ing now in
worked.. his will in me, (yes, in me,) But I'm bound...... by sin no
light...... in them I see, (none for me,) Fash-ion, fol - ly, pride have
stood... 'twixt God and me, (God and me,) Praise His name!.... are left be-
Ca-naan, (now in Canaan,) For the Son........ hath made me free.
lon-ger, (bound no longer,)
left me, (they have left me,)
hind me, (left be-hind me,)
made me free,
REFRAIN.
I am dwell-ing now in Ca-naan, now in Ca-naan,
I am dwell - ing now in Ca - naan, Je - sus'
Je - sus' blood a-vails for me, yes, for me; I am free from con-dem-
blood........ avails for me; I am free .... from con-dem

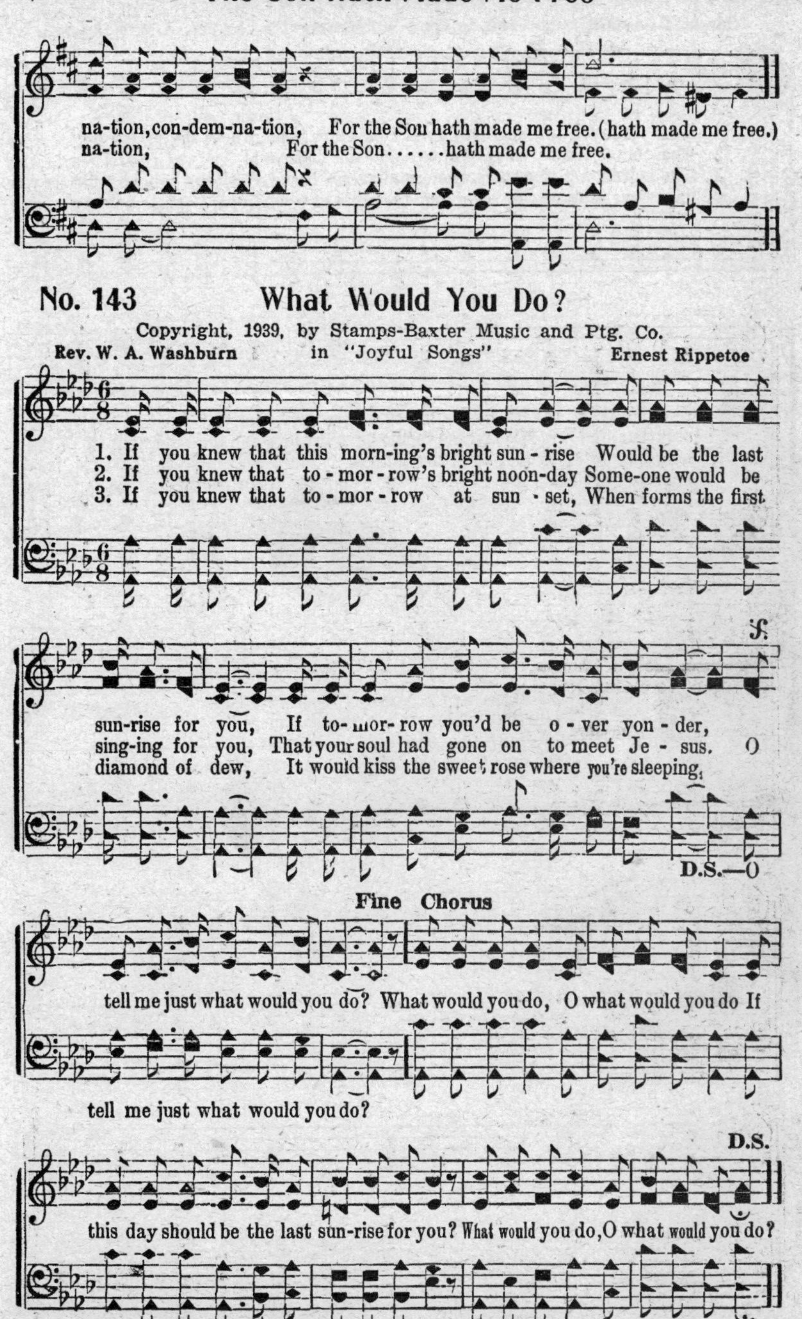
The Son Hath Made Me Free
na-tion, con-dem-na-tion, For the Son hath made me free. (hath made me free.)
na-tion, For the Son...... hath made me free.
No. 143 What Would You Do?
Copyright, 1939, by Stamps-Baxter Music and Ptg. Co.
Rev. W. A. Washburn in "Joyful Songs" Ernest Rippetoe
1. If you knew that this morn-ing's bright sun - rise Would be the last sun-rise for you, If to-mor-row you'd be o - ver yon - der,
2. If you knew that to - mor - row's bright noon-day Some-one would be sing-ing for you, That your soul had gone on to meet Je - sus. O
3. If you knew that to - mor - row at sun - set, When forms the first diamond of dew, It would kiss the sweet rose where you're sleeping;
D.S.
Fine Chorus
tell me just what would you do? What would you do, O what would you do If
tell me just what would you do?
D.S.
this day should be the last sun-rise for you? What would you do, O what would you do?

No. 144 Lord, Send Me

M. W. S. Copyright, 1893, by John McPherson. Used by per. M. W. Spencer

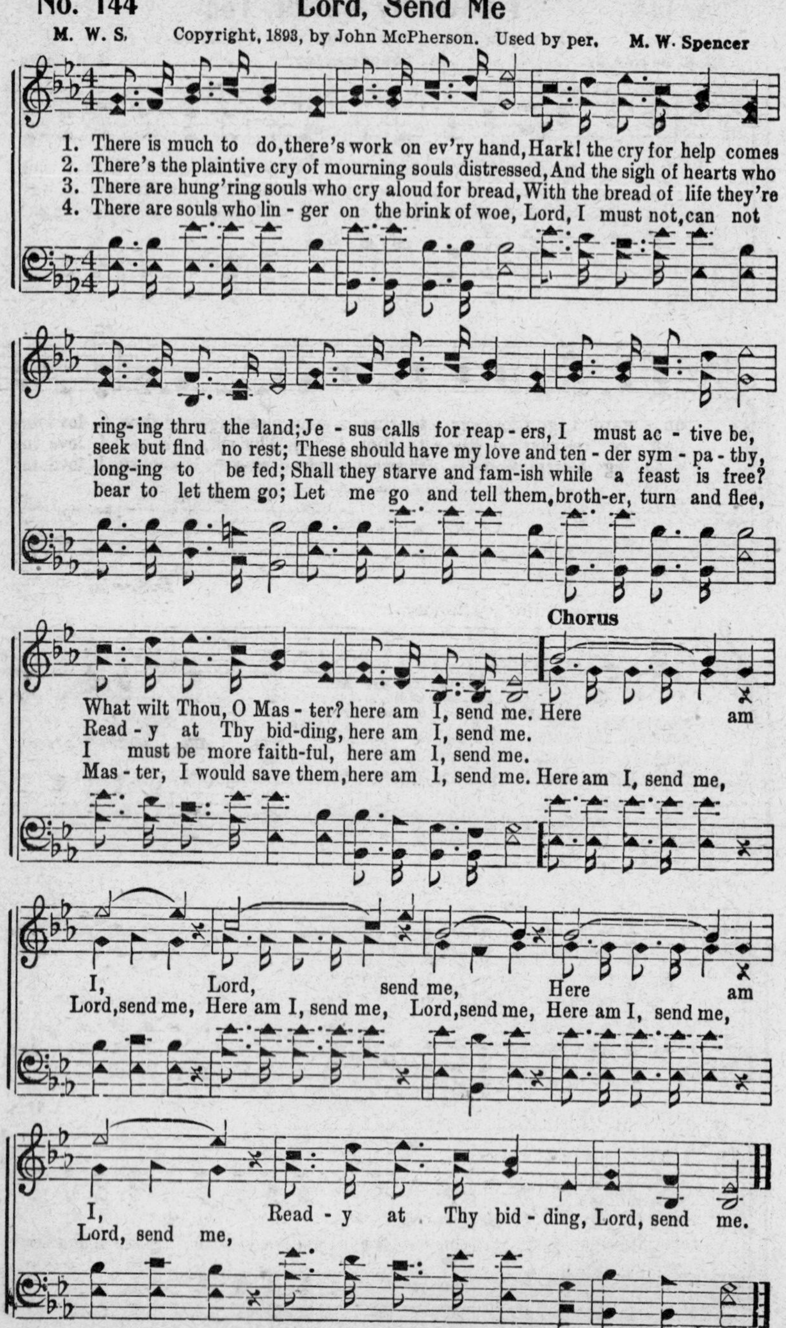
1. There is much to do, there's work on ev'ry hand, Hark! the cry for help comes
2. There's the plaintive cry of mourning souls distressed, And the sigh of hearts who
3. There are hung'ring souls who cry aloud for bread, With the bread of life they're
4. There are souls who lin - ger on the brink of woe, Lord, I must not, can not
ring-ing thru the land; Je - sus calls for reap - ers, I must ac - tive be,
seek but find no rest; These should have my love and ten - der sym - pa - thy,
long-ing to be fed; Shall they starve and fam-ish while a feast is free?
bear to let them go; Let me go and tell them, broth-er, turn and flee,
Chorus
What wilt Thou, O Mas - ter? here am I, send me. Here am
Read - y at Thy bid-ding, here am I, send me.
I must be more faith-ful, here am I, send me.
Mas - ter, I would save them, here am I, send me. Here am I, send me,
I, Lord, send me, Here am
Lord, send me, Here am I, send me, Lord, send me, Here am I, send me,
I, Read - y at Thy bid - ding, Lord, send me.
Lord, send me,

No. 145 I Love My Savior, Too

J. R. Baxter, Jr. J. B. Coats

1. Je - sus, my heav'nly King, loves me, I know, Prais-es to Him I sing, on - ward I go; Close - ly to Him I cling, bless-ings still flow, I love my Sav - ior, too.
2. Walk-ing with Him each day, love light doth shine, Do - ing His will al - way, nev - er re - pine; Kneel-ing to Him I pray, "Thy will, not mine," I love my
3. Hap - py to serve my friend, lean on His arm, Rapture will nev - er end, noth - ing a - larm; Voic - es will sweet - ly blend, un - der His charm, I love my

D.S.—In ev - 'ry - thing I do.

Fine Chorus

I love my Sav - - - - ior, He loves me, too;
Yes, I tru - ly love my bless-ed Sav - ior, bless-ed Savior, And He ev - er loves me, yes, He loves me, too;

I seek His fa - - - - vor
Humbly now I seek His grace and fa - vor, grace and fa - vor

D.S.

No. 146 I'd Rather Have Jesus

L. G. P. in "Thankful Hearts" Luther G. Presley

1. Men strive for the wealth of this wide, wick-ed world, They seek af - ter hon-
2. They seem not to know that their treasures will rust And thieves oft - en break
3. What prof - it is found in earth's sil - ver and gold? How sad at the close
or and fame; (worldly fame;) So lav - ish- ly sporting their diamonds and pearls,
thru and steal; (oft-en steal;) Con-tent- ed with pleasure, they fol-low their lust,
of life's day, (fleeting day,) If for the exchange one must lose his own soul,
They put the dear Sav-ior to shame.
With sor-row their des-ti - ny seal.
From heaven's door be turned a - way.
Chorus
I'd rath- er live
I'd rath - - - er live in
in that bright ci - ty, Own earth's sil-ver and gold,
heav - - en Than to own all earth's sil-ver and gold, I'd
I'd rath-er have Je - sus my Sav- ior Than a
rath - - - er have Je - - - sus Than the diamonds of a pal-

I'd Rather Have Jesus
pal-ace to hold; I'd rath-er be just a poor beg-gar,
ace to hold; .... I'd rath - - er be a beg - - gar, Live
Live in a shack by the road, Than here to own
in a lit-tle shack by the road,........ Than to own .... all earth's
all of earth's treasures, With no ti - tle to a fu-ture a-bode.
treas - ures, to a fu-ture a - bode........
No. 147 It Is the Hour of Prayer
J. L. Hale
1. It is the hour of pray'r; Draw near and bend the knee, And
2. O'er-wea-ried with the heat And bur-den of the day, Now
3. O bless-ed is the hour That lifts our hearts on high! Like
4. Tho dark may be our lot; Our eyes be dim with care, These
fill the calm and ho - ly air With voice of mel - o - dy.
let us rest our wan - d'ring feet, And gath - er here to pray.
sun-light when the tem - pests low'r, Pray'r to the soul is nigh.
sad-d'ning tho'ts shall trou - ble not This ho - ly hour of pray'r.

No. 148 He'll Wipe All Tears Away

Mrs. J. M. Hunter | J. R. Baxter, Jr., owner | J. R. Baxter, Jr.

1. As day by day I jour-ney, I'm wea - ry oft and worn; But to my heart a mes-sage On wings of love is borne: It tells me there is com-ing A bright and hap-py day, When God, my heav'nly Father, Will wipe all tears a-way.
2. Tho man -y dis - ap-point-ments A-round my path may fall, I'll call them "His appointments," For He is rul - ing all; He notes the smallest sparrow, He hears His children pray, And by and by, in mer-cy, He'll wipe all tears a-way.
3. Look up, ye heav-y - heart-ed, Look up and trust your King; His dear ones are pro-tect-ed Beneath His shelt'ring wing; Tho dark the clouds may gather, He'll send the sun's glad ray, And in His word He tells us He'll wipe all tears a-way.

Chorus

He'll wipe all tears a -way, He'll wipe all tears a -way; Our kind and
He will wipe all tears a-way, Yes, He will wipe all tears a-way;
lov - ing Father will wipe all tears a-way; He''ll wipe all tears a-way, He'll
Will wipe all tears a-way; He will wipe all tears away, Yes,

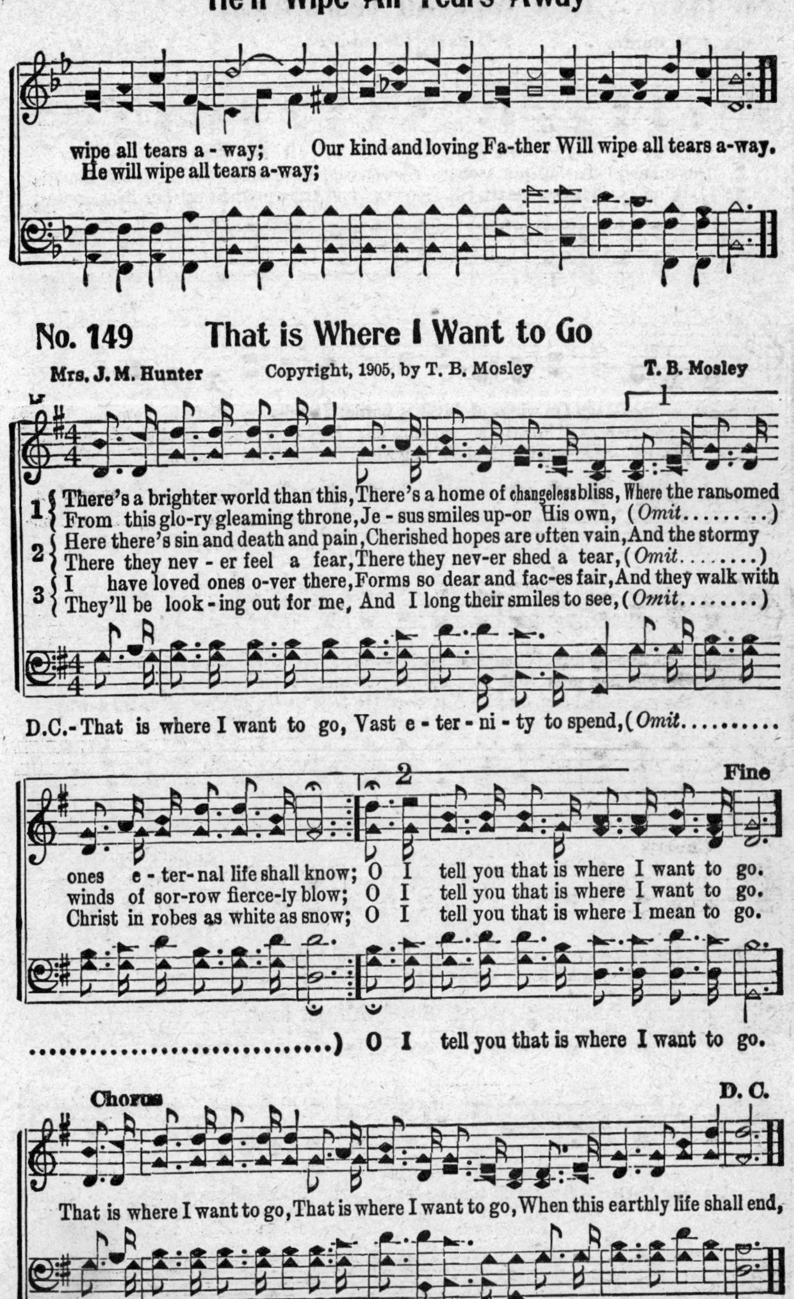
He'll Wipe All Tears Away
wipe all tears a - way; Our kind and loving Fa-ther Will wipe all tears a-way.
He will wipe all tears a-way;
No. 149 That is Where I Want to Go
Mrs. J. M. Hunter
Copyright, 1905, by T. B. Mosley
T. B. Mosley
1
1 There's a brighter world than this, There's a home of changeless bliss, Where the ransomed
From this glo-ry gleaming throne, Je - sus smiles up-on His own, (Omit........)
2 Here there's sin and death and pain, Cherished hopes are often vain, And the stormy
There they nev - er feel a fear, There they nev-er shed a tear, (Omit........)
3 I have loved ones o-ver there, Forms so dear and fac-es fair, And they walk with
They'll be look - ing out for me, And I long their smiles to see, (Omit........)
D.C.- That is where I want to go, Vast e - ter - ni - ty to spend, (Omit..........
2
Fine
ones e - ter - nal life shall know; O I tell you that is where I want to go.
winds of sor-row fierce-ly blow; O I tell you that is where I want to go.
Christ in robes as white as snow; O I tell you that is where I mean to go.
..........................) O I tell you that is where I want to go.
Chorus
D. C.
That is where I want to go, That is where I want to go, When this earthly life shall end,

No. 150 Praise Him! Praise Him!

"I will sing praises unto my God."—Ps. 146: 2

Fanny J. Crosby — Copyright, 1869, by Biglow & Main — Chester G. Allen

1. Praise Him! praise Him! Je - sus, our bless-ed Re-deem-er! Sing, O earth—His
2. Praise Him! praise Him! Je - sus, our bless-ed Re-deem-er! For our sins He
3. Praise Him! praise Him! Je - sus, our bless-ed Re-deem-er! Heav'nly por - tals,

won- der- ful love pro - claim! Hail Him! hail Him! high-est arch-an-gels in
suf-fered, and bled, and died; He our rock, our hope of e - ter- nal sal-
loud with ho- san - nas ring! Je - sus, Sav - ior, reign-eth for - ev - er and

D.S.—Praise Him! praise Him! tell of His ex - cel-lent

Fine

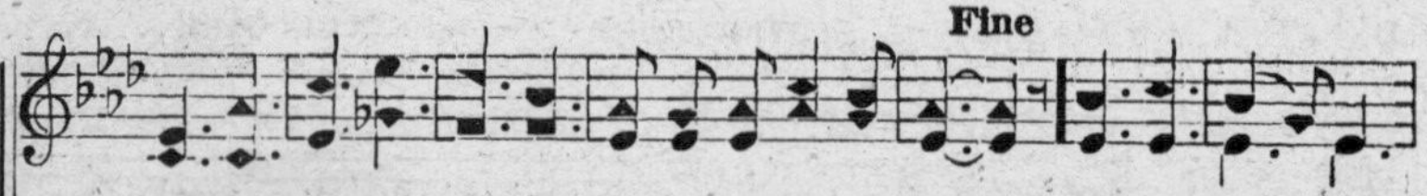

glo-ry, Strength and hon-or give to His ho - ly name! Like a shep - herd,
va - tion, Hail Him! hail Him! Je-sus the cru-ci - fied. Sound His prais - es!
ever; Crown Him! crown Him! Prophet and Priest and King! Christ is com- ing!

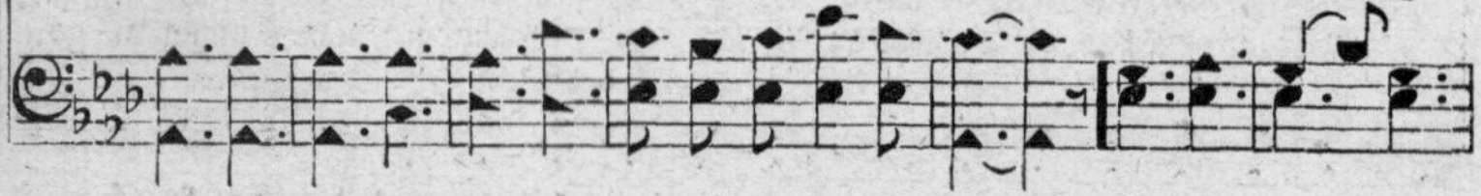

greatness, Praise Him! praise Him! ever in joyful song!

D.S.

Je-sus will guard His children, In His arms He carries them all day long;
Je-sus who bore our sor-rows, Love un-bound-ed, won-der-ful deep and strong;
o- ver the world vic-to-rious, Pow'r and glo - ry un - to the Lord be- long;

No. 151 When the Saints Go Marching In

Arr. Luther G. Presley in "Starlit Crown" Arr. Virgil O. Stamps

1. I'm just a wea-ry pil-grim, Plodding thru this world of sin;
2. My fa - ther loved the Sav-ior, What a sol - dier he had been!
3, And moth - er, may God bless her, I can see her now, as then;
4. Up there I'll see the Sav - ior Who re-deemed my soul from sin,
Get - ting read - y for that ci - ty When the saints go march-ing in.
But his steps will be more stead-y
With a robe of white a-round her
With ex-tend - ed hands He'll greet me
Saints go march-ing
Chorus
When the saints go marching in, When the saints go
When the saints march-ing in, Saints go
march - ing in; Lord I want to be in that
march-ing go march-ing in O
num-ber When the saints go march-ing in.
that number, Saints go march-ing go marching in.
count - less num-ber,

No. 152 Nailed to the Cross

Mrs. Frank A. Breck
Grant Colfax Tullar

Duet ad lib.

1. There was One who was will-ing to die in my stead, That a soul so un-worth-y might live, And the path to the cross He was will-ing to tread, All the sins of my life to for-give.
2. He is ten-der and lov-ing and pa-tient with me, While He cleans-es my heart of its dross, But "there's no con-dem-na-tion," I know I am free, For my sins are all nailed to the cross.
3. I will cling to my Sav-ior and nev-er de-part — I will joy-ful-ly jour-ney each day, With a song on my lips and a song in my heart, That my sins have been taken a-way.

Chorus

pp

They are nailed to the cross, they are nailed to the cross, O how much He was will-ing to bear! With what anguish and loss, Je-sus went to the cross! But He car-ried my sins with Him there.

Rit.

No. 153 Tell Me the Old, Old Story

KATE HANKEY

W. H. DOANE

1. Tell me the old, old sto - ry Of un - seen things a - bove, Of Je - sus
2. Tell me the sto - ry slow - ly, That I may take it in— That won-der-
3. Tell me the sto - ry soft - ly, With earnest tones, and grave; Re-mem-ber,
4. Tell me the same old sto - ry, When you have caused to fear That this world's

and his glo - ry, Of Je - sus and his love. Tell me the sto - ry
ful re - demp - tion, God's rem - e - dy for sin. Tell me the sto - ry
I'm the sin - ner Whom Je-sus came to save. Tell me the sto - ry
emp - ty glo - ry, Is cost-ing me too dear; Yes, and when that world's

sim - ply, As to a lit - tle child, For I am weak and wea - ry, And
oft - en, For I for - get so soon; The "ear - ly dew" of morn - ing, Has
al - ways, If you would real-ly be, In a - ny time of trou - ble, A
glo - ry Is dawn-ing on my soul, Tell me the old, old sto-ry: "Christ

Chorus

helpless and de - filed.
passed a-way at noon. Tell me the old, old sto - ry, Tell me the old, old
com-fort-er to me.
Je-sus makes thee whole."

sto - ry, Tell me the old, old sto - ry Of Je - sus and His love.

No. 154
Watching You
J. M. H.
R. E. Winsett. owner, Used by per.
J. M. Henson
1. All a - long on the road to the soul's true a-bode, There's an Eye
2. As you make life's great flight, keep the pathway of right,
3. Fix your mind on the goal, that sweet home of the soul, There's an Eye
watch-ing you; Ev - 'ry step that you take this great Eye is a-wake,
God will warn not to go in the path of the foe,
watch-ing you; Nev - er turn from the way to the king-dom of day,
Chorus
There's an Eye watch-ing you. Watching you, watch-ing
There's an Eye watch-ing you. Watch-ing you,
you, Ev-'ry day mind the course you pursue; Watching you,
watching you, Watching you
watch-ing you, There's an all - see - ing Eye watch-ing you.
watch-ing yon,

No. 155 The Kingdom Coming

Mrs. M. B. C. Slade — Used by per. — R. M. McIntosh

1. From all the dark plac - es of earth's hea-then rac - es, O see how the
2. The sun - light is glanc-ing o'er arm - ies ad-vanc- ing, To con-quor the
3. With shout-ing and sing-ing, and ju - bi - lant ring-ing, Their arms of re-

thick shad - ows fly! The voice of sal - va - tion a - wakes ev - 'ry
king - doms of sin; Our Lord shall pos - sess them, His pres - ence shall
bel - lion cast down, At last ev - 'ry na - tion, the Lord of sal-

D.S.—The earth shall be full of His knowl - edge and

Fine — Chorus

na - tion, Come o - ver and help us, they cry.
bless them, His beau - ty shall en - ter them in. The king - dom is
va - tion, Their King and Re - deem - er shall crown!

glo - ry, As wa - ters that cov - er the sea.

D.S.

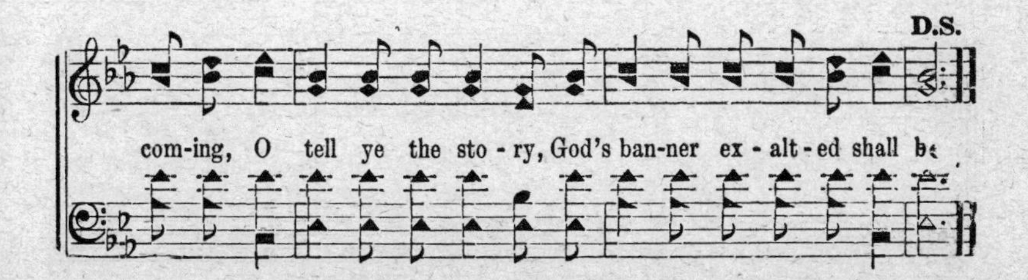
com-ing, O tell ye the sto - ry, God's ban-ner ex - alt - ed shall be

No. 156 I'll Be A Friend To Jesus
Rev. Johnson Oatman
J. W. Dennis, owner
J. W. Dennis
1. They tried my Lord..........and Mas-ter, With no one to .... de-
2. The world may turn.......... a-gainst Him, I'll love Him to.......... the
3. I'll do what He .... may bid me; I'll go where He.........may
4. To all who need.......... a Sav-ior, My Friend I rec - - - om-
fend; With-in the halls...... of Pi - late He stood without...... a
end, And while on earth......I'm liv - ing, My Lord shall have...... a
send; I'll try each fly - - ing mo-ment To prove that I'm...... His
mend, Be-cause He bro't..... sal - va - tion, Is why I am..... His
Chorus
friend. I'll be a friend............ to Je - sus,
I'll be a friend to Je - sus,
My life for Him.... .... I'll spend; I'll be a friend.........
My life for Him I'll spend; I'll be a friend
to Je - sus, Un - til my years .... shall end.
to Je - sus, Un - til my years shall end.

No. 157 He's a Wonderful Savior to Me

Virgil P. Brock | Blanche Kerr Brock

1. I was lost in sin but Je-sus rescued me, He's a won-der-ful Sav-ior to me; I was bound by fear but Je-sus set me free, He's a
2. He's a Friend so true, so pa-tient and so kind, He's a won-der-ful Sav-ior to me; Ev-'ry-thing I need in Him I al-ways find, He's a
3. He is al-ways near to comfort and to cheer, He's a won-der-ful Sav-ior to me; He for-gives my sins, He dries my ev-'ry tear, He's a
4. Dearer grows the love of Je-sus day by day, He's a won-der-ful Sav-ior to me; Sweeter is His grace while pressing on my way, He's a
So won-der-ful!
won-der-ful Sav-ior to me.............
So won-der-ful!
CHORUS.
For He's a won-der-ful Sav-ior to me,
won-der-ful!
He's a won-der-ful Sav-ior to me;
won-der-ful!
I was lost in sin, but Je-sus took me in, He's a won-der-ful Sav-ior to me.

No. 158 'Tis So Sweet to Trust in Jesus

Mrs. Louisa M. R. Stead — Wm. J. Kirkpatrick

1. 'Tis so sweet to trust in Je - sus, Just to take Him at His word,
2. O how sweet to trust in Je - sus, Just to trust His cleans-ing blood;
3. Yes, 'tis sweet to trust in Je - sus, Just from sin and self to cease;
4. I'm so glad I learned to trust Thee, Precious Je - sus, Sav - ior, Friend;

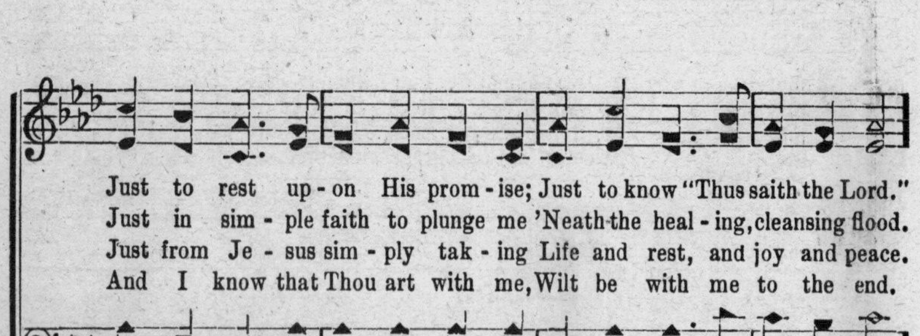
Just to rest up - on His prom - ise; Just to know "Thus saith the Lord."
Just in sim - ple faith to plunge me 'Neath the heal - ing, cleansing flood.
Just from Je - sus sim - ply tak - ing Life and rest, and joy and peace.
And I know that Thou art with me, Wilt be with me to the end.

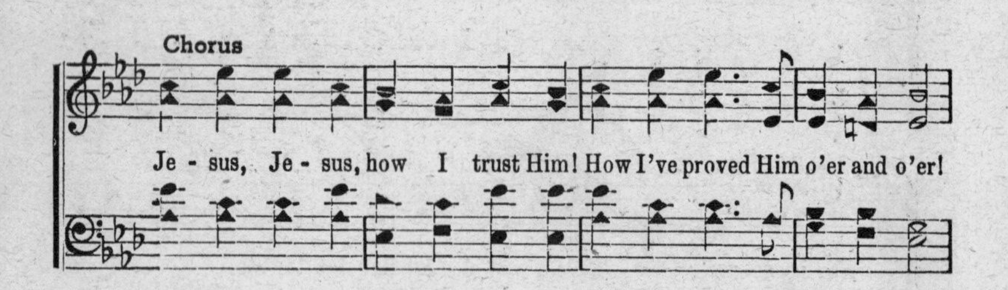
Chorus
Je - sus, Je - sus, how I trust Him! How I've proved Him o'er and o'er!

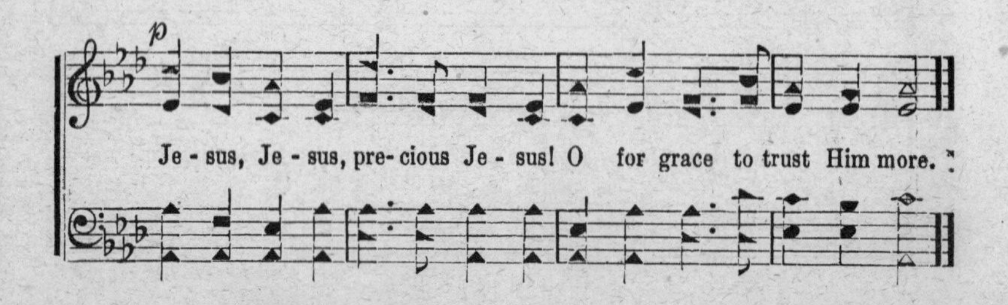
p
Je - sus, Je - sus, pre- cious Je - sus! O for grace to trust Him more.

No. 159 When the Redeemed are Gathering In
Property of W. H. Dutton, Comanche, Tex.
Rev. Johnson Oatman, Jr.
Used by per.
W. H. Dutton
1. I am think-ing of the rap-ture in our bless-ed home on high, When the re-deemed...... are gath-er-ing in;............. How we'll raise the heav'nly an-them in that ci-ty in the sky, When the re-deemed..... are gath-er-ing in.
2. There will be a great pro-ces-sion o-ver on the streets of gold, O what mu-sic, O what sing-ing o'er the ci-ty will be rolled,
3. Saints will sing redemption's sto-ry with their voic-es clear and strong, Then the an-gels all will lis-ten, for they cannot join that song,
4. Then the Sav-ior will give or-ders to pre-pare the ban-quet board, And we'll hear His in-vi-ta-tion, "Come, ye blessed of the Lord,"
When the redeemed are gathering in, are gath-er-ing in;
When the redeemed are gath-er-ing in. (are gath-er-ing in.)
Fine
Chorus
When the re-deemed........... are gath-er-ing in,........... Washed like the snow,.... and free from all sin;...........
How we will shout,............... and how we will sing,........ (Omit D.S.)........
D.S.

No. 160 The Pearly White City

Rev. 21:2

A. F. I. Arthur F. Ingle

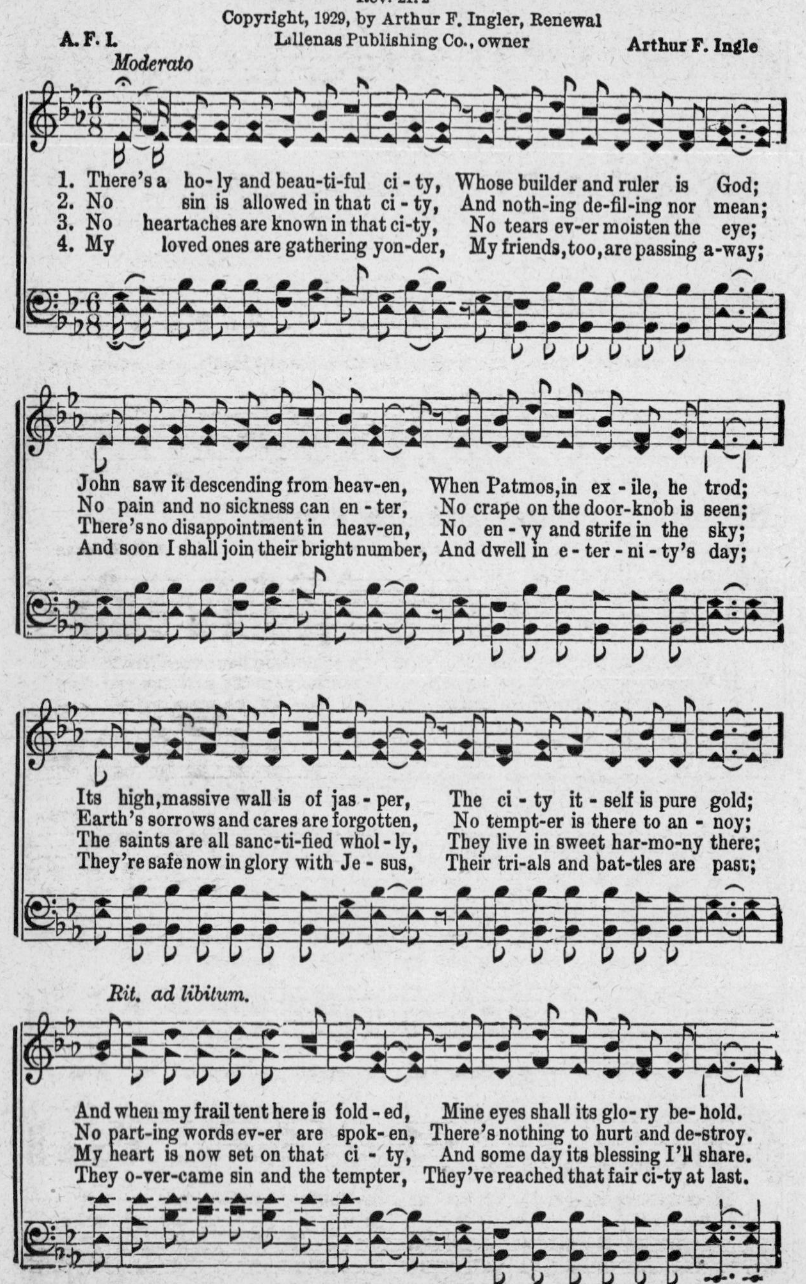
Moderato
1. There's a ho-ly and beau-ti-ful ci-ty, Whose builder and ruler is God;
2. No sin is allowed in that ci-ty, And noth-ing de-fil-ing nor mean;
3. No heartaches are known in that ci-ty, No tears ev-er moisten the eye;
4. My loved ones are gathering yon-der, My friends, too, are passing a-way;
John saw it descending from heav-en, When Patmos, in ex-ile, he trod;
No pain and no sickness can en-ter, No crape on the door-knob is seen;
There's no disappointment in heav-en, No en-vy and strife in the sky;
And soon I shall join their bright number, And dwell in e-ter-ni-ty's day;
Its high, massive wall is of jas-per, The ci-ty it-self is pure gold;
Earth's sorrows and cares are forgotten, No tempt-er is there to an-noy;
The saints are all sanc-ti-fied whol-ly, They live in sweet har-mo-ny there;
They're safe now in glory with Je-sus, Their tri-als and bat-tles are past;
Rit. ad libitum.
And when my frail tent here is fold-ed, Mine eyes shall its glo-ry be-hold.
No part-ing words ev-er are spok-en, There's nothing to hurt and de-stroy.
My heart is now set on that ci-ty, And some day its blessing I'll share.
They o-ver-came sin and the tempter, They've reached that fair ci-ty at last.

The Pearly White City
Chorus Slow
In that bright city, pearly white city, I have a mansion, an harp, and a crown;
Rit. ad lib.
Now I am watching, waiting and longing, For the white city that's soon coming down.
No. 161 He Makes Me Forget
Jame Rowe
J. M. Henson, owner
J. M. Henson
1. When-ev-er a storm sweepeth o'er me Or something has caused me to fret;
2. When-ev-er the temp-ter as-sails me, When thorns in the pathway are met;
3. His love will up-hold me and keep me, Till tri - als no more will be met;
Fine
I think of the love of my Sav-ior And then all my cares I for - get.
I think of the One who is with me And then all my cares I for - get.
And then in His presence, up yon-der, His love I shall nev- er for - get.
D.S. Yes, praise Him for-ev- er and ev - er, He keeps a glad song in my soul.
Chorus
D.S.
He makes me for-get all my tri - als, He caus- es my bur-dens to roll;

No. 162 When Our Lord Shall Come Again

Rev. J. Oatman, Jr
PROPERTY OF R. L. FERGUSON
R. L. Ferguson
1. When up - on........ the clouds of heav - en, (clouds of heaven,) Christ shall
2. Will His com - ing bring re - joic-ing? (bring re-joic-ing?) Or will
3. Will you join....... in lam - en - ta-tion? (lam - en-ta-tion?) Or the
4. Work and pray...... till Je - sus calls you, (Je - sus calls you,) Help to
come.... to earth a - gain, (to earth a-gain,) Will the world...... be glad to
it......... bring tears and pain? (bring tears and pain?) Are you read - y to re-
an - gel's glad re-frain? (their glad refrain?) Will you help.... His peo-ple
gath - er in the grain, (the golden grain,) Then with joy...... you'll meet the
see Him, (glad to see Him,) When our Lord... shall come a - gain?
ceive Him, (to re-ceive Him,)
crown Him, (help to crown Him,)
Sav-iour, (meet the Saviour,)
shall come again?
Refrain
There'll be sing-ing, there'll be shout-ing, There'll be
There'll be singing, there'll be shouting, shouting, shouting,
sor-row,... there'll be pain; There'll be weep-ing,
There'll be sorrow, there'll be pain, heart-rending pain; There'll be weeping

When Our Lord Shall Come Again

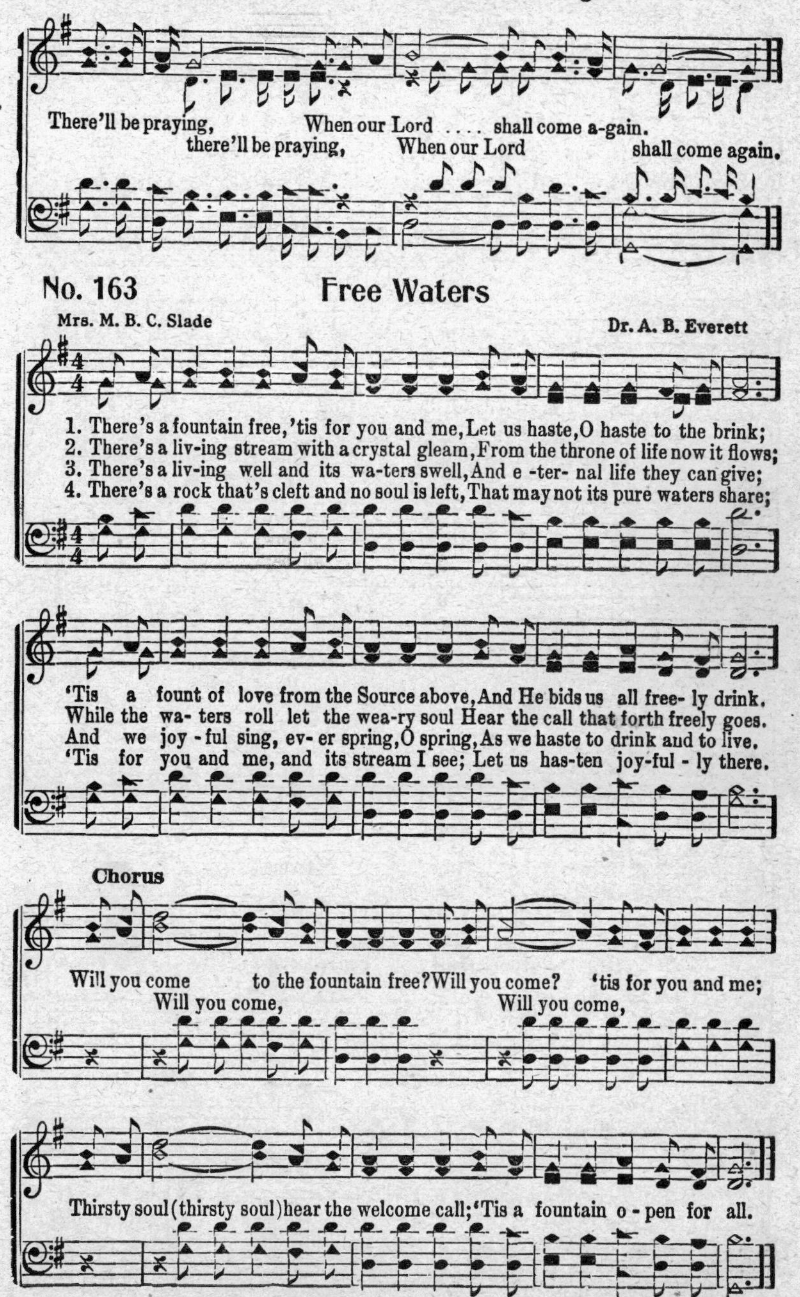

There'll be praying, When our Lord .... shall come a-gain.
there'll be praying, When our Lord shall come again.
No. 163
Free Waters
Mrs. M. B. C. Slade
Dr. A. B. Everett
1. There's a fountain free, 'tis for you and me, Let us haste, O haste to the brink;
2. There's a liv-ing stream with a crystal gleam, From the throne of life now it flows;
3. There's a liv-ing well and its wa-ters swell, And e-ter-nal life they can give;
4. There's a rock that's cleft and no soul is left, That may not its pure waters share;
'Tis a fount of love from the Source above, And He bids us all free-ly drink.
While the wa-ters roll let the wea-ry soul Hear the call that forth freely goes.
And we joy-ful sing, ev-er spring, O spring, As we haste to drink and to live.
'Tis for you and me, and its stream I see; Let us has-ten joy-ful-ly there.
Chorus
Will you come to the fountain free? Will you come? 'tis for you and me;
Will you come, Will you come,
Thirsty soul (thirsty soul) hear the welcome call; 'Tis a fountain o-pen for all.

No. 164
Redeemed
James Rowe
S. A. Ganus, owner By per.
S. A. Ganus
1. Sweet is the song............ I am sing-ing to - day;......
2. Great is my joy .... now as on-ward I go; ......
3. Pre - cious in - deed........... is my Sav - ior to me; ......
.... I'm re - deemed!.... I'm re - deemed!.... Trou-ble and
.... I'm re - deemed!.... I'm re - deemed!.... All the way
.... I'm re - deemed!.... I'm re - deemed! ... Hap- py in
sor - row .... have van-ished a - way;..........
homeward .... my prais-es shall flow;..........
glo - ry............ some day I shall be; .... I have
Chorus
I have been redeemed! I'm re - deemed by love di - vine,
been re-deemed! I'm redeemed by love divine,
Glo-ry, glo-ry, Christ is mine, Christ is mine, All to him I
Christ is mine, All to him

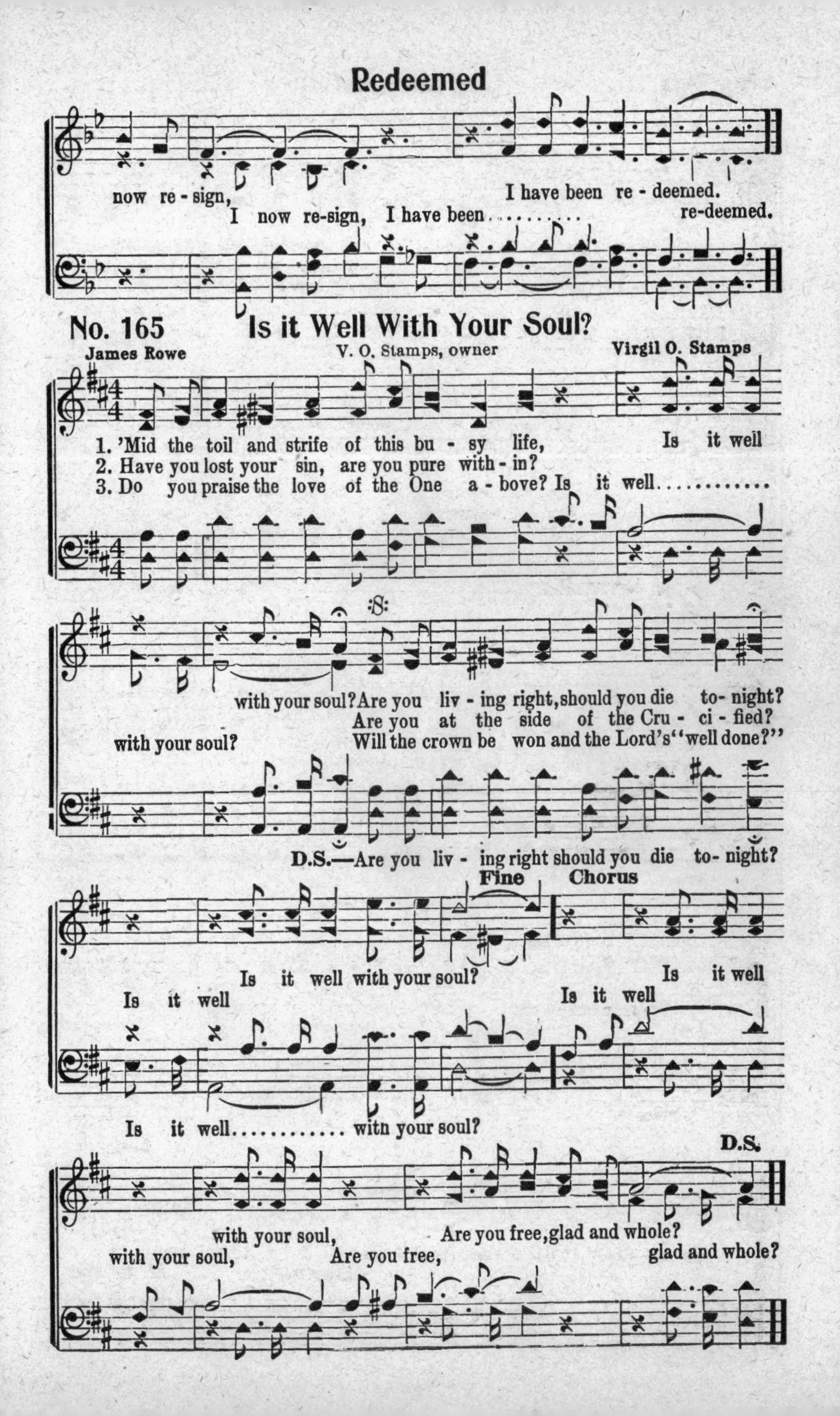
Redeemed
now re-sign, I have been re-deemed.
I now re-sign, I have been......... re-deemed.
No. 165 Is it Well With Your Soul?
James Rowe
V. O. Stamps, owner
Virgil O. Stamps
1. 'Mid the toil and strife of this bu-sy life, Is it well
2. Have you lost your sin, are you pure with-in?
3. Do you praise the love of the One a-bove? Is it well............
with your soul? Are you liv-ing right, should you die to-night?
Are you at the side of the Cru-ci-fied?
with your soul? Will the crown be won and the Lord's "well done?"
D.S.—Are you liv-ing right should you die to-night?
Fine
Chorus
Is it well with your soul? Is it well
Is it well Is it well
Is it well............ with your soul?
D.S.
with your soul, Are you free, glad and whole?
with your soul, Are you free, glad and whole?

No. 166 The Glory Train

This Arr. Copyright, 1939, by Stamps-Baxter Music and Ptg. Co.,

Mrs. J. B. Vaughan in "Favorite Song and Hymns" John B. Vaughan

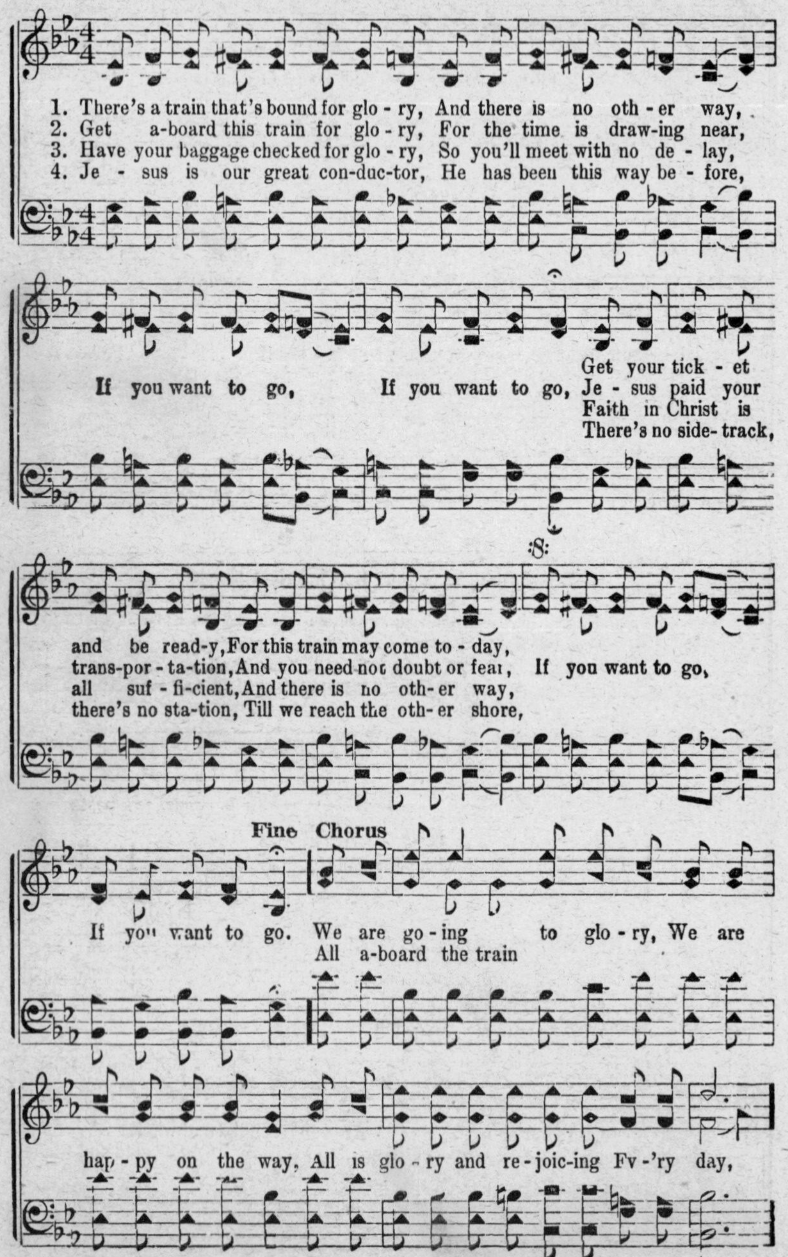

1. There's a train that's bound for glo - ry, And there is no oth - er way,
2. Get a-board this train for glo - ry, For the time is draw-ing near,
3. Have your baggage checked for glo - ry, So you'll meet with no de - lay,
4. Je - sus is our great con-duc-tor, He has been this way be - fore,
If you want to go, If you want to go,
Get your tick - et and be read-y, For this train may come to - day,
Je - sus paid your trans-por - ta-tion, And you need not doubt or fear,
Faith in Christ is all suf - fi-cient, And there is no oth-er way,
There's no side-track, there's no sta-tion, Till we reach the oth-er shore,
If you want to go,
If you want to go.
Fine
Chorus
We are go - ing to glo - ry, We are
All a-board the train
hap - py on the way, All is glo - ry and re - joic-ing Ev - 'ry day,

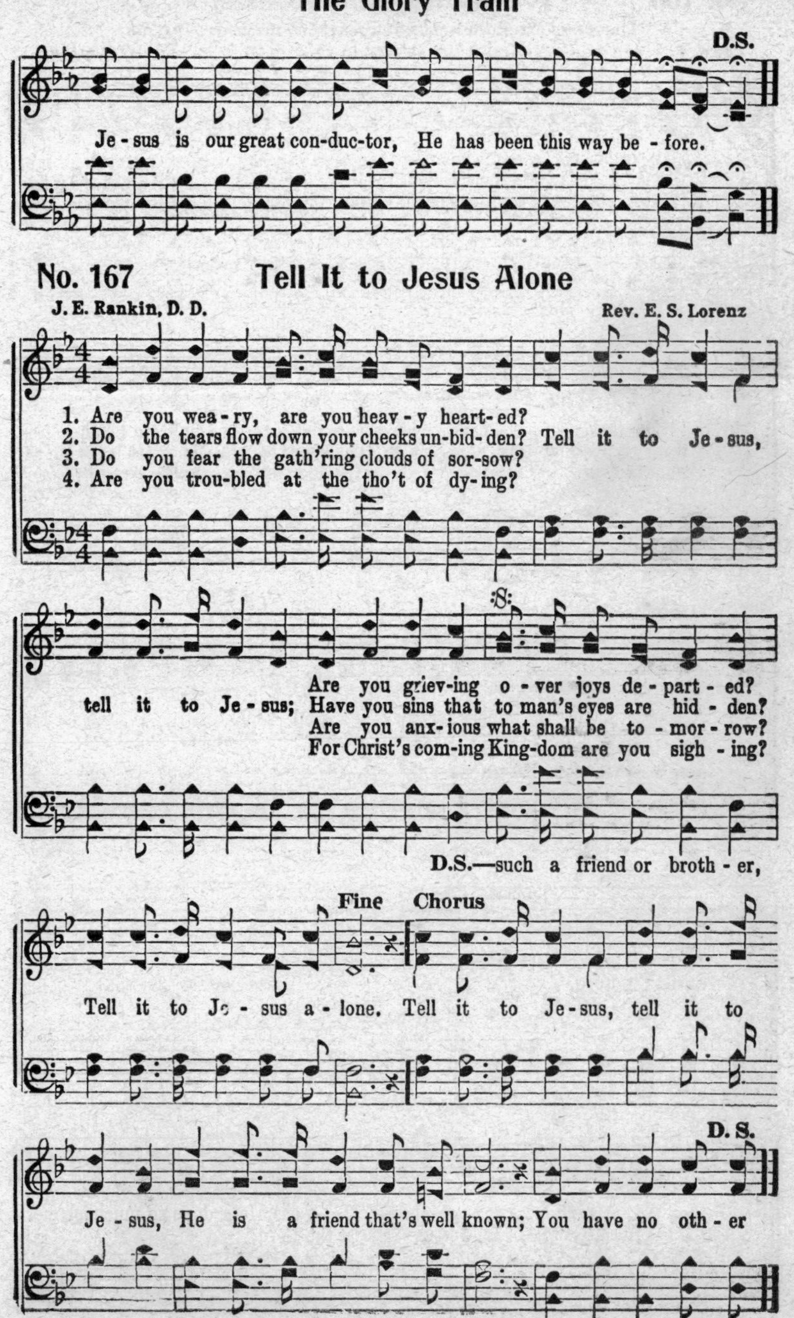
The Glory Train
D.S.
Je - sus is our great con-duc-tor, He has been this way be - fore.
No. 167
Tell It to Jesus Alone
J. E. Rankin, D. D.
Rev. E. S. Lorenz
1. Are you wea - ry, are you heav - y heart- ed?
2. Do the tears flow down your cheeks un-bid- den? Tell it to Je - sus,
3. Do you fear the gath'ring clouds of sor-sow?
4. Are you trou-bled at the tho't of dy-ing?
Are you griev-ing o - ver joys de - part - ed?
tell it to Je - sus; Have you sins that to man's eyes are hid - den?
Are you anx- ious what shall be to - mor - row?
For Christ's com-ing King-dom are you sigh - ing?
D.S.—such a friend or broth - er,
Fine
Chorus
Tell it to Je - sus a - lone. Tell it to Je-sus, tell it to
D. S.
Je - sus, He is a friend that's well known; You have no oth - er

No. 168 A Soul Winner for Jesus

"The law of the Lord is perfect, converting the soul."—Ps. 19:7

J. W. F. Copyright, Renewal, 1935, by Quartet Music Co. J. W. Ferrill

1. I want to be a soul winner for Je-sus ev'-ry day, He does so much for me;
I want to aid the lost sinner to leave his erring way, And be from bondage free.

2. I want to be a soul winner and bring the lost to Christ, That they His grace may know;
I want to live for Christ ever, and do His blessed will, Be-cause He loves me so.

3. I want to be a soul winner till Jesus calls for me, To lay my burdens down;
I want to hear Him say, servant, "You've gathered many sheaves, Receive a starry crown."

Chorus

A soul.......... winner for Je - sus, A soul........... winner for
winner for Je -sus Christ the Lord, winner for Je- sus

Je - sus, O let me be each day; A soul............. win-ner for
Christ the Lord, win-ner for Je- sus

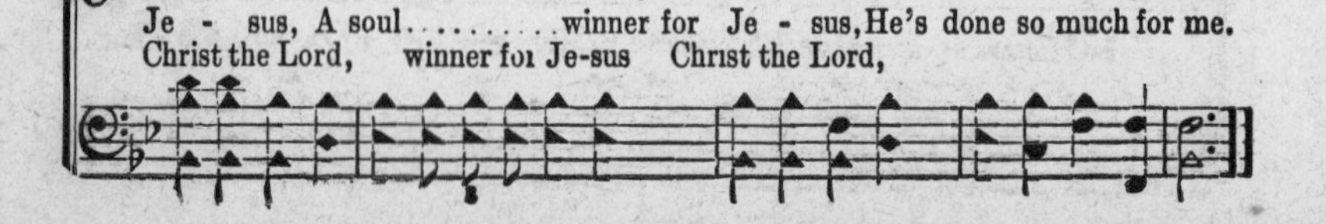

Je - sus, A soul......... winner for Je - sus, He's done so much for me.
Christ the Lord, winner for Je-sus Christ the Lord,

No. 169
Elijah's God
Copyright, 1939, by Stamps-Baxter Music and Ptg. Co.
in "Favorite Songs and Hymns"
W. J. H.
W. J. Henry
1. There was a man in old - en days, E - li - jah was his name, Be-
2. He gath-ered all the priests of Baal, To call up - on their god, They
3. Then to the top of Car-mel's mount, The ho - ly proph-et went, And
cause that sin did so abound He prayed and stopped the rain; And for three years or
cried to him the whole day long, He answered not a word; But when E - li - jah
prayed un-to the Lord a-gain, That rain once more be sent; He poured his heart out
D.S.—Yes, He con-trols the
more we're told, They nev-er had a show'r, For God in heav-en answered then, E-
called on God, Be-fore the peo-ple there, The Lord sent down the fire from heav'n, Be-
to his God, Nor was his pray'r in vain, The clouds again in heav'n were seen, God
u - ni-verse, All things obey His word, And when by faith we call on Him, Our
Fine
Refrain
li - jah's prayer of pow'r.
cause He heard his pray'r.
sent a might - y rain.
E - li - jah's God still lives to - day, O bless - ed
hum - ble pray'r is heard.
D.S.
be His name, And when His children to Him pray, He an-swers still the same;

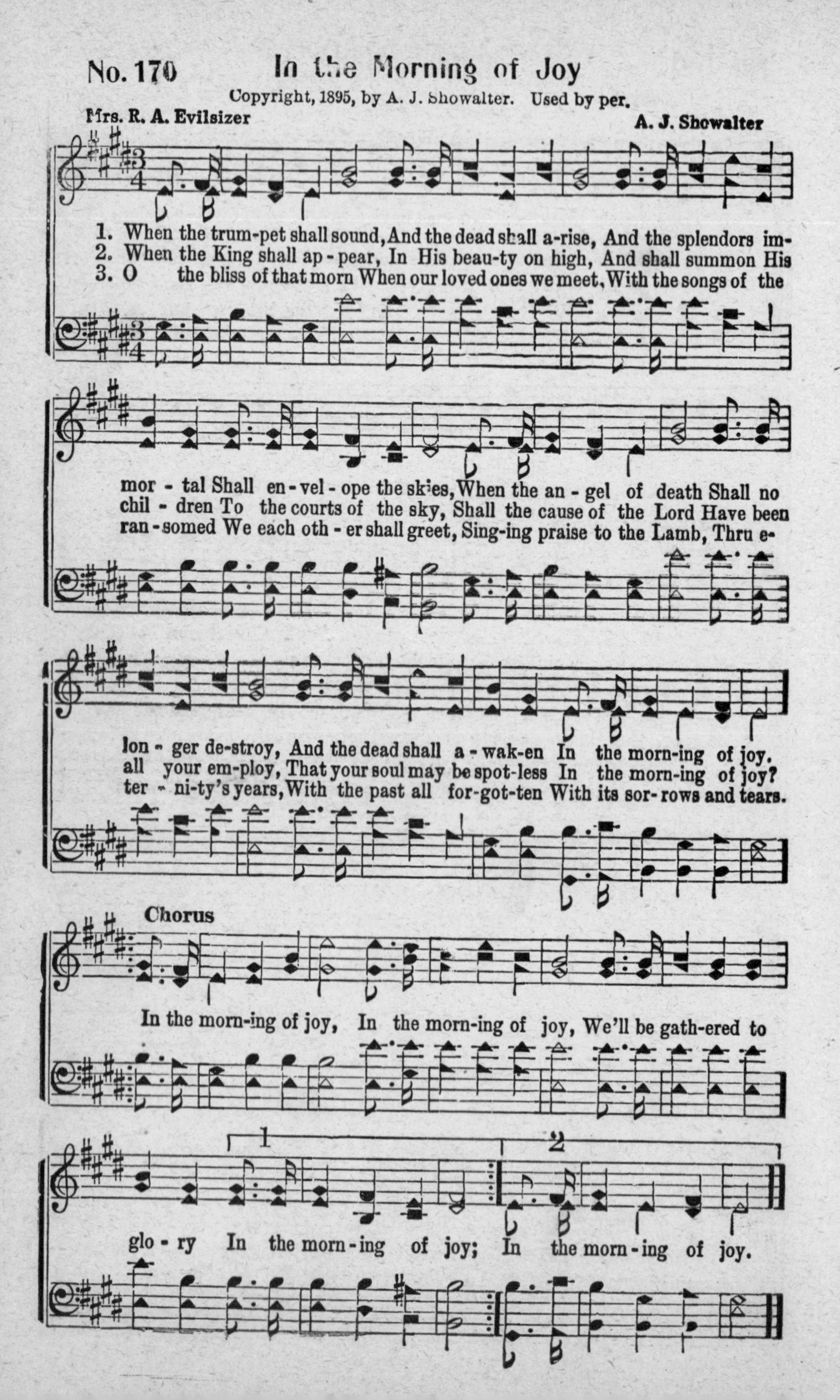
No. 170
In the Morning of Joy
Copyright, 1895, by A. J. Showalter. Used by per.
Mrs. R. A. Evilsizer
A. J. Showalter
1. When the trum-pet shall sound, And the dead shall a-rise, And the splendors im-
2. When the King shall ap - pear, In His beau-ty on high, And shall summon His
3. O the bliss of that morn When our loved ones we meet, With the songs of the
mor - tal Shall en-vel - ope the skies, When the an - gel of death Shall no
chil - dren To the courts of the sky, Shall the cause of the Lord Have been
ran - somed We each oth - er shall greet, Sing-ing praise to the Lamb, Thru e-
lon - ger de-stroy, And the dead shall a - wak-en In the morn-ing of joy.
all your em-ploy, That your soul may be spot-less In the morn-ing of joy?
ter - ni-ty's years, With the past all for-got-ten With its sor-rows and tears.
Chorus
In the morn-ing of joy, In the morn-ing of joy, We'll be gath-ered to
1
2
glo - ry In the morn - ing of joy; In the morn - ing of joy.

No. 171 Will the Circle be Unbroken

Ada R. Habershon — Chas. H. Gabriel

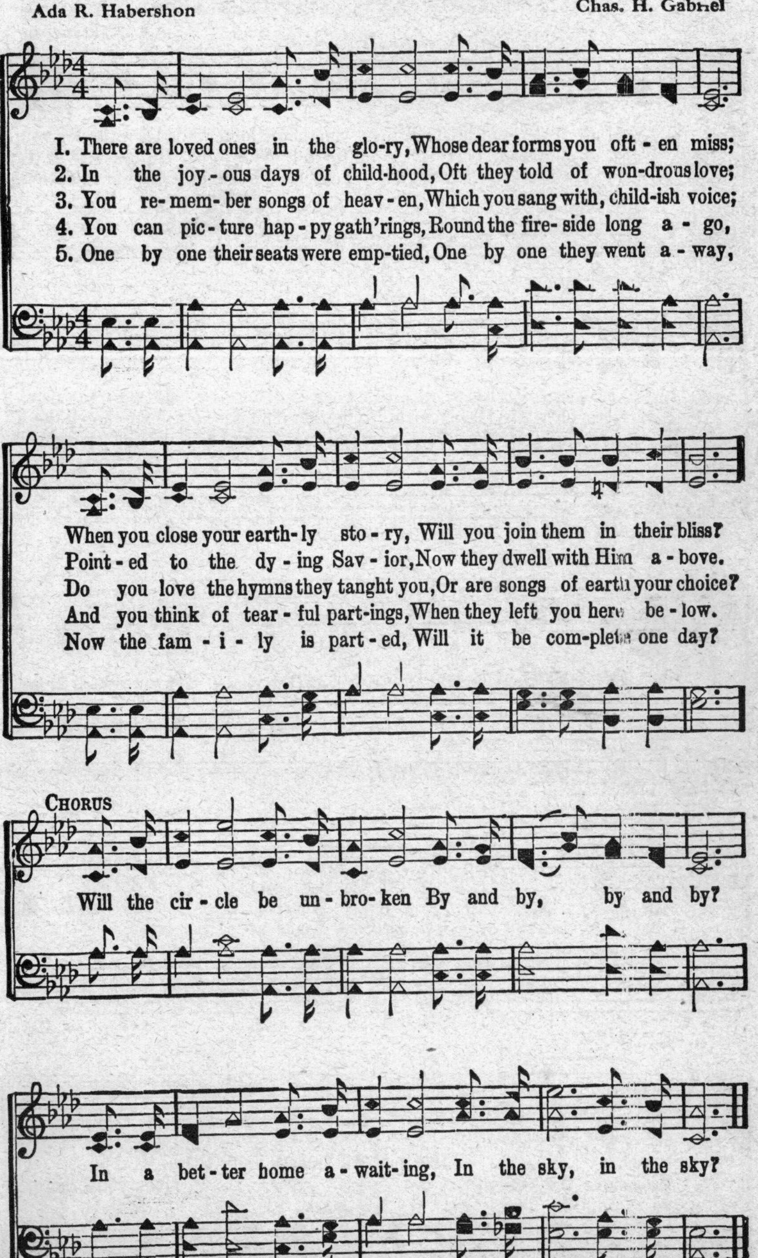
1. There are loved ones in the glo-ry, Whose dear forms you oft - en miss;
2. In the joy - ous days of child-hood, Oft they told of won-drous love;
3. You re- mem- ber songs of heav - en, Which you sang with, child-ish voice;
4. You can pic - ture hap - py gath'rings, Round the fire- side long a - go,
5. One by one their seats were emp-tied, One by one they went a - way,
When you close your earth- ly sto - ry, Will you join them in their bliss?
Point - ed to the dy - ing Sav - ior, Now they dwell with Him a - bove.
Do you love the hymns they tanght you, Or are songs of earth your choice?
And you think of tear - ful part-ings, When they left you here be - low.
Now the fam - i - ly is part - ed, Will it be com-plete one day?
CHORUS
Will the cir - cle be un - bro- ken By and by, by and by?
In a bet- ter home a - wait- ing, In the sky, in the sky?

No. 172 Kneel At the Cross

Stamps-Baxter Music & Ptg. Co., owners

C. E. M. Chas. E. Moody

1. Kneel at the cross, Christ will meet you there, Come while He waits for you;
2. Kneel at the cross, There is room for all Who would His glo - ry share;
3. Kneel at the cross, Give your i - dols up, Look un - to realms a-bove;
List to His voice, Leave with Him your care And be - gin life a new.
Bliss there a-waits, Harm can ne'er be-fall Those who are an-chored there.
Turn not a - way To life's sparkling cup; Trust on - ly in His love.
Chorus
Kneel.......... at the cross,......... Leave..........
Kneel at the cross, Kneel at the cross, Leave ev -'ry care,
ev - 'ry care;............ . Kneel........... at the
Leave ev - 'ry care; Kneel at the cross,
cross,............ Je - sus will meet you there...........
Kneel at the cross, meet you there.

No. 173 I'll Make It My Home

Copyright, 1930, by The Stamps-Baxter Music Co.
Mrs. L. J. Morris
C. C. Stafford
1. I've heard of a beau - ti - ful ci - ty a - bove, Where no one can
2. I've heard of a ci - ty with streets of pure gold, Where treas-ures can
3. I've heard of a ci - ty where stands the great throne, And an - gels in -
4. So pa - tient - ly, lov - ing - ly trust - ing my Lord, Till I shall be
go a - stray; And since I am trust - ing His won - der - ful love, I'll
not de - cay; Where love's bless-ed sto - ry with rapt - ure is told, I'll
white ar - ray Are prais - ing my Lord, with my loved and His own, I'll
called a - way, I la - bor and wait, for I know His re - ward My
Chorus
make it my home some day. I'll make it my home some day, ...
make it my home some day.
make it my home some day.
soul shall en - joy some day.
some day,
When shad - ows have passed a - way; (a - way;) A man - sion of
love is wait - ing a - bove, I'll make it my home some day. (some day.)

No. 174
I'm Saved
G. T B.
Property of G. T. Byrd
Rev. G. T. Byrd
1. 'Twas Je - sus my Sav - ior who par-doned my sins, I'm saved,
2. Sin's pleas- ure no long - er my soul will en - snare,
3. No e - vil com - pan - ions can lead me a - stray,
4. And now I am hap - py in Je - sus my King, I'm saved,so
saved, saved; And now the new life I will sure - ly be - gin,
I know I will en - ter those man-sions so fair.
For Je - sus has turned all my night in - to day,
sweet- ly saved; And thru the vast a - ges His prais - es I'll sing,
Chorus
I'm saved, saved, saved. O glo - ry to Je - sus, my
I'm saved, so sweet - ly saved.
soul is re-deemed, I'm saved, saved, saved; O glo - ry to
I'm saved,so sweet- ly saved;
Je - sus my soul is re-deemed, I'm saved, saved, saved.
I'm saved,so sweet- ly saved.

No. 175 The Book That Never Grows Old

Lizzie De Armond · Owned by R. E. Winsett · J. R. Baxter, Jr.

1. There's a wonderful Book that appeals to my heart, A mine of riches untold, Ev'ry word is a jewel of luster divine, The Book that never grows old.
2. Like a beacon of light doth it shine thru the years, To lead us safe to the fold, Thru the clouds that arise, gleaming brightly afar,
3. When the billows of life would my bark overwhelm, This anchor surely will hold, Grounded deep in God's love are its promises sure,
Chorus
It never grows old, no never grows old, The word of the Father above, It never grows old, no never grows old, Praise God for the Book of His love!

No. 176 Sweetest Mother

Copyright, 19—, by Will M. Ramsey. Stamps-Baxter Music Co., owners
Gertrude Stoddard Dennstedt
Will M. Ramsey
1. She's a lit - tle old fash-ioned, That sweet moth-er of mine, There are
2. She's a lit - tle old fash-ioned, That sweet moth-er of mine, Tho
3. She's a lit - tle old fash-ioned, She stays close - ly at home, So
man - y whose beau - ty Will my moth-er's out-shine; She's a lit - tle old
e - ven her plain-ness Now my heartstrings en-twine; Oth - er hands may be
calm and con - tent - ed Al - tho oth - ers may roam; And in ten - der young
D.S.—glo - ry a-
fash-ioned As I plain - ly can see But she is for - ev - er Sweet-est
whit - er But none oth - er so dear For they smoothed my pil-low For
childhood 'Twas a shel - ter for me And she who so graced it, Dear-est
round her, God a - bides it may be And she is for - ev - er Sweet-est
Fine Chorus
moth-er to me.
man - y a year. She's a lit - tle old fashioned, But she's sweet-er each
ev - er shall be.
moth-er to me.
D.S.
day, I a - dore her plain feat-ures And her thin locks of gray; There's a

No. 177 Heaven is Nearer Since Mother is There

Blanche C. Patterson in "Harbor Bells No. 6" Luther L. Lovett

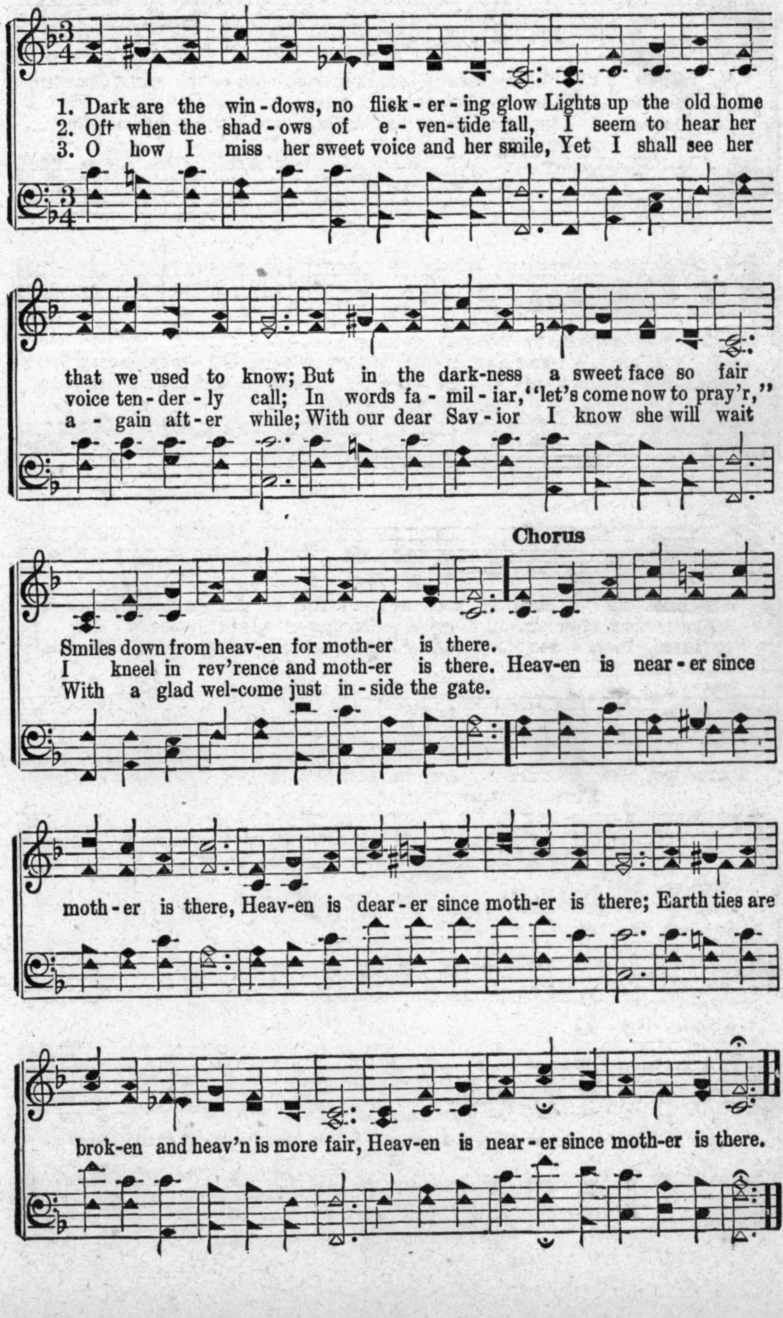

1. Dark are the win-dows, no flick-er-ing glow Lights up the old home that we used to know; But in the dark-ness a sweet face so fair Smiles down from heav-en for moth-er is there.
2. Oft when the shad-ows of e-ven-tide fall, I seem to hear her voice ten-der-ly call; In words fa-mil-iar, "let's come now to pray'r," I kneel in rev'rence and moth-er is there.
3. O how I miss her sweet voice and her smile, Yet I shall see her a-gain aft-er while; With our dear Sav-ior I know she will wait With a glad wel-come just in-side the gate.

Chorus

Heav-en is near-er since moth-er is there, Heav-en is dear-er since moth-er is there; Earth ties are brok-en and heav'n is more fair, Heav-en is near-er since moth-er is there.

No. 178
Wonderful Jesus
James Rowe
J. P. Denton, owner
J. P. Denton
1. Won-der-ful Je-sus! glo-ri-ous friend! He will be with me
2. Won-der-ful Je-sus! show-ing the way In-to the bless-ed
3. Won-der-ful Je-sus! all thru the night He will en-fold me,
un-to the end, Cheer-ing, up-hold-ing, keep-ing me strong,
king-dom of day; Guid-ing my foot-steps, hold-ing con-trol,
giv-ing me light; Then when the morn-ing breaks on the shore,
Chorus
Fear-less and loy-al, shield-ing from wrong.
Mak-ing me hap-py, keep-ing me whole. Won-der-ful Je-sus!
This He will whis-per, "Mine ev-er-more."
mar-vel-ous King! Ev-er His praise my spir-it shall sing, When I be-
hold His glo-ri-fied face, How I shall praise His won-der-ful grace!

No. 179
I'll Fly Away
Copyright, 1932, in "Wonderful Message"
Hartford Music Co., owner
A. E. B.
Albert E. Brumley
1. Some glad morn-ing when this life is o'er, I'll fly a-
2. When the shad-ows of this life have grown,
3. Just a few more wea-ry days and then, fly a-way
way;
fly a-way;
To a home on God's ce-les-tial shore,
Like a bird from pris-on bars has flown,
To a land where joys shall nev-er end,
Refrain
I'll fly a-way.
fly a-way, fly a-way.
I'll fly a-
fly a-way,
way, O glo-ry, I'll fly a-way;
fly a-way,
When I die,
in the morning,
Hal-le-lu-jah, by and by, I'll fly a-way.
fly a-way, fly a-way.

No. 180 There Shall be Showers of Blessing
El Nathan
James McGranahan
M 63 = ♩
1. "There shall be show-ers of bless-ing"—This is the prom-ise of love;
2. "There shall be show-ers of bless-ing"—Precious, re - viv - ing a - gain,
3. "There shall be show-ers of bless-ing"—Send them up - on us, O Lord!
4. "There shall be show-ers of bless-ing"—O that to - day they might fall,
There shall be sea - sons re - fresh - ing, Sent from the Sav - ior a - bove.
O - ver the hills and the val - leys Sound of a - bun-dance of rain.
Grant to us now a re - fresh - ing, Come, and now hon - or Thy Word!
Now as to God we're con-fess - ing, Now as on Je - sus we call!
Chorus.
Show - - - ers of bless - ing, Show-ers of bless-ing we need;
Show - ers, show-ers
Mer - cy-drops round us are fall - ing, But for the show-ers we plead.

No. 181
Jesus is Calling
Fanny J. Crosby
George C. Stebbins
1. Je - sus is ten - der - ly call - ing thee home—Call - ing to - day,
2. Je - sus is call - ing the wea - ry to rest--Call - ing to - day,
3. Je - sus is wait - ing, O come to Him now—Wait - ing to - day,
4. Je - sus is plead - ing, O list to His voice—Hear Him to - day,
call - ing to - day; Why from the sun-shine of love wilt thou roam
call - ing to - day; Bring Him thy bur - den, and thou shalt be blest;
wait - ing to - day; Come with thy sins, at His feet low - ly bow;
hear Him to - day; They who be - lieve on His name shall re - joice;
Far - ther and far - ther a - way?
He will not turn you a - way.
Come, and no lon - ger de - lay.
Quick - ly a - rise and a - way.
Chorus
Call - ing to - day!
Call - ing, call - ing to - day, to - day!
Call - ing to - day! .... Je - - sus is
Call - ing, call - ing to - day, to - day! Je - sus is ten - der - ly
call - - ing, Is ten - der - ly call - ing to - day.
call - ing to - day,

No. 182 Is Thy Heart Right With God?

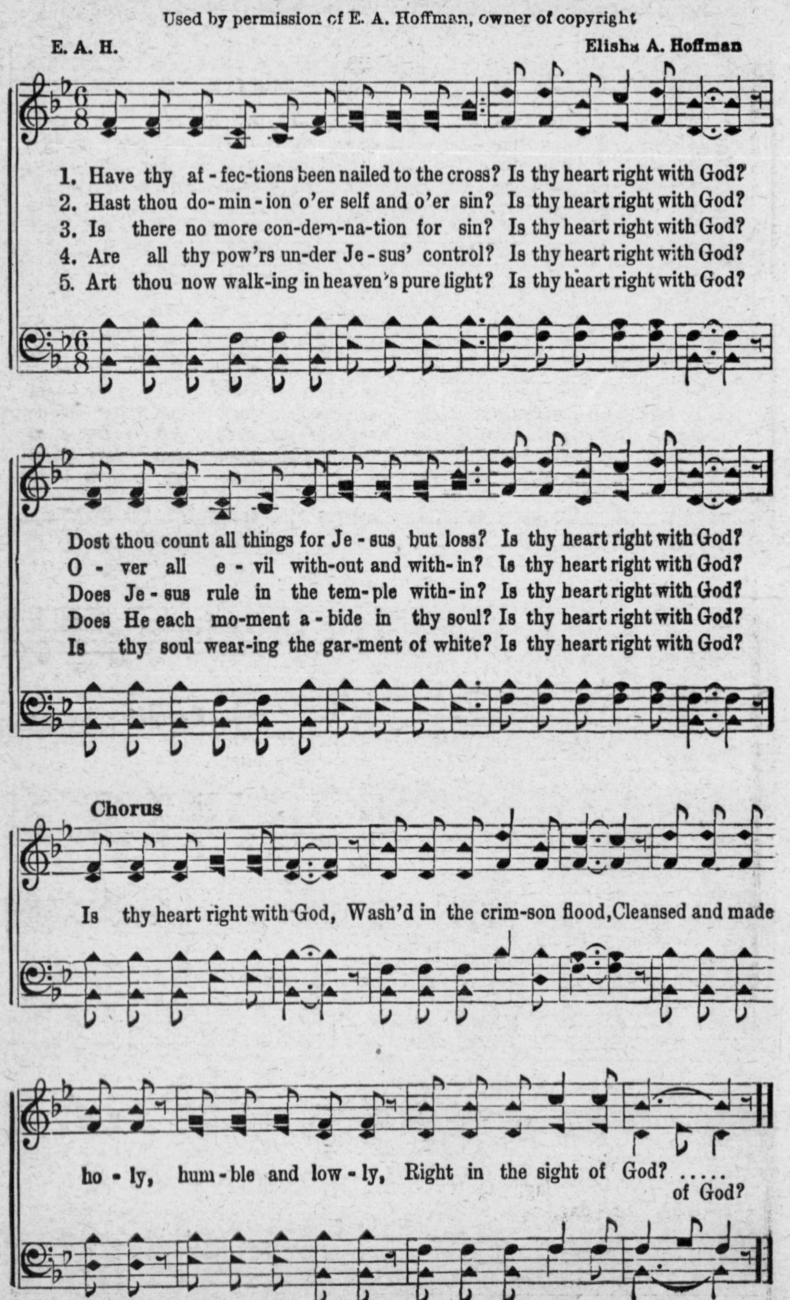
Used by permission of E. A. Hoffman, owner of copyright
E. A. H.
Elisha A. Hoffman
1. Have thy af - fec-tions been nailed to the cross? Is thy heart right with God?
2. Hast thou do- min - ion o'er self and o'er sin? Is thy heart right with God?
3. Is there no more con-dem-na-tion for sin? Is thy heart right with God?
4. Are all thy pow'rs un-der Je - sus' control? Is thy heart right with God?
5. Art thou now walk-ing in heaven's pure light? Is thy heart right with God?
Dost thou count all things for Je - sus but loss? Is thy heart right with God?
O - ver all e - vil with-out and with- in? Is thy heart right with God?
Does Je - sus rule in the tem- ple with- in? Is thy heart right with God?
Does He each mo-ment a - bide in thy soul? Is thy heart right with God?
Is thy soul wear-ing the gar-ment of white? Is thy heart right with God?
Chorus
Is thy heart right with God, Wash'd in the crim-son flood, Cleansed and made
ho - ly, hum - ble and low - ly, Right in the sight of God? .....
of God?

No. 183 I'm Going Through

The original and all arrangements of this song is the Copyright Property
Herbert Buffum
of R. E. Winsett
Arr. by R. E. Winsett
1. Lord, I have start-ed to walk in the light Shin-ing up-
2. Man-y they are who start in the race, But with the
3. I'd rath-er walk with Je-sus a-lone, And have for a
4. O brother, now will you take up the cross? Give up the
on me from heav-en so bright; I bade the world and its fol-lies a-
light they re-fused to keep pace; Oth-ers ac-cept it be-cause it is
pil-low, like Ja-cob, a stone; Liv-ing each moment with His face in
world, and count it as dross; Sell all thou hast, and give to the
Chorus
dieu, I've start-ed in, Je-sus, and I'm go-ing thru.
new; But not ver-y man-y ex-pect to go thru. I'm go-ing thru, yes,
view Than shrink from my pathway and fail to go thru.
poor, Then go thru with Je-sus and those who en-dure.
I'm go-ing thru; I'll pay the price, what-ev-er oth-ers do, I'll take the
way with the Lord's despised few, I'm go-ing thru, Je-sus, I'm go-ing thru.

No. 184
Beautiful Gleanings Bring
F. L. Eiland
Copyright, 1899, by F. L. Eiland. Used by per.
J. W. Acuff
1. Go, in ear - ly morn-ing, in - to the har -vest white, Sing a song of
2. For the faint and wea - ry, car - ry a smile of cheer, With the sad and
3. In the name of Je - sus, gath- er the sheaves to- day, Read the pre-cious
glad - ness la - bor with all your might; Let the words of Je - sus
drear - y, weep-ing an anx- ious tear; To the heart that's ach - ing
prom - ise, wag - es, He you will pay; Go with great re - joic - ing
o - ver the na - tion ring, With the com - ing eve - ning,
un - der a load of care, Lend a hand of com - fort,
glean - ing from fields of sin, Thrust thy glow - ing sic - kle,
Chorus
beau - ti - ful glean-ings bring. See the beau - ti - ful har-vest white!
cov - er its ail - ings there.
bring - ing the har - vest in. See you there,
Go, and la - bor with all your might; Let your
Go, ye there,
Let them there

Beautiful Gleanings Bring

Repeat chorus softly
an-thems of glad-ness ring, Go, and beau-ti - ful glean-ings bring!
Go, ye now,
No. 185
I'm On the Rock
"God only is my Rock."—Psa. 62 : 2
Mrs. B. Davis
Copyright, 1906, by Jno. T. Benson
Arr. Jno. T. Benson
1. The pit - falls in sin's aw - ful path Once caught and held me fast,
2. Old Sa - tan led thru mire and sand, And thorns be - fore me cast,
3. On sin's wild sea I'll sail no more, All dan - ger now is past,
4. I have es - caped the burn - ing sand, The des - ert's fier - y blast,
But Je - sus came and saved from wrath, I'm on the Rock at last.
But, by the Sav - ior's might - y pow'r, I'm on the Rock at last.
The rag - ing tem - pests all are o'er, I'm on the Rock at last.
I'm bound for heav - en's shin - ing strand, I'm on the Rock at last.
Chorus
I'm on the Rock at last, at last, I'm on the Rock at last;
My feet have found a rest - ing place, I'm on the Rock at last.

No. 186 It Is Well With My Soul
H. G. Stafford
P. P. Bliss
1. When peace like a river, attendeth my way, When sorrows like sea-billows roll, Whatever my lot, Thou hast taught me to say, "It is well, it is well with my soul."
2. Tho' Satan should buffet, tho' trials should come, Let this blest assurance control, That Christ hath regarded my helpless estate, And hath shed His own blood for my soul.
3. My sin—O the bliss of this glorious tho't!—My sin—not in part but the whole, Is nailed to His cross and I bear it no more, Praise the Lord, praise the Lord, O my soul!
4. And, Lord, haste the day when the faith shall be sight, The clouds be rolled back as a scroll, The trump shall resound, and the Lord shall descend, "Even so" it is well with my soul.
Chorus
It is well, It is well, with my soul, with my soul, It is well, it is well with my soul.

No. 187 Our Savior Left Alone
Copyright, 1932, by H. N. Lincoln. International copyright secured
James and Lincoln Stamps-Baxter Music and Ptg. Co., owners H. N. Lincoln
1. In Geth-sem - a - ne, dark, sad and lone, Grief - la - den at close of day:
2. Lat - er on, fac - ing Pi - late He stood, His death was the rab-ble's plea,
3. All a - lone, up to Cal - v'ry He went, So weak while He bore His load;
4. O the shame of that throne-crown, complete, Deep wounds in His sa - cred side;
5. To the dark, dis-mal grave did de-scend, Laid low in the si - lent tomb;
Chorus - In the world's darkest hour, all a - lone, For sins did our Lord a - tone;
Fine
There was naught but the wind's cheerless moan, Where Je-sus had gone to pray.
Yet so hum-ble, so meek, pure and good, No word of complaint made He.
Heart so sad, precious form low - ly bent, A - lone on that drear - y road.
Cru - el nails in His hands and His feet, What suff'ring be-fore He died!
"As He said" from the grave did as - cend, From death took its sting and gloom.
Then tri-um-phant o'er death and the grave, He rose all man-kind to save.
His dis - ci - ples He left, watch to keep, To them was His grief yet un-known;
They a-bused Him and led Him a - way, This King who forsook home and throne;
Pe - ter loved, had His friendship denied, And Ju - das so base - ly had gone;
As He closed His dear eye-lids in death, Much more of His love to make known;
"Thrice appeared" unto those that He loved, Trans-fig-ured, de - part - ing a - lone;
D.C.
In their weak-ness they soon fell a-sleep, Our dear Savior was left a - lone.
"Cru-ci-fy Him" they cried on that day, Je - sus bore all that shame a-lone.
Fond dis-ci-ples had fled from His side, Leaving Him there to die a - lone.
Still for - giv - ing to His latest breath, Yet for-sak-en by all a - lone.
From the earth to His throne was removed, Where He pleads for His loved, and own.

No. 188 Death Is Only a Dream

Owned by H. A. R. Horton and R. M. McIntosh. Used by permission
Rev. C. W. Ray
Music and Chorus by A. J. Buchanan
Effective as a solo
1. Sad - ly we sing and with trem - u - lous breath, As we stand by the
2. Why should we weep when the wea - ry ones rest, In the bos - om of
3. Naught in the riv - er the saints should ap - pall, Tho it fright- ful- ly
4. O - ver the tur - bid and on - rush - ing tide Doth the light of e-
mys - tic - al stream, In the val - ley and by the dark
Je - sus su - preme, In the man - sions of glo - ry pre-
dis - mal my seem, In the arms of their Sav - ior no
ter - ni - ty gleam, And the ran - somed the dark - ness and
riv - er of death, And yet 'tis no more than a dream.
pared for the blest? For death is no more than a dream.
ill can be - fall, They find it no more than a dream.
storm shall out - ride, To wake with glad smiles from their dream.
Chorus
On - ly a dream, on - ly a dream Of glo - ry beyond the dark stream, How
p
m
peaceful the slumber, how hap - py the waking, For death is on - ly a dream.

No. 189
Gathering Home
Miss Mariana B. Slade
Used by per.
R. M. McIntosh
1. Up to the beau-ti-ful Giv-er of life,—Gath-er-ing home! gath-er-ing home! Up to the dwell-ing where com-eth no strife, The dear ones are gath-er-ing home.
2. Up to the ci-ty where fall-eth no night,—Gath-er-ing home! gath-er-ing home! Up where the Sav-ior's own face is the light, The dear ones are gath-er-ing home.
3. Up to the beau-ti-ful man-sions a-bove,—Gath-er-ing home! gath-er-ing home! Safe in the arms of His in-fi-nite love, The dear ones are gath-er-ing home.
Chorus
Gath-er-ing home! .... gath-er-ing home! ....
Gath-er-ing home! gath-er-ing home!
Nev-er to sor-row more, nev-er to roam; Gath-er-ing home! ..... gath-er-ing home! .... God's children are gathering home!
Gathering home! gathering home!
Repeat pp ad lib.

No. 190 Safe in the Arms of Jesus.

Fanny J. Crosby. W. H. Doane.

M. 80 = ♩

1. Safe in the arms of Je - sus, Safe on His gen - tle breast—
There by His love o'er - shad - ed Sweet-ly my soul shall rest.
Hark! 'tis the voice of an - gels, Borne in a song to me,
O - ver the fields of glo - ry, O - ver the jas - per sea.

2. Safe in the arms of Je - sus, Safe from cor-rod - ing care;
Safe from the world's temp-ta - tions, Sin can - not harm me there.
Free from the blight of sor - row, Free from my doubts and fears;
On - ly a few more tri - als, On - ly a few more tears.

3. Je - sus, my heart's dear ref - uge, Je - sus has died for me;
Firm on the Rock of A - ges, Ev - er my trust shall be.
Here let me wait with pa - tience, Wait till the night is o'er;
Wait till I see the morn - ing Break on the gold - en shore.

D. C.—*Safe in the arms of Je - sus, Safe on His gen - tle breast—*
There by His love o'er - shad - ed Sweet - ly my soul shall rest.

FINE. D. C.

No. 191 What Would You Give in Exchange?
Copyright, 1940, Renewal. Stamps-Baxter Music & Ptg. Co., owners
F. J. Berry
J. H. Carr
1. Broth - er a - far from the Sav - ior to - day, Risk-ing your soul for the
2. Mer - cy is call - ing you, won't you give heed? Must the dear Sav- ior still
3. More than the sil - ver and gold of the earth,—More than all jew- els thy
4. If, when you stand at the bar by and by, When you are weighed in the
things that de - cay, O if to - day God should call it a - way,
ten - der - ly plead? Risk not your soul, it is pre- cious in - deed;
spir - it is worth! God, the Cre - a - tor, has giv - en it birth!
bal - ance on high, You should be sen-tenced for - ev - er to die!
Fine Chorus
What would you give in ex-change for your soul? What would you give?
in ex-change?
D.S.-What would you give in exchange for your soul?
What would you give? What would you give in ex-
in ex-change?
D. S.
change for your soul? O if to - day God should call it a - way,

No. 192
Some Glad Day
W. M. R.
Stamps-Baxter Music and Ptg. Co., owners
Will M. Ramsey
1. O bless-ed tho't...... sweet rest will come,...... Some glad day.... .
2. These heavy bur - - dens we'll lay down,......
3. Our suff'ring too .... will soon be past,........
4. All war and strife...... will soon be o'er,........
1. O blessed tho't sweet rest will come, Some glad day
af - ter while;.... When all our earth - - ly toil is done,..........
When we re - ceive........ our heav'nly crown,........
When we shall find........ sweet rest at last,........
We'll find sweet peace.... on heaven's shore,........
after while; When all our earthly toil is done, our toil is done,
Chorus
Fine
There'll come a glad day af - ter while, O af - ter while,
af - ter while. af-ter while,
D.S.-There'll come a glad day af - ter while, (after while.)
D.S.
af - ter while, There'll come a glad day af - ter while,
af - ter while, af - ter while,

No. 193 There's a Crown for Your Cross

Miss Ada Powell Austin Hazelwood, owner Used by per, Austin Hazelwood

1. There's a crown for your cross, when the teardrops that stray Will be driv-en for-
2. There's a crown for your cross when the daylight shall dawn, When the night's dreary
3. There's a crown for your cross where the sweet flowers grow, On the banks where bright
4. There's a crown for your cross and a pow - er di-vine, There's a love all a-
ev - er a - way; Where the cares that oppress will at last be laid down, You'll be
shad-ows are gone; You will meet with glad smiles and nev- er a frown, You'll be
wa - ters doth flow; Where the Sav-ior a-waits at the beau-ti-ful gate, You'll be
round you will shine; Where the cross for the crown is for- ev-er laid down, You'll be
Chorus
giv - en a beau-ti- ful crown. There's a crown for your cross, there is gain for your
loss, You'll be giv - en a crown for your cross;.... There's a beau-ti- ful crown
when your cross is laid down, You'll be giv - en a beau-ti - ful crown.

No. 194 Prepare to Meet Thy God

(From a sermon by Rev. J. F. Haley, July, 1909)

J. H. S. J. H. Stanley, owner J. H. Stanley

1. Care-less soul, why will you lin - ger, Wand'ring from the fold of God?
2. Why so tho't-less are you stand-ing While the fleet - ing years go by,
3. Hear you not the earn-est plead-ings Of your friends that wish thou well?
4. If you spurn the in - vi - ta - tion Till the Spir - it shall de- part,
Hear you not the in - vi - ta - tion? O pre-pare to meet thy God.
And your life is spent in fol - ly? O pre-pare to meet thy God.
And per-haps be - fore to - mor - row You'll be called to meet your God.
Then you'll see your sad con - di - tion, Un - pre-pared to meet thy God.
Chorus
Care-less soul, ... O heed the warn-ing, ... For your
O careless soul, heed the warning,
life .... will soon be gone; ...... O how sad .... to
will soon be gone, O yes, your life will soon be gone; to face the judgment,
face the judgment, ... Un-pre-pared .... to meet thy God.
O how sad to face the judgment, Unprepared to meet thy God.

No. 195 He Whispers Sweet Peace to Me

W. M. R. Will M. Ramsey

1. Sometime when mis - giv - ings dark - en the day, And faith's light I can - not see; I ask my dear Lord to bright-en the way, He whis - pers sweet peace to me.
2. I could not go on with-out Him I know, The world would o'er whelm my soul; For I could not see the right way to go, When temp - ta - tions o'er me roll.
3. I trust Him thru faith, by faith hold His hand, And sometimes my faith is weak, And then when I ask Him to take com-mand, It seems that I hear Him speak.
4. He speaks in a still, small voice we are told, A voice that dis- pels all fear; And when I'm in doubt, or trou-bled in soul, That still small voice I can hear.

Chorus

Yes, He whis-pers sweet peace to me, He whis-pers to me, He whis-pers sweet peace to me, When
He whis-pers to me, ... He whis-pers sweet peace to me, ...

I am cast down in spir - it and soul, He whispers sweet peace to me.

No. 196 Will Jesus Find Us Watching?

"Let us not sleep, as do others; but let us watch and be sober."—1 Thes. 5:6

Fanny J. Crosby Copyright, 1876, by W. H. Doane. Used by per. W. H. Doane

1. When Je - sus comes to re - ward His serv-ants, Wheth-er it be
2. If at the dawn of the ear - ly morn-ing, He shall call us
3. Have we been true to the trust He left us? Do we seek to
4. Bless - ed are those whom the Lord finds watch-ing, In His Glo - ry
noon or night, Faith - ful to Him will He find us watch-ing,
one by one, When to the Lord we re - store our tal - ents,
do our best! If in our hearts there is naught con - demns us,
they shall share; If He shall come at the dawn or mid-night,
Chorus
With our lamps all trimmed and bright?
Will He an-swer thee, "Well done?" O can we say, we are read-y,
We shall have a glo - rious rest.
Will He find us watch- ing there?
broth-er? Read- y for the soul's bright home? Say will He find you and
me still watch-ing, Wait - ing, wait - ing when the Lord shall come?

No. 197 Sin Can Never Enter There

Rev. 21: 27

C. W. Naylor Copyright, 1902, by B. E. Warren. R. E. Winsett, owner B. E. Warren

1. Heav-en is a ho - ly place, filled with glo - ry and with grace,
2. If you hope to dwell at last, when your life on earth is past,
3. You may live in sin be-low, heav-en's grace re - fuse to know,
4. If you cling to sin till death, when you draw your lat - est breath,
Sin can nev - er en - ter there; All with - in its gates are pure,
In that home so bright and fair, You must here be cleans'd from sin,
But you can - not en - ter there; It will stop you at the door,
You will sink in dark de-spair, To the re - gions of the lost
from de - file - ment kept se - cure, Sin can nev - er en - ter there.
have the life of Christ with - in, Sin can nev - er en - ter there.
bar you out for - ev - er - more, Sin can nev - er en - ter there.
thus to prove at aw - ful cost, Sin can nev - er en - ter there.
Chorus
Sin can nev- er en - ter there, Sin can nev- er en- ter there; So, if at the
judg-ment bar, sin -ful spots your soul shall mar, You can nev- er en - ter there.

No. 198 Savior, Lead Me, Lest I Stray
F. M. D.
Frank M. Davis
1. Sav - ior, lead me lest I stray, Gen - tly lead me all the way; I am safe when by Thy side, I would in Thy love a - bide.
2. Thou, the ref - uge of my soul, When life's storm - y bil - lows roll; I am safe when Thou art nigh, All my hopes on Thee re - ly.
3. Sav - ior, lead me then at last, When the storm of life is past, To the land of end - less day, Where all tears are wiped a - way.
1. Sav - ior, lead me, lest I stray, Gen- tly lead me all the way; I am safe when by Thy side I would in Thy love a-bide.
Chorus
Lead me, lead me, Sav - ior, lead me, lest I stray;........ Gen - tly down the stream of time, Lead me, Sav-ior, all the way.
lest I stray
stream of time,
all the way.

No. 199 Did You Think to Pray?

"Be careful for nothing; but in every thing by prayer and supplication with thanksgiving let your requests be made known unto God."—Phil. 4: 6.

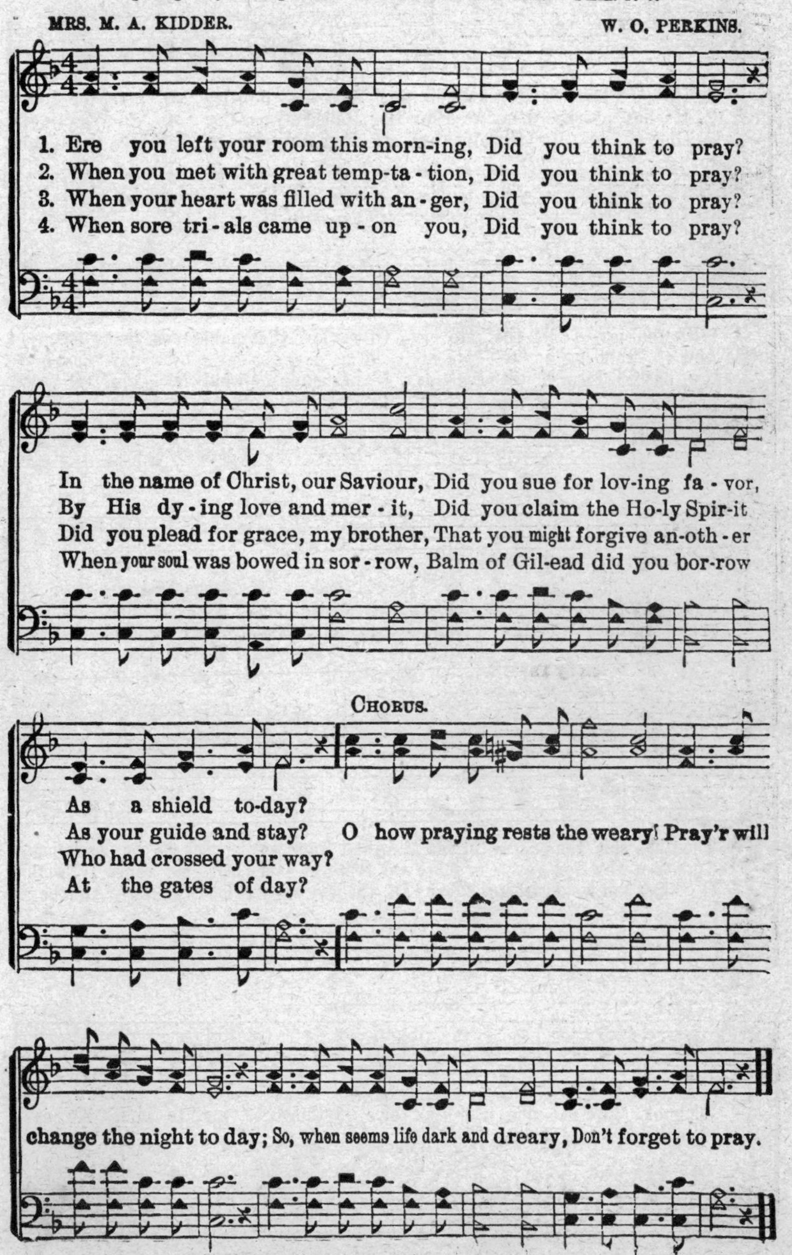
MRS. M. A. KIDDER.
W. O. PERKINS.
1. Ere you left your room this morn-ing, Did you think to pray?
2. When you met with great temp-ta-tion, Did you think to pray?
3. When your heart was filled with an-ger, Did you think to pray?
4. When sore tri-als came up-on you, Did you think to pray?
In the name of Christ, our Saviour, Did you sue for lov-ing fa-vor,
By His dy-ing love and mer-it, Did you claim the Ho-ly Spir-it
Did you plead for grace, my brother, That you might forgive an-oth-er
When your soul was bowed in sor-row, Balm of Gil-ead did you bor-row
As a shield to-day?
As your guide and stay?
Who had crossed your way?
At the gates of day?
CHORUS.
O how praying rests the weary! Pray'r will
change the night to day; So, when seems life dark and dreary, Don't forget to pray.

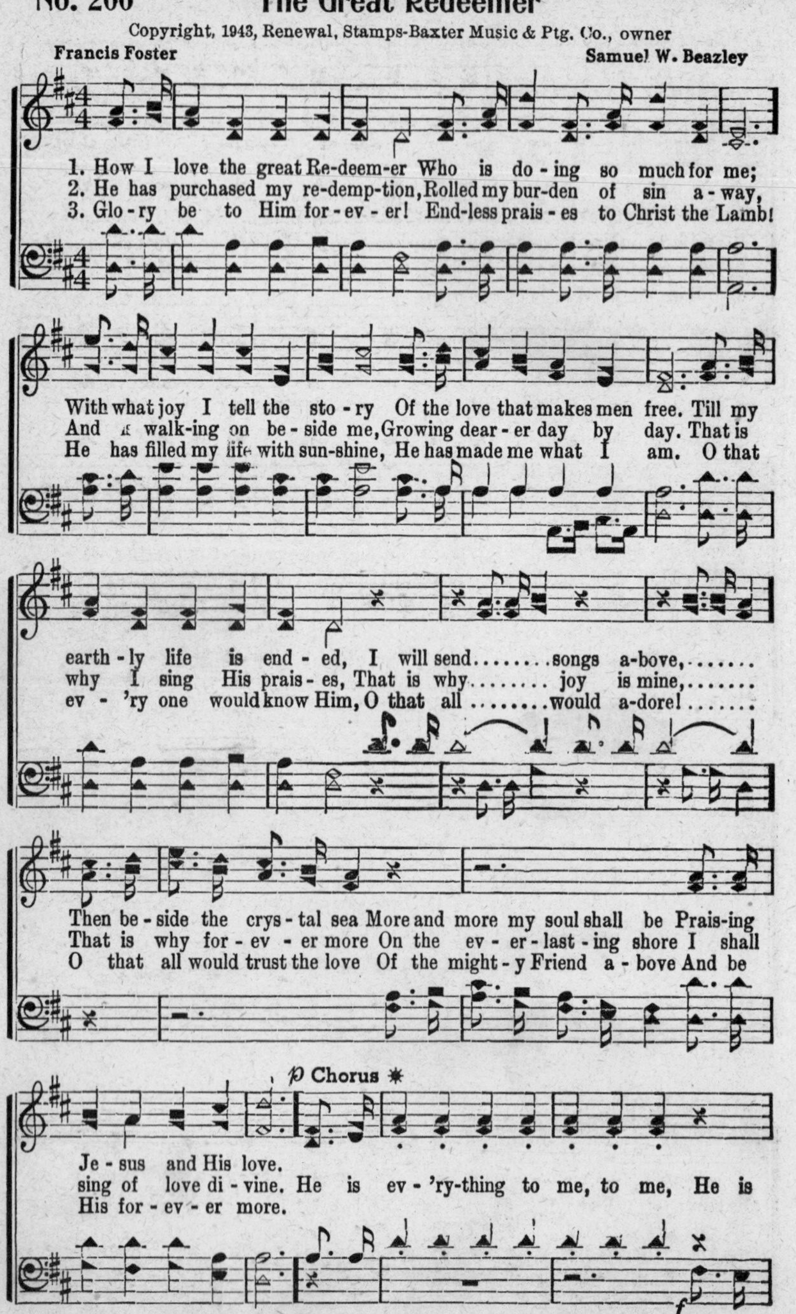
No. 200
The Great Redeemer
Copyright, 1943, Renewal, Stamps-Baxter Music & Ptg. Co., owner
Francis Foster
Samuel W. Beazley
1. How I love the great Re-deem-er Who is do-ing so much for me;
2. He has purchased my re-demp-tion, Rolled my bur-den of sin a-way,
3. Glo-ry be to Him for-ev-er! End-less prais-es to Christ the Lamb!
With what joy I tell the sto-ry Of the love that makes men free. Till my
And is walk-ing on be-side me, Growing dear-er day by day. That is
He has filled my life with sun-shine, He has made me what I am. O that
earth-ly life is end-ed, I will send........songs a-bove,.......
why I sing His prais-es, That is why........ joy is mine,.......
ev-'ry one would know Him, O that all ....would a-dore!.......
Then be-side the crys-tal sea More and more my soul shall be Prais-ing
That is why for-ev-er more On the ev-er-last-ing shore I shall
O that all would trust the love Of the might-y Friend a-bove And be
Je-sus and His love.
sing of love di-vine.
His for-ev-er more.
p Chorus *
He is ev-'ry-thing to me, to me, He is
f

*Bass to be sung loud. The other parts subdued and semi-staccato.

The Great Redeemer

He is ev - 'ry - thing to me, And ev - 'ry-thing shall
ev - 'ry-thing to me, And ev - 'ry-thing shall al-ways
al - ways be; I will nev - er cease to raise A
be; I will nev - er cease to raise A song of
song of glad - ness in His praise; Here, and in the
glad - ness in His praise; Here, and in the world a-
world a - bove, My soul shall sing of sav - ing love;
bove, My soul shall sing of sav-ing love; Life and
Life and light and joy is He, The precious Friend who died for me.
light and joy is He, The precious Friend who died for me.

No. 201 I Know Somebody's List'ning

A. E. B.
Albert E. Brumley
1. Tho a pil-grim, a stranger, a beggar I be As here I go trav-el-ing
2. Thru the troubles and tri-als and darkest of night He speaks and I hear His kind
3. Let the world amble on like the Bab'lon of old With beau-ty and charm to al-
on, Tho dearest of friends will not lis-ten to me And chide me for trusting God's
voice, Thru darkness He giveth me comfort and light, He keeps me, in Him I re-
lure, My hope in the heav-en-ly treasures untold Is far more ex-ceeding and
Son; Tho the world in its fol-ly, its sin and its shame, Neg-lect-ful-ly
joice; What more could I ask when the shadows grow dim And kindred and
sure; My Re-deem-er will an-swer my sad fee-ble plea And guide me each
turns me a - way, I still have my Sav - ior, O praise His sweet name, He
loved ones be - tray, What more could I cher-ish than Je - sus the Friend Who
hour of the day, A won-der-ful, won-der-ful Sav - ior is He Who
hears ev-'ry-thing that I say..........
Chorus
Know somebody's list'ning,
ev-'ry-thing that I say. I know............ somebody's

I Know Somebody's List'ning
know somebody's list'-ning, Hears ev - 'ry thing that I say,
list'-ning .... And hears ev -'ry thing that I say, ... I
Know somebody answers, know somebody answers, Pray'r
know............ some-bod-y an-swers.......... Ev-'ry pray'r that I
that I se - cret - ly pray; Know somebody loves me know somebody
se - cret - ly pray;.......... I know.......... some-bod-y loves me......
loves me, Nev - er will turn me a - way, Je - - -
...... And nev - er will turn me a - way,.......... 'Tis Je-sus the
sus of Mount Calvary And He hears ev'ry thing that I say...........
Sav - ior of ev'ry thing that I say.

No. 202 Anywhere Is "Home"

J. M. Henson — Morris and Henson, owners — Homer F. Morris

1. Earth-ly wealth and fame May nev-er come to me,
Earth-ly wealth and hon-ored fame
2. Oft I'm tossed a-bout And driv-en by the foe,
Oft I'm tossed, am tossed a-bout
3. I will la - - - bor on Till I am called a-way,
I will la-bor, la-bor on,

And a pal - - - ace fair, Here mine may nev-er be;
And an earth-ly pal-ace fair,
Sad with-in, with-out Wher-ev-er I may go;
Sad with-in and sad with-out,
Till the morn shall dawn, Of that e-ter-nal day;
Till the morn at last shall dawn,

But let come what may, If Christ for me doth care,
But let come, let come what may,
But I press a-long Still look-ing up in pray'r,
So I press, I press a-long,
Look-ing un - - - to Him, Who keeps me in His care,
Ev-er look-ing un-to Christ

An-y-where is home, If He is on-ly there.
An-y-where is home, sweet home,
For it's home, sweet home, If Christ is on-ly there.
O I know 'tis home, sweet home,
An-y-where is home, If Christ, my Lord is there.
An-y-where is home, sweet home, on-ly there.

Anywhere Is "Home"

Chorus
An - y - where is home, Let come and go what may,
An - y-where sweet home, come what may,
An - y - where I roam, He keeps me all the way;
An - y - where I chance to roam, each day;
So for His dear sake, My cross I'll meek - ly bear,
So far my dear Mas-ter's sake
An - y - where is home, If Christ, my Lord, is there.
An - y-where sweet home, on - ly there.

No. 203 Jesus, Hold My Hand

A. E. B. Albert E. Brumley

1. As I trav - el thru this pil - grim land There is a Friend who
2. Let me trav - el in the light di - vine That I may see the
3. When I wan - der thru the val - ley dim To - ward the set - ting

walks with me, Leads me safe - ly thru the sink - ing sand, It is the
bless - ed way; Keep me that I may be whol ly Thine And sing re-
of the sun, Lead me safe - ly to a land of rest If I a

Christ of Cal - va - ry; This would be my pray'r, dear Lord, each
demption's song some day; I will be a sol-dier brave and
crown of life have won; I have put my faith in Thee, dear

day To help me do the best I can, For I need Thy light to
true And ev - er firm - ly take a stand, As I on - ward go and
Lord, That I may reach the gold - en strand, There's no oth - er friend on

guide me day and night, Bless - ed Je - sus, hold my hand.
dai - ly meet the foe, Bless - ed Je - sus, hold my hand.
whom I can de - pend, Bless - ed Je - sus, hold my hand.

Jesus, Hold My Hand

Chorus
Bless-ed Je - sus, hold my hand, Yes, I need Thee
Je - - - sus, hold my hand, I need Thee ev - 'ry
ev - 'ry hour, Thru this land, this pil - grim land
hour, Thru this pil - grim land, Pro-
By Thy sav-ing pow'r; Hear my plea, my fee - ble plea,
tect me by Thy pow'r; Hear my fee-ble plea,
Lord, dear Lord, look down on me, When
O Lord, look down on me, When I kneel in
I kneel in pray'r, Bless - ed Je-sus, hold my hand.
pray'r I hope to meet you there,

No. 204 **I'd Rather Be an Old-Time Christian**

(THAN ANYTHING I KNOW)

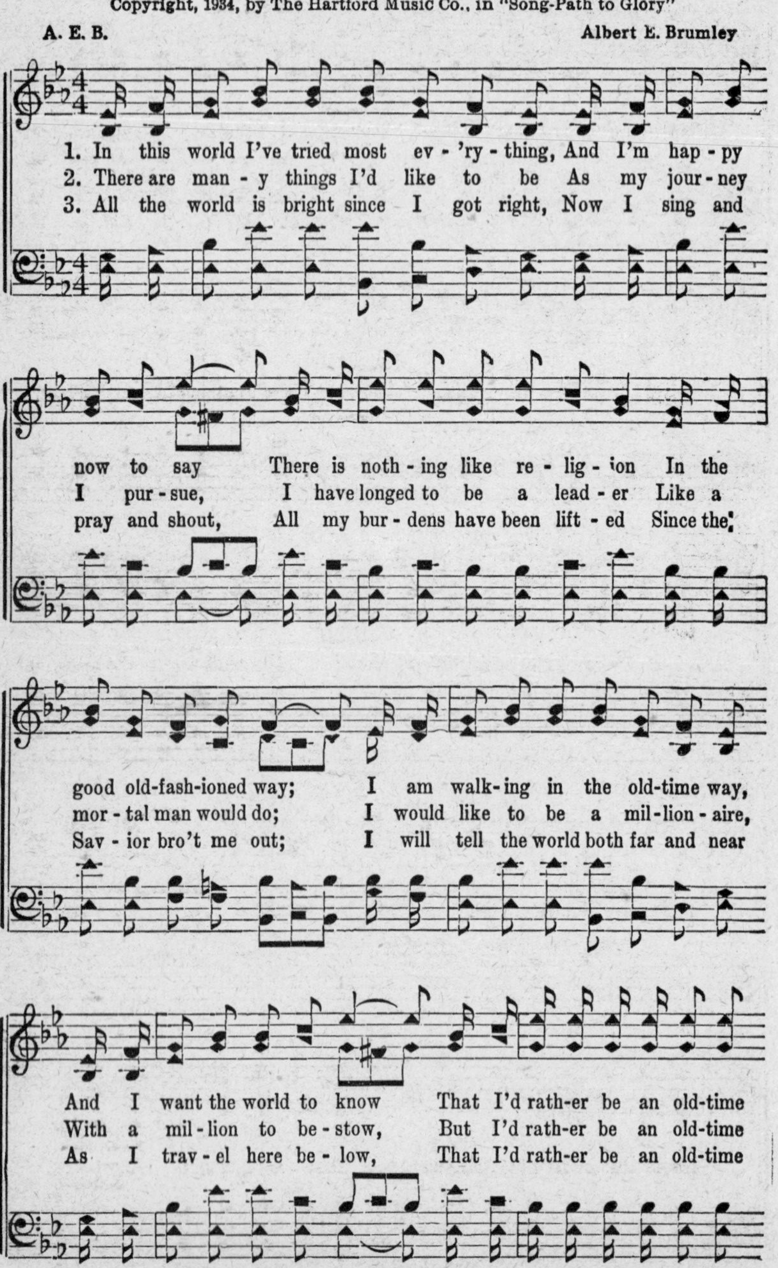
A. E. B.
Albert E. Brumley
1. In this world I've tried most ev - 'ry - thing, And I'm hap - py now to say There is noth - ing like re - lig - ion In the good old-fash-ioned way; I am walk-ing in the old-time way, And I want the world to know That I'd rath-er be an old-time
2. There are man - y things I'd like to be As my jour - ney I pur - sue, I have longed to be a lead - er Like a mor - tal man would do; I would like to be a mil-lion - aire, With a mil - lion to be - stow, But I'd rath-er be an old-time
3. All the world is bright since I got right, Now I sing and pray and shout, All my bur - dens have been lift - ed Since the Sav - ior bro't me out; I will tell the world both far and near As I trav - el here be - low, That I'd rath-er be an old-time

I'd Rather Be an Old-Time Christian

Chorus
Chris-tian(Lord,) Than an-y-thing I know. I'd rath-er be an old-time
Christian(Lord,) Than an-y-thing I know, There's nothing like an old-time
Chris-tian With a Chris-tian love to show; I'm walk-ing in the grand old
high-way, And I'm tell-ing ev-'ry-where I go, That I'd
rath-er be an old-time Christian(Lord,) Than an-y-thing I know.

No. 205 Just a Little While

E. M. B. — E. M. Bartlett

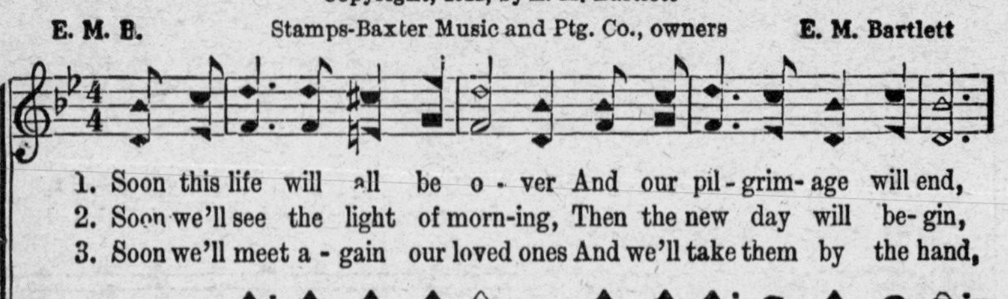

1. Soon this life will all be o - ver And our pil - grim - age will end,
2. Soon we'll see the light of morn-ing, Then the new day will be - gin,
3. Soon we'll meet a - gain our loved ones And we'll take them by the hand,

Soon we'll take our heav'n-lv jour-ney, Be at home a - gain with friends;
Soon we'll hear the Fa - ther call - ing, "Come, my chil - dren en - ter in;"
Soon we'll press them to our bos - om O - ver in the prom-ised land;

Heav-en's gates are stand - ing o - pen, Wait - ing for our en-trance there,
Then we'll hear a choir of an - gels, Sing - ing out the vic - t'ry song,
Then we'll be at home for - ev - er, Thru - out all e - ter - ni - ty,

Some sweet day we're go - ing o - ver, All the beau-ties there to share.
All our trou - bles will be end - ed And we'll live with heaven's throng.
What a bless - ed, bless - ed morn-ing That e - ter - nal morn will be!

Just a Little While

Chorus
Just a lit - tle while to stay here, Just a lit - tle while to
stay here, stay here,
wait, Just a lit - tle while to la - bor In the path that's
to wait, la - bor, la - bor,
al-ways straight, Just a lit - tle more of
that's al-ways straight and nar-row
trou - - ble In this low and sin - ful state;
trou - ble, trou - ble, sin - ful state;
Then we'll enter heaven's por - tals, Sweeping thru the pearly gates.
por-tals, por-tals, pearl-y gates

No. 206 Master, the Tempest is Raging
Miss M. A. Baker
H. R. Palmer
1. Mas - ter, the tem - pest is rag - ing! The bil - lows are toss - ing
2. Mas - ter, with an - guish of spir - it I bow in my grief to-
3. Mas - ter, the ter - ror is o - ver, The el - e- ments sweet - ly
high! The sky is o'er-shad-owed with black-ness, No shel - ter or
day; The depths of my sad heart are trou - bled — O wak - en and
rest; Earth's sun in the calm lake is mir - rored, And heav-en's with-
help is nigh; Car - est Thou not that we per - ish? How canst Thou
save, I pray; Tor - rents of sin and of an - guish Sweep o'er my
in my breast; Lin - ger, O bless - ed Re - deem - er! Leave me a
lie a - sleep, When each mo - ment so mad - ly is threat-'ning A
sink - ing soul; And I per - ish! I per - ish! dear Mas - ter O
lone no more; And with joy I shall make the best har - bor, And
Chorus
grave in the an - gry deep?
hast - en, and take con - trol. The winds and the waves shall o-
rest on the bliss - ful shore.

Master, the Tempest is Raging
p
pp
bey Thy will, Peace, be still! Wheth-er the wrath of the
Peace, be still, peace, be still!
cres.
storm-tossed sea, Or demons or men, or what-ev-er it be, No
wa-ters can swal-low the ship where lies The Mas-ter of o-cean, and
ff
m
earth, and skies; They all shall sweet-ly o-bey Thy will, Peace, be still!
p
pp
peace, be still! They all shall sweet-ly o-bey Thy will, Peace, peace, be still!

No. 207 I Guess I'm Just a Little Old Fashioned

A. E. B. Albert E. Brumley

1. Here so man - y are break-ing tra - di - tions That are sa - cred the
2. O they say I'm old fash-ioned for trust - ing In the sto - ry of
3. In this world that is doubt-ing and chang-ing, Chang-ing ways that are

whole world a - round, Seek-ing on - ly for rich - es and pleas- ures
long, long a - go, And they say I've an old fash-ioned fan - cy
old for the new, There's a need for the old - time re - li - gion

That so free- ly in this life a - bound; But I still love the pre-cious old
Just be-cause I be-lieve it is so; Well, the whole world can call me old
And the pray'rs of the Christians so true; May the Sav-ior who rul - eth in

Bi - ble, 'Tis my com-fort, my guide and my stay, O I guess I'm just a
fash - ioned, They can call me what-ev-er they may, But I'll still be just a
heav - en Hear the old fashioned pray'rs that we pray, May He keep us just a

lit - tle old fash - ioned But I still love the old fash-ioned way.
lit - tle old fash - ioned For I still love the old fash-ioned way.
lit - tle old fash - ioned For I still love the old fash-ioned way.

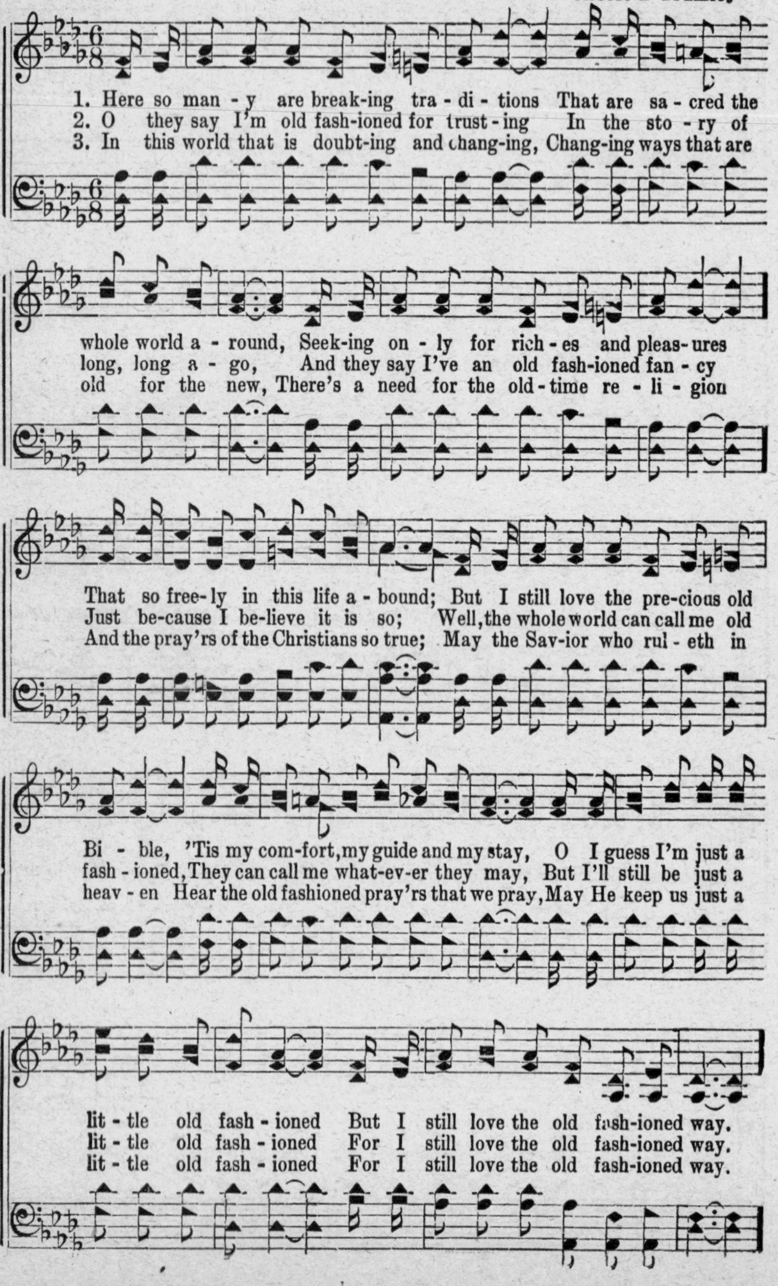

I Guess I'm Just a Little Old Fashioned

Chorus
O I guess I'm just a lit - tle old fash - ioned, But I still love the
old fash-ioned way, Lord, I care not for the world and its glo - ry,
Or the life that is mod-ern and gay; But I still love the songs a-bout
Je - sus And I still love the Bi - ble so true, O I guess I'm just a
lit - tle old fash - ioned, But my Sav - ior was old fashioned, too.

No. 208 I'll Meet You in the Morning

Respectfully dedicated to my wife, Goldie, and sons, Billey Joe, Albert E. Jr., Thomas Rexton, Robert Bartlett and Jackie Stamps.—A. E. B.

A. E. B. Albert E. Brumley

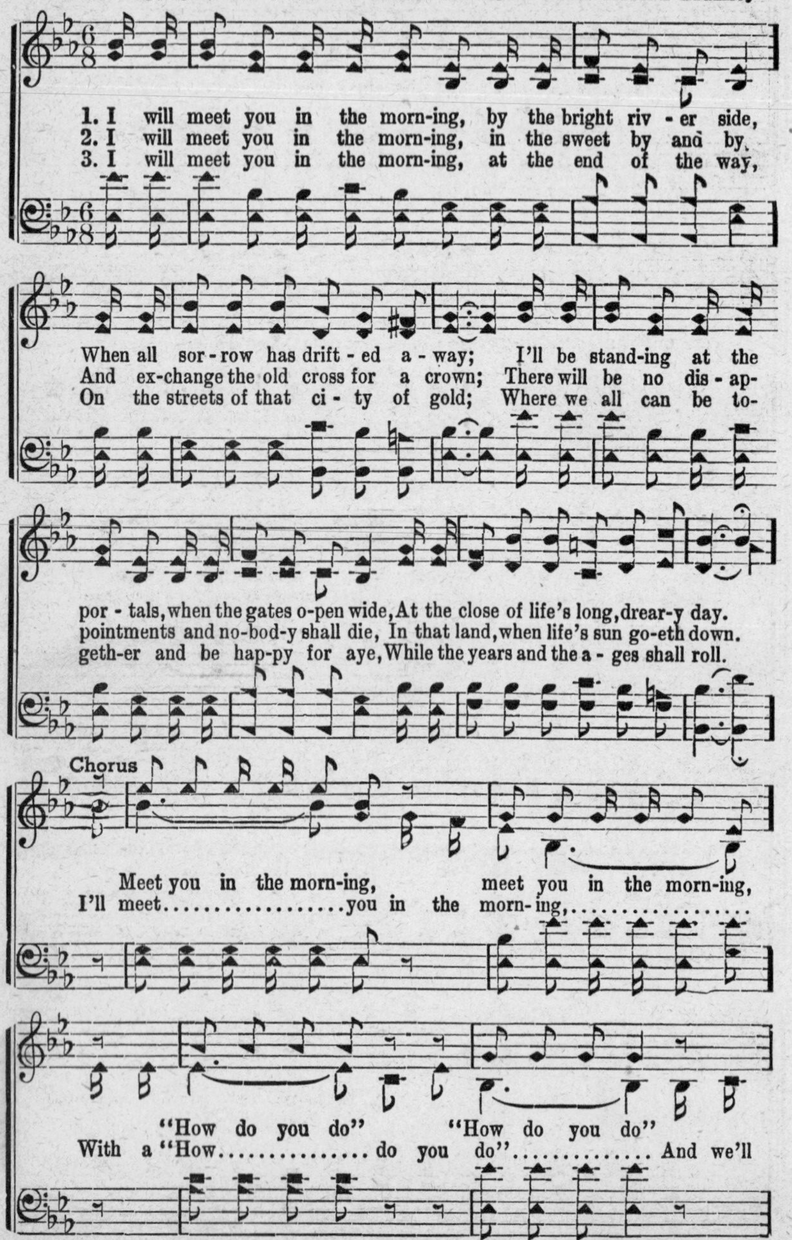
1. I will meet you in the morn-ing, by the bright riv - er side,
2. I will meet you in the morn-ing, in the sweet by and by,
3. I will meet you in the morn-ing, at the end of the way,
When all sor-row has drift - ed a - way; I'll be stand-ing at the
And ex-change the old cross for a crown; There will be no dis - ap-
On the streets of that ci - ty of gold; Where we all can be to-
por - tals, when the gates o-pen wide, At the close of life's long, drear-y day.
pointments and no-bod-y shall die, In that land, when life's sun go-eth down.
geth-er and be hap-py for aye, While the years and the a - ges shall roll.
Chorus
Meet you in the morn-ing, meet you in the morn-ing,
I'll meet.................you in the morn- ing,.................
"How do you do" "How do you do"
With a "How............... do you do"............... And we'll

I'll Meet You in the Morning

Sit down by the riv - er, sit down by the riv - er,
sit down................ by the riv - er.................And with
Rap-ture our "auld" acquaintance re-new; Know me in the morn-
rap-ture "auld" acquaintance re - new;..........You'll know............
ing, know me in the morn-ing, Smiles that I wear,
me in the morning,.............By the smiles...........that I
smiles that I wear, Meet you in the morning, meet you in the morning,
wear,...... When I meet you........... in the morn-ing,............
Ci - ty, ci - ty built, that ci - ty built four square.
In the ci - ty that is built four square.................

No. 209

We Shall Understand

James Rowe — Mrs. T. B. Mosley, Albertville, Ala., owner — T. B. Mosley

Soprano Solo
1. Some - time the veil of life shall rise, Some -
2. Some-where your soul and mine shall know Why
3. Some - how the mys - ter - y will die, And
time the light we all shall see Shine
un - der bur - dens now we bend, Why
those who loved and passed a - way, Who
out a - cross un - cloud - ed skies, And make things
some have joy and oth - ers woe, Why some fall
left us here a - lone to sigh, Will hold our
plain to you and me; Then we shall
far and some as - cend; O yes, 'twill
hands a - gain some day; For ev - 'ry-
know why we are here Up - on this
all be plain at last, The light will
thing made clear will be, When we have

We Shall Understand
storm - y, troub - led land, For God at
shine at God's com - mand, These cloud - ed
reached the bet - ter land, Some - how, when
last will make it clear, We shall un - der - stand.
days will soon be past, We shall un - der - stand.
all the shad - ows flee, We shall un - der - stand.
Chorus
Some-time our eyes will see, Some-where
Some-time (some - time) our eyes will see, Some-
made plain 'twill be, Some - how when shad-ows
where (some - where) made plain 'twill be, Some - how (some-
flee, We'll un - - der-stand.
how) when shad-ows flee, We'll un - der-stand, we'll un - der-stand.

No. 210 I Would Not Miss It—Would You?
Copyright, 1939, by Stamps-Baxter Music and Ptg. Co.
Herbert Buffum
in "Joyful Songs"
Virgil O. Stamps
1. If Christ should return in the clouds before night, I would not miss it, would
2. We've prayed for a might-y re - vi - val to come, I would not miss it, would
3. When sin-ners cry out as they cried long a - go, I would not miss it, would
you? And ris - ing to greet Him His saints took their flight; O
you? It will come when with - in our own hearts 'tis be - gun; O
you? And Chris - tians the full - ness of God's love would know; O
I would not miss it, would you? When those in the tomb once a-gain live
I would not miss it, would you? When God shall come forth in the same old-
I would not miss it, would you? When wrongs are made right and forgiveness
a - new, And once more a - rise and ap - pear on our view, When for-
time pow'r, And on those who look old-time bless-ings will show'r, Sup-
is sought, And free - ly be - stowed as of old we are taught; When
ev - er and ev-er with earth we are thru, O I would not miss it, would you?
pos-ing it does come this ver- y same hour! O I would not miss it, would you?
no man but love owes his fellowman ought, O I would not miss it, would you?

I Would Not Miss It—Would You?

Chorus
The bless - ed Re-deem - er Is soon to
Bless-ed Re-deem - er, bless-ed Re-deem - er, Soon to ap-pear,
ap-pear, The time of "the com - ing
is soon to ap-pear, Time of His com-ing, time of His com - ing,
A - gain" draw - eth near; With shouting and sing- ing till
The time of His com - ing draw-eth near;
all heav-en rings, We'll crown Him for-ev - er the King of all kings, With
mem'ries that saddened for-e'er taken wings, O I would not miss it, would you?

No. 211
The Palace of Prayer
Copyright, 1935, by The Stamps-Baxter Music Co.,
in "Harbor Bells No. 4"
Rev. B. B. Edmiaston
A. G. Godley
1. There's a won - der - ful life - giv - ing sto - ry, Of a pal - ace of
2. When con - fus - ion of earth would con - found me, When my spir - it is
3. When the shad - ows of sor - row come o'er me, When my bur - dens are
4. So I'll live near this pal - ace of bless - ing, To it's courts I will
beau - ty most rare; How the an - gels of peace come from glo - ry,
wea - ry with care, Heaven's qui - et comes gent - ly a - round me,
heav - y to bear, An - gel voic - es in mer - cy im - plore me
oft - en re - pair; For I feel my dear Sav - ior's ca - ress - ing,
Meet - ing us in the pal - ace of pray'r.
When I en - ter the pal - ace of pray'r.
To en - ter the pal - ace of pray'r.
In the beau - ti - ful pal - ace of pray'r.
Chorus
In the won - der - ful pal - ace of
dim. ad lib.
beau - ty, . . . We may leave ev - 'ry sor - row and care, ... And re -
and love,
ev - 'ry care,
ceive a new vision of du - ty; . . Je - sus meets us in the pal - ace of pray'r.
from a bove;

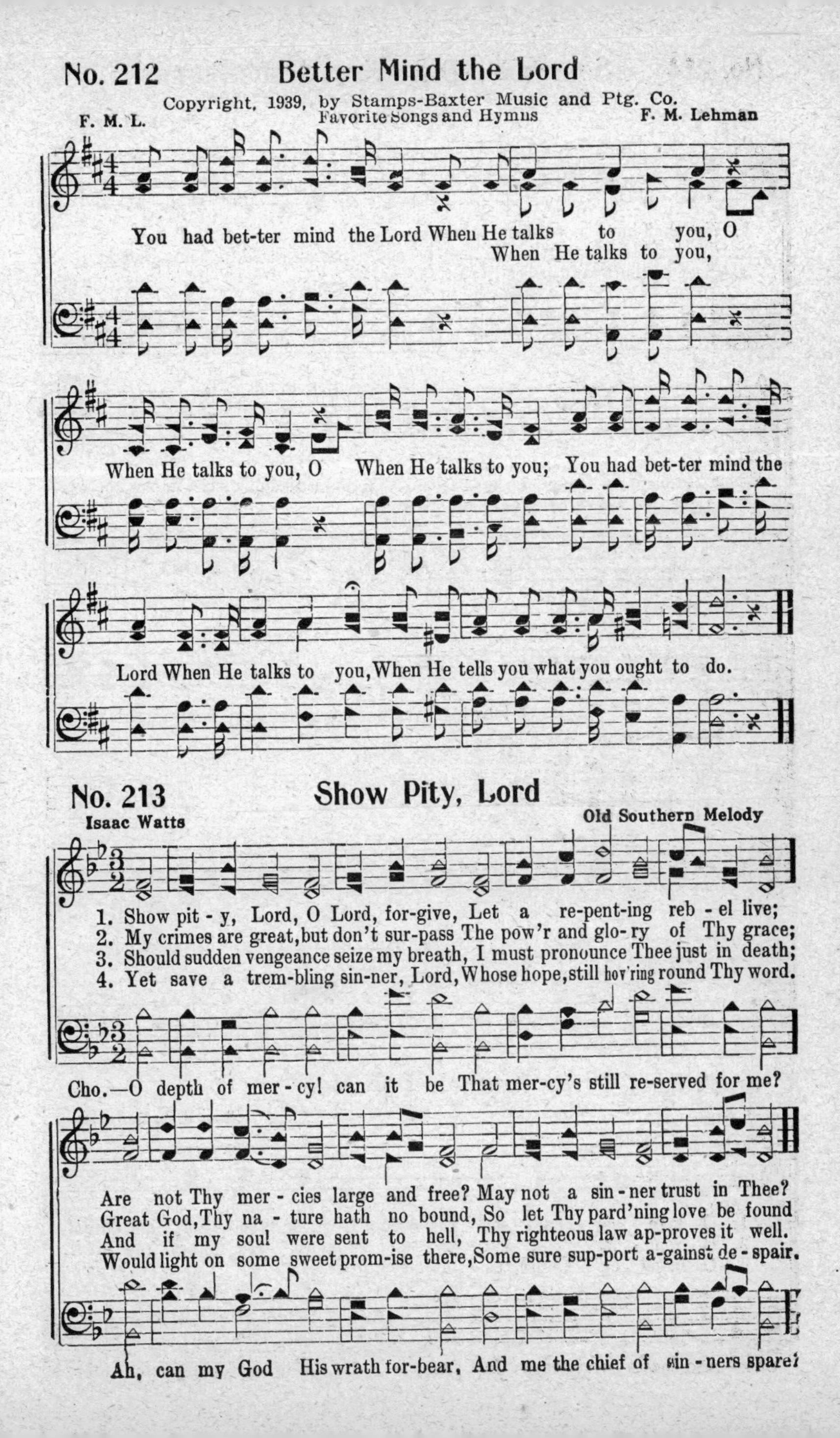
No. 212
Better Mind the Lord
Copyright, 1939, by Stamps-Baxter Music and Ptg. Co.
Favorite Songs and Hymns
F. M. L.
F. M. Lehman
You had bet-ter mind the Lord When He talks to you, O
When He talks to you,
When He talks to you, O When He talks to you; You had bet-ter mind the
Lord When He talks to you, When He tells you what you ought to do.
No. 213
Show Pity, Lord
Isaac Watts
Old Southern Melody
1. Show pit - y, Lord, O Lord, for-give, Let a re-pent-ing reb - el live;
2. My crimes are great, but don't sur-pass The pow'r and glo - ry of Thy grace;
3. Should sudden vengeance seize my breath, I must pronounce Thee just in death;
4. Yet save a trem-bling sin-ner, Lord, Whose hope, still hov'ring round Thy word.
Cho.—O depth of mer - cy! can it be That mer-cy's still re-served for me?
Are not Thy mer - cies large and free? May not a sin - ner trust in Thee?
Great God, Thy na - ture hath no bound, So let Thy pard'ning love be found
And if my soul were sent to hell, Thy righteous law ap-proves it well.
Would light on some sweet prom-ise there, Some sure sup-port a-gainst de - spair.
Ah, can my God His wrath for-bear, And me the chief of sin - ners spare?

No. 214 Some Glad Day When Jesus Comes
Copyright, 1937, by Stamps-Baxter Music Co.
in "Starlit Crown"
F. M. L
Frank M. Lynn
1. We shall have a wondrous home in glo-ry,
2. All earth's sins and strife will then be end-ed, Some glad day, some glad day,
3. Bless-ed tho't we'll sweet-ly rest for- ev- er,
Where we'll sing with saints the blessed sto- ry,
When to heav-en's home we have as-cend-ed, Some glad day when Je-sus comes.
Aft - er we have crossed be-yond the riv-er,
Chorus
O.......... how I long to meet Him! Some glad day, some glad day!
When He comes, O
O .... 'twill be joy to greet Him! Some glad day when Jesus comes.
Glo-ry, glo-ry,
No. 215 Enough For Me
E. A. H.
Rev. E. A. Hoffman
1. O love sur - pass - ing knowledge! O grace, so full and free!
2. O won - der - ful sal - va - tion! From sin He makes me free!
3. O blood of Christ, so pre-cious, Poured out on Cal - va - ry!
Cho.—And that's e - nough for me, O that's e - nough for me:

Enough For Me

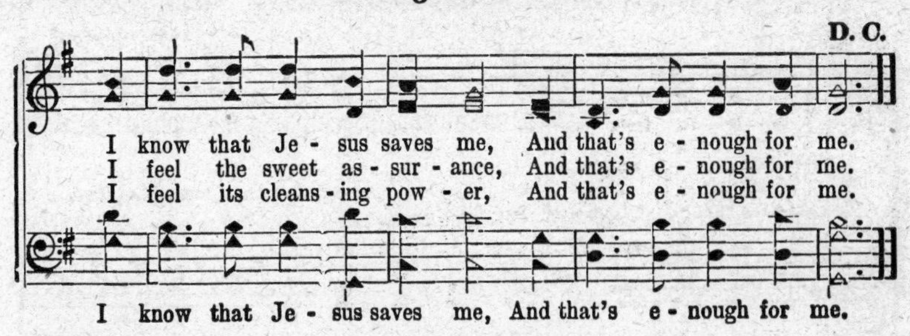
D. C.
I know that Je - sus saves me, And that's e - nough for me.
I feel the sweet as - sur - ance, And that's e - nough for me.
I feel its cleans - ing pow - er, And that's e - nough for me.
I know that Je - sus saves me, And that's e - nough for me.

No. 216 Parting Hand

"A Farewell Hymn"—1 Thes. 3:9 Jeremiah Ingals, 1805

1. My dear - est friends, in bonds of love, Our hearts in sweet - est un - ion prove;
2. How sweet the hours have passed a-way, When we have met to sing and pray;
3. And since it is God's ho - ly will We must be part - ed for a while;
4. How oft I've seen the flow-ing tears, And heard you tell your hopes and fears;

Your friend-ship's like a draw- ing band, Yet we must take the part-ing hand
How loath I've been to leave the place Where Je - sus shows His smil-ing face,
In sweet sub- mis-sion all in one, We'll say, "Our Fa-ther's will be done,"
Your hearts with love have seemed to flame, Which makes me hope we'll meet a-gain,

D.S. And when I see that we must part, You draw like chords a-round my heart.
D.S. But du - ty makes me un - der-stand That we must take the part - ing hand.
D.S. Fight on, you'll win the hap - py shore, Where parting hands are known no more.
D.S. O taste His grace, in all that land We'll no more take the part -ing hand.

Your presence sweet, your un - ion dear, Your words de-light - ful to my ear,
O could I stay with friends so kind, How would it cheer my strug-gling mind!
Dear fel - low youth in Chris-tian ties, Who seek for man-sions in the skies,
Ye mourn-ing souls, in sad sur-prise, Je - sus re-mem-bers all your cries;

No. 217
Redeeming Love
William Cowper
A. S. Kieffer
1 There is a foun - tain filled with blood, Drawn from Im-man-uel's veins,
And sin - ners plunged be-neath that flood Lose all their guilt - y stains.
2 The dy - ing thief re - joiced to see That foun - tain in his day,
And there may I, though vile as he, Wash all my sins a - way.
3 Thou dy - ing Lamb, Thy pre-cious blood Shall nev - er lose its pow'r,
Till all the ran-somed sons of God Are saved to sin no more.
D.C.—And then I hope to sing this love In sweet - er strains on high.
Chorus
D.C.
Re-deem - ing love has been my theme, And shall be till I die;
No. 218
Mear
John Fawcett
The Importance of Religion.—Phil. 3:8
Welsh Air
1. Re - lig - ion is the chief con - cern Of mor-tals here be - low;
2. More needful this than glitt' - ring wealth Or aught the world be - stows;
3. Re - lig - ion should our thoughts en-gage A-midst our youth - ful bloom;
4. O may my heart, by grace re-newed, By my Re-deem - er's throne;
5. Let deep re - pent - ance, faith and love, Be joined with god - ly fear;
May I its great im-port-ance learn, Its sov - 'reign vir - tue know.
Not rep - u - ta - tion, food or health, Can give us such re - pose.
'Twill fit us for de - clin - ing age, And for the aw - ful tomb.
And be my stub - born will sub - dued, His gov - ern-ment to own.
And all my con - ver - sa-tion prove My heart to be sin - cere.

No. 219
There'll Be No Sorrow There
Mrs. Mary S. B. Dana
Rev. C. R. Dunbar
1. O sing to me of heav'n, When I am called to die;
2. When cold and slug - ish drops, Roll off my mar - ble brow;
3. When the last mo - ment comes, O watch my dy - ing face,
4. Then to my rapt - ured ear, Let one sweet song be giv'n;
Cho.—There'll be no sor - row there, There'll be no sor - row there;
D.C.
Sing songs of ho - ly ec - sta - cy, To waft my soul on high.
Break forth in songs of joy - ful - ness, Let heav'n be - gin be - low.
To catch the bright se - raph - ic gleam, Which on each fea - ture plays.
Let mu - sic cheer me last on earth, And greet me first in heav'n.
In heav'n a - bove where all is love, There'll be no sor - row there.
No. 220
Will the Waters Be Chilly
I. Watts
Arr.
Refrain
1 Show pit - y, Lord, O Lord for - give;
Let a re - pent - ing reb - el live,
2 Are not Thy mercies large and free? Pre - pare me Lord to die.
May not a sin - ner trust in Thee? Pre - pare me Lord to die.
Will the
3 My sins are great but don't surpass,
The pow'r and glo - ry of Thy grace,
4 Here on my heart the bur - den lies,
And past of - fenc - es pain my eyes,
1
2
wa - ters be chil - ly? Will the wa - ters be chil - ly? When I am called to die.

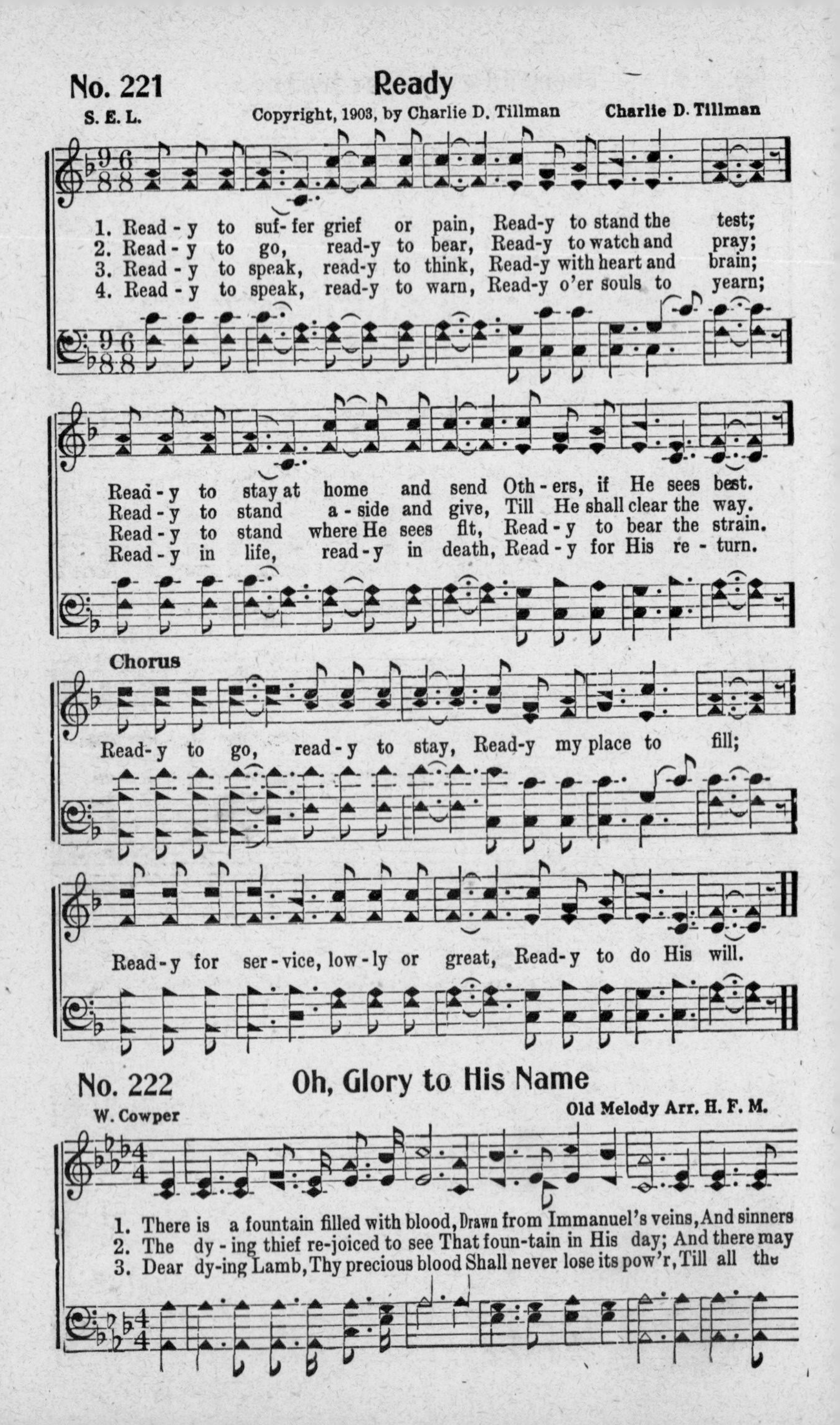
No. 221
Ready
S. E. L.
Copyright, 1903, by Charlie D. Tillman
Charlie D. Tillman
1. Read - y to suf- fer grief or pain, Read-y to stand the test;
2. Read - y to go, read-y to bear, Read-y to watch and pray;
3. Read - y to speak, read-y to think, Read-y with heart and brain;
4. Read - y to speak, read-y to warn, Read-y o'er souls to yearn;
Read - y to stay at home and send Oth - ers, if He sees best.
Read - y to stand a - side and give, Till He shall clear the way.
Read - y to stand where He sees fit, Read - y to bear the strain.
Read - y in life, read - y in death, Read - y for His re - turn.
Chorus
Read- y to go, read - y to stay, Read-y my place to fill;
Read - y for ser - vice, low - ly or great, Read - y to do His will.
No. 222
Oh, Glory to His Name
W. Cowper
Old Melody Arr. H. F. M.
1. There is a fountain filled with blood, Drawn from Immanuel's veins, And sinners
2. The dy - ing thief re-joiced to see That foun-tain in His day; And there may
3. Dear dy-ing Lamb, Thy precious blood Shall never lose its pow'r, Till all the

Oh, Glory to His Name

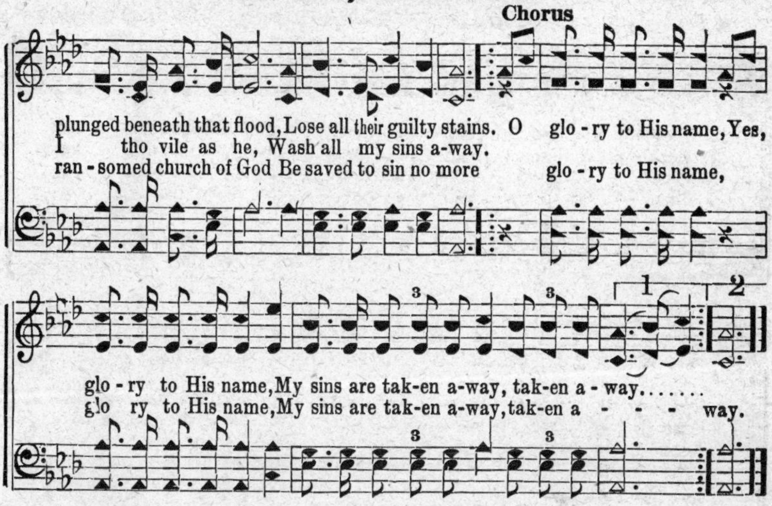

Chorus

plunged beneath that flood, Lose all their guilty stains. O glo - ry to His name, Yes,
I tho vile as he, Wash all my sins a-way.
ran - somed church of God Be saved to sin no more glo - ry to His name,

glo - ry to His name, My sins are tak-en a-way, tak-en a - way.......
glo ry to His name, My sins are tak-en a-way, tak-en a - - - - way.

No. 223 Listen to the Voice of Jesus

Jennie Wilson — Homer F. Morris

1. In the day time's gold-en light, Lis - ten to the voice of Je - sus;
2. While in downward paths you roam, Lis - ten to the voice of Je - sus;
3. Long - ing for a pur - er life, Lis - ten to the voice of Je - sus;
4. Find - ing par-don for your soul, Lis - ten to the voice of Je - sus;

In the sol- emn gloom of night, Lis - ten to the voice of Je - sus. (Fine)
He is bid-ding you come home, Lis - ten to the voice of Je - sus.
Seek-ing rest from e - vil strife, Lis - ten to the voice of Je - sus.
Yield-ing all to His con - trol, Lis - ten to the voice of Je - sus.

D.S.—Weary one, by sin un - done, Lis- ten to the voice of Je - sus.

Refrain

He is call - ing, ev - er call-ing, Clear and sweet His words are fall-ing, (D. S.)

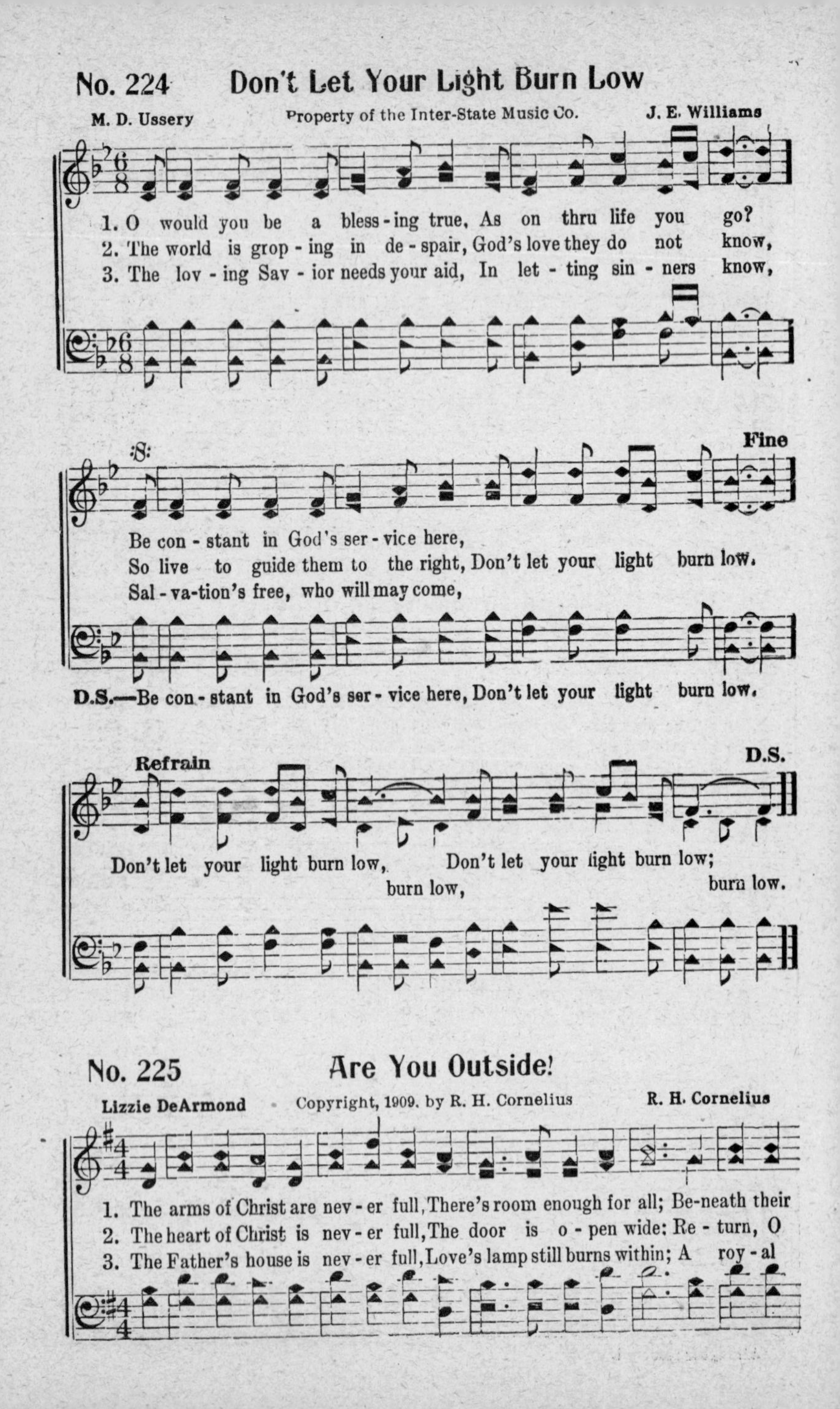
No. 224
Don't Let Your Light Burn Low
M. D. Ussery
Property of the Inter-State Music Co.
J. E. Williams
1. O would you be a bless-ing true, As on thru life you go?
2. The world is grop-ing in de-spair, God's love they do not know,
3. The lov-ing Sav-ior needs your aid, In let-ting sin-ners know,
Fine
Be con-stant in God's ser-vice here,
So live to guide them to the right, Don't let your light burn low.
Sal-va-tion's free, who will may come,
D.S.—Be con-stant in God's ser-vice here, Don't let your light burn low.
Refrain
D.S.
Don't let your light burn low, Don't let your light burn low;
burn low,
burn low.
No. 225
Are You Outside!
Lizzie DeArmond
Copyright, 1909, by R. H. Cornelius
R. H. Cornelius
1. The arms of Christ are nev-er full, There's room enough for all; Be-neath their
2. The heart of Christ is nev-er full, The door is o-pen wide; Re-turn, O
3. The Father's house is nev-er full, Love's lamp still burns within; A roy-al

Are You Outside!
Refrain
ten - der lov - ing clasp, No one can ev - er fall.
wand'ring one, return, There's rest and peace in-side. Are you out-side unsaved? Are you
welcome waits each guest, A pardon free from sin.
outside unsaved? Are you out-side so near your home? Christ calls you, come this way.
No. 226 O Come, Angel Band
Jefferson Hascall
W. B. Bradbury
1 { My lat - est sun is sink - ing fast, My race is near - ly run,
My strong - est tri - als now are past, My tri - umph is be - gun! }
2 { I know I'm near - ing ho - ly ranks Of friends and kin - dred dear;
I brush the dew of Jordan's banks, The cross - ing must be near; }
3 { I've al - most gained my heav'n-ly home, My spir - it loud - ly sings;
The ho - ly ones, be - hold, they come! I hear the noise of wings, }
4 { O bear my long - ing heart to Him Who bled and died for me;
Whose blood now clean - ses from all sin, And gives me vic - to - ry. }
Refrain f
O come, an-gel band, come, and around me stand, O bear me a - way on your
snow - y wings To my im - mor - tal home my im - mor - tal home.
1
2

No. 227 I Will Arise and Go to Jesus

Arr. by H. F. Morris
1. Come, ye sin - ners, poor and need - y, Weak and wounded, sick and sore;
2. Now, ye need - y, come and welcome; God's free boun - ty glo - ri - fy;
3. Let not conscience make you lin - ger, Nor of fit - ness fondly dream;
4. Come, ye wea - ry, heav - y lad - en, Bruised and mangled by the fall;
Cho.— I will a - rise and go to Je - sus, He will em-brace me in His arms;
D. C. Chorus
Je - sus read - y stands to save you, Full of pit - y, love and pow'r.
True be - lief and true re - pent - ance, Ev - 'ry grace that brings you nigh.
All the fit - ness He re - quir - eth Is to feel your need of Him.
If you tar - ry till you're bet - ter, You will nev - er come at all.
In the arms of my dear Sav - ior, O there are ten thousand charms.
No. 228 Passing Away
Chas. Wesley
Arr. by H. F. Morris
1 { And must I be to judg-ment bro't And an - swer in that day,
For ev - 'ry vain and i - dle tho't And ev - 'ry word I say?
2 { Yes, ev - 'ry se - cret of my heart Shall short - ly be made known,
And I re - ceive my just de - sert For all that I have done.
3 { How care - ful then, ought I to be With what re - lig - ious fear,
Who such a strict ac - count must give For my be - hav - ior here.
Chorus
1 2
We are pass - ing a - way, We are pass - ing a - way;
To the great judg-ment..... day.

No. 229
Not Made With Hands
Arr.
Old Melody Arr.
1. Christ went a build-ing to pre-pare, Not made with hands; And 'twill be decked with
2. Put on the ar-mor of our God, Not made with hands; And take the path our
3. With shield of faith de-fy the foe, Not made with hands; Un-til you hear the
4. Then come up, children, get your crown, Not made with hands; When you have laid your
Fine Chorus
jew-els rare, Not made with hands.
Cap-tain trod, Not made with hands. I know (I know,) I know (I know,)
trump-et blow, Not made with hands.
ar-mor down, Not made with hands.
D.S.
I have an-oth-er build-ing; I know (I know,) I know (I know.)
No. 230
Windham
I. Watts
The broad and narrow way.—Matt. 7. 12, 14
Daniel Read, 1786
1. Broad is the road that leads to death, And thousands walk to-geth-er there,
2. "De-ny thy-self and take thy cross," Is the Re-deem-er's great command;
3. The fear-ful soul that tries and faints, And walks the way of God no more,
But wis-dom shows a nar-row path, With here and there a trav-el-er.
Na-ture must count her gold but dross, If she would gain this heav'nly land.
Is but es-teemed al-most a saint, And makes his own de-struc-tion sure.

No. 231 When I Can Read My Title Clear
Isaac Watts
(PISGAH)
J. C. Leroy
1. When I can read my ti-tle clear To mansions in the skies,
2. Should earth a-gainst my soul en-gage, And fie-ry darts be hurled,
3. Let care like a wild deluge come And storms of sorrow fall,
4. There shall I bathe my wea-ry soul In seas of heav'nly rest,
D. C.—And wipe my weep-ing eyes, And wipe my weeping eyes;
D. C.—And face a frown-ing world, And face a frowning world;
D. C.—My God, my heav'n, my all, My God, my heav'n, my all;
D. C.—A - cross my peace-ful breast, A - cross my peaceful breast;
D.C.
I'll bid fare-well to ev-'ry fear, And wipe my weep-ing eyes.
Then I can smile at Sa-tan's rage And face a frown-ing world.
Thro Christ I'll safe-ly reach my home, My God, my heav'n, my all.
And not a wave of trou-ble roll A-cross my peace-ful breast.
No. 232 Children of the Heavenly King
John Cennick, 1742
Arr. H. F. Morris
1. Child-ren of the heav'nly King, As ye jour-ney sweet-ly sing;
2. Ye are trav'ling home to God, In the way the fa-thers trod;
3. Fear not breth-ren, joy-ful stand On the bor-ders of your land;
4. Lord sub-mis-sive make us go, Glad-ly leav-ing all be-low;
Sing our Sav-ior's wor-thy praise, Glo-rious is His works and ways.
They are hap-py now and ye Soon their hap-pi-ness shall see.
Je-sus Christ, our Fa-ther's Son, Bids you un-dis-mayed go on.
On-ly Thou our lead-er be, And we still will fol-low Thee.

No. 233
The Unseen Han d
A. J. S.
Owned by Author
A. J. Sims
1. There is an un - seen hand to me, That leads thru ways I can-not see;
2. His hand has led thru shad-ows drear, And while it leads I have no fear;
3. I long to see my Sav-ior's face And sing the sto-ry "Saved by Grace"
While go - ing thru this world of woe, This hand still leads me as I go.
I know 'twill lead me to that home, Where sin nor sor-row e'er can come.
And there up - on that Gold-en Strand, I'll praise Him for His guid - ing hand.
Chorus
1
2
I'm trusting to the unseen hand, That guides me thru this weary land;
And some sweet day I'll reach that strand, Still guided by the (Omit) un-seen hand,
No. 234
Jesus Loves Even Me
P. P. B.
"God is Love."—John 4: 8
P. P. Bliss
1 I am so glad that our Father in heav'n Tells of His love in the Book He has giv'n;
Won-der ful things in the Bi-ble I see, This is the dearest, that Je-sus loves me.
2 Tho I for-get Him and wander a-way, Still He doth love me wher-ev-er I stray;
Back to His dear loving arms would I flee, When I remember that Jesus loves me.
3 O there is on - ly one song I can sing, When in His beau-ty I see the great King;
This shall my song in e - ter - ni-ty be, "O what a wonder that Jesus love me."
Chorus
1
2
I am so glad that Jesus loves me, Je-sus loves me, Je-sus loves me, e-ven me.

No. 235 Our Coming King

Copyright, 1939, by Stamps-Baxter Music & Ptg. Co.
J. D. C.
J. D. (Main Line) Coons
Je - sus is the on - ly Sav-ior, Loud-ly let the anthems ring; Je - sus
Je - sus is the great Bap-tiz-er, Glo - ry, hal - le - lu - jah sing! On, in
1
2
is the mighty Heal-er, Glad - ly the mes-sage bring,
Him we go re-joic-ing, (Omit)................... He is our com-ing King.
No. 236 On the Main Line
Copyright, 1939, by Stamps-Baxter Music & Ptg. Co.
J. D. C.
J. D. (Main Line) Coons
I'm out on the main line to-night, I'm out on the main line to-night; With
Je - sus, my Pi - lot, I'm bound to go thru, I'm out on the main line to-night.

(Main Line) Coons, Glad Tidings Bible Institute 1441 Ellis St., San Francisco, Calif.

No. 237 The Light of the World is Jesus

Copyright, 1903, by A. J. Showalter

A. J. S. A. J. Showalter

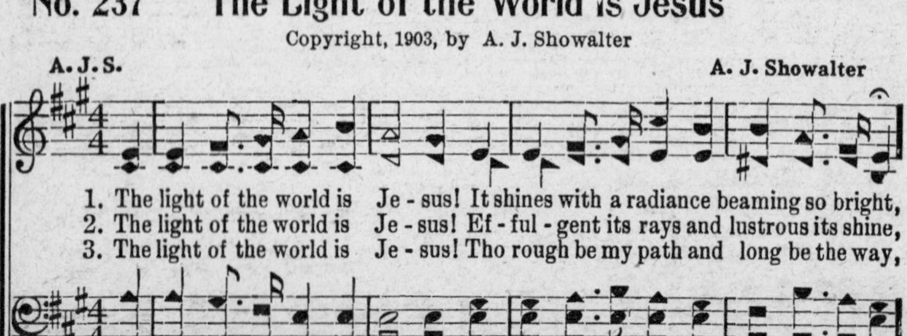
1. The light of the world is Je - sus! It shines with a radiance beaming so bright,
2. The light of the world is Je - sus! Ef - ful - gent its rays and lustrous its shine,
3. The light of the world is Je - sus! Tho rough be my path and long be the way,

The Light of the World is Jesus
Fine
Dis-pel-ling the gloom and darkness of night,
No clouds can obscure its beams so di-vine, The light of the world is Je - sus!
It leads to those mansions, fairer than day,
Chorus
The light of the world, The light of the world is Je - sus! It
of the world, light of the world,
D.S.
shines on the way, Turns night in - to day,
on the way, shines on the way, in- to day, night in - to day,
No. 238
Savior, in Thy Mercy Hear Us
A. J. S.
A. J. Showalter
1. Sav-ior, in Thy mer-cy hear us, Bless us while we pray; Have compassion
Speak to us a - long life's journey, Fill our hearts with love; May Thy ho - ly
2. We con-fess our sins and coldness, We have gone a-stray; But in mer - cy
Help us do the humblest du - ty With a pur-pose strong, Trusting in Thy
on Thy chil-dren, Turn us not a - way;
spir - it guide (Omit..................) us To our home a - bove.
hear our plead-ing, Turn out night to day;
love to cheer (Omit.........................) us All the way a - long.

No. 239 Lord, Revive Us

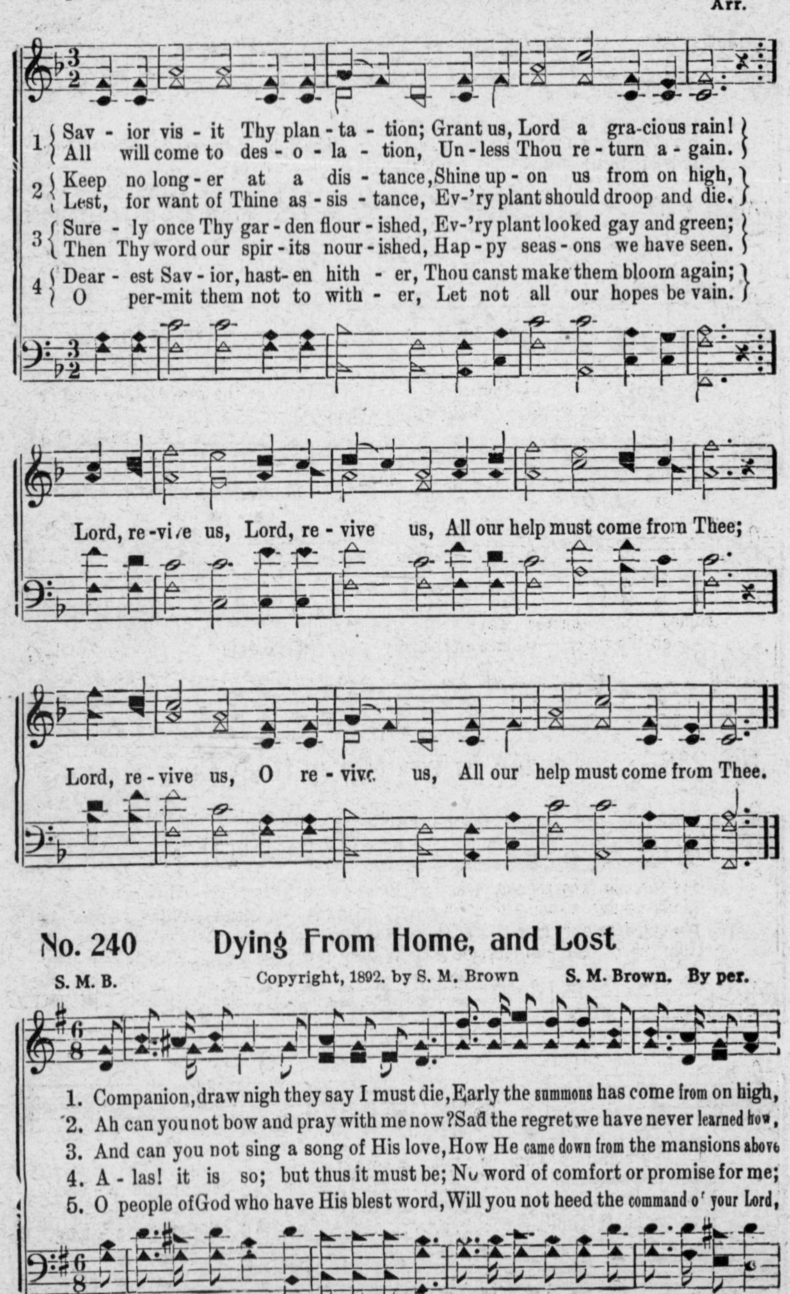
Arr.
1. Sav - ior vis - it Thy plan - ta - tion; Grant us, Lord a gra-cious rain!
All will come to des - o - la - tion, Un - less Thou re - turn a - gain.
2. Keep no long - er at a dis - tance, Shine up - on us from on high,
Lest, for want of Thine as - sis - tance, Ev-'ry plant should droop and die.
3. Sure - ly once Thy gar - den flour - ished, Ev-'ry plant looked gay and green;
Then Thy word our spir - its nour - ished, Hap - py seas - ons we have seen.
4. Dear - est Sav - ior, hast- en hith - er, Thou canst make them bloom again;
O per-mit them not to with - er, Let not all our hopes be vain.
Lord, re - vive us, Lord, re - vive us, All our help must come from Thee;
Lord, re - vive us, O re - vive us, All our help must come from Thee.
No. 240 Dying From Home, and Lost
S. M. B.
Copyright, 1892, by S. M. Brown
S. M. Brown. By per.
1. Companion, draw nigh they say I must die, Early the summons has come from on high,
2. Ah can you not bow and pray with me now? Sad the regret we have never learned how,
3. And can you not sing a song of His love, How He came down from the mansions above
4. A - las! it is so; but thus it must be; No word of comfort or promise for me;
5. O people of God who have His blest word, Will you not heed the command of your Lord,

Dying From Home, and Lost

Fine
The way is so dark, and yet I must go, O that such sorrow you never may know?
To come before Him, who only can save, Leading in triumph thru death and the grave.
To bleed and to die on Cal-va-ry's tree, Bringing sal-va-tion to sinners like me?
To die with-out God; or hope in His Son, Covered in darkness, bereaved and undone
And publish to all of Adam's lost race, Pardon, forgiveness, salvation thru grace?
D.S.—Only a song, 'twill comfort and cheer, Only a word from that book so dear.
Chorus
D.S.
On-ly a pray'r, on-ly a tear, O if sis-ter and moth-er were here;
No. 241
I Shall Not Be Moved
Arr. Copyright, 1939, by Stamps-Baxter Music and Ptg. Co.
H. F. M.
Arr.
1. Glo-ry hal-le-lu-jah, I shall not be moved; Anchored in Je-ho-vah,
2. In His love a-bid-ing, I shall not be moved; And in Him con-fid-ing,
3. Tho all hell as-sail me, I shall not be moved; Je-sus will not fail me,
4. Tho the tempest rag-es, I shall not be moved; On the Rock of A-ges,
D.C.—I shall not be, I shall not be moved, I shall not be,
D. C.
I shall not be moved; Just like a tree that's planted by the waters, I shall not be moved.
I shall not be moved: Just like a tree that's planted by the waters, I shall not be moved.

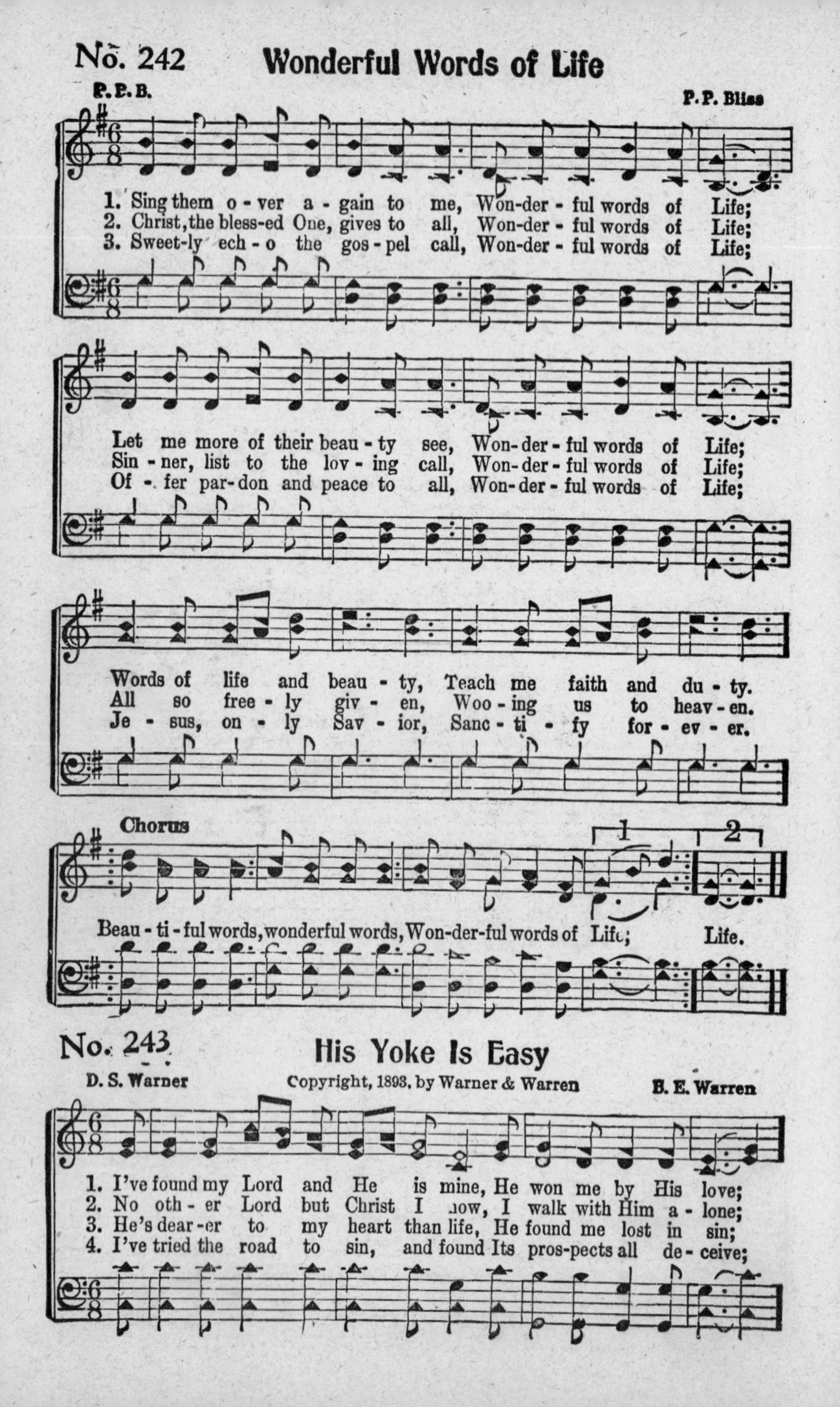
No. 242 Wonderful Words of Life
P. P. B.
P. P. Bliss
1. Sing them o - ver a - gain to me, Won-der - ful words of Life;
2. Christ, the bless-ed One, gives to all, Won-der - ful words of Life;
3. Sweet-ly ech - o the gos - pel call, Won-der - ful words of Life;
Let me more of their beau - ty see, Won-der - ful words of Life;
Sin - ner, list to the lov - ing call, Won-der - ful words of Life;
Of - fer par - don and peace to all, Won-der - ful words of Life;
Words of life and beau - ty, Teach me faith and du - ty.
All so free - ly giv - en, Woo - ing us to heav - en.
Je - sus, on - ly Sav - ior, Sanc - ti - fy for - ev - er.
Chorus
1
2
Beau - ti - ful words, wonderful words, Won-der-ful words of Life; Life.
No. 243 His Yoke Is Easy
D. S. Warner
Copyright, 1893, by Warner & Warren
B. E. Warren
1. I've found my Lord and He is mine, He won me by His love;
2. No oth - er Lord but Christ I know, I walk with Him a - lone;
3. He's dear - er to my heart than life, He found me lost in sin;
4. I've tried the road to sin, and found Its pros-pects all de - ceive;

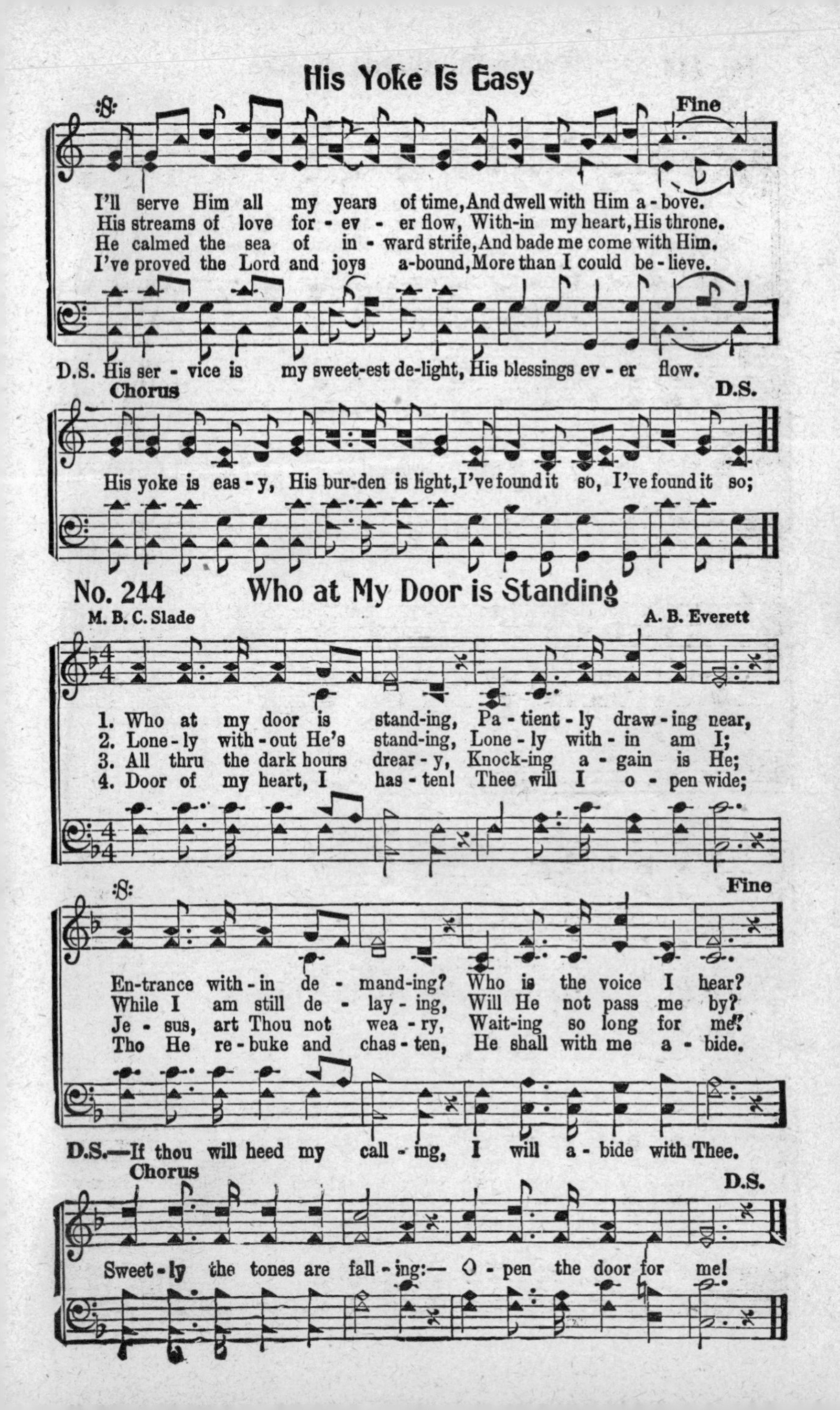
His Yoke Is Easy
Fine
I'll serve Him all my years of time, And dwell with Him a-bove.
His streams of love for-ev-er flow, With-in my heart, His throne.
He calmed the sea of in-ward strife, And bade me come with Him.
I've proved the Lord and joys a-bound, More than I could be-lieve.
D.S. His ser-vice is my sweet-est de-light, His blessings ev-er flow.
Chorus
D.S.
His yoke is eas-y, His bur-den is light, I've found it so, I've found it so;
No. 244 Who at My Door is Standing
M. B. C. Slade
A. B. Everett
1. Who at my door is stand-ing, Pa-tient-ly draw-ing near,
2. Lone-ly with-out He's stand-ing, Lone-ly with-in am I;
3. All thru the dark hours drear-y, Knock-ing a-gain is He;
4. Door of my heart, I has-ten! Thee will I o-pen wide;
Fine
En-trance with-in de-mand-ing? Who is the voice I hear?
While I am still de-lay-ing, Will He not pass me by?
Je-sus, art Thou not wea-ry, Wait-ing so long for me?
Tho He re-buke and chas-ten, He shall with me a-bide.
D.S.—If thou will heed my call-ing, I will a-bide with Thee.
Chorus
D.S.
Sweet-ly the tones are fall-ing:— O-pen the door for me!

No. 245 Come, Humble Sinner
Mrs. E. Jones
Arr.
1 { Come, humble sin - ner, in whose breast A thousand tho'ts re-volve;
Come with your guilt and fear op-pressed, And make this last re-solve. }
2 { I'll go to Je - sus, tho my sin Hath like a mountain rose;
I know His courts, I'll en - ter in, What - ev - er may op -pose. }
3 { Pros-trate I'll lie be - fore His throne, And there my guilt con-fess;
I'll tell Him I'm a wretch un - done, With-out His sov'reign grace. }
4 { I shall not per - ish if I go, I am re - solved to try;
For if I stay a - way, I know, I must for - ev - er die. }
Chorus
O you must be a lov - er of the Lord, ...
O you must be a lov - er of the Lord, (of the Lord,)
1
2
O you must be a lov - er of the Lord, (of the Lord,)
Or you can't go to heav-en when you (Omit..............) die.
No. 246 O Save Me At the Cross
Fanny J. Crosby
Arr.
1. Lov - ing Sav - ior, hear my cry, Hear my cry, hear my cry, Trembling,
2. I have sinned, but Thou hast died, Thou hast died, Thou hast died; In Thy
3. Tho I per - ish, I will pray, I will pray, I will pray; Thou of
4. Thou hast said Thy grace is free, Grace is free, grace is free; Have com-
5. On - ly faith will par-don bring, Par-don bring, par-don bring; In that

O Save Me At the Cross
Chorus
to Thy arms I fly, O save me at the cross.
mer - cy let me hide, O save me at the cross.
life the liv-ing way, O save me at the cross. Dear Je-sus, re-ceive me,
pas-sion Lord, on me, O save me at the cross.
faith to Thee I cling, O save me at the cross.
No mo would I grieve Thee; Now, blessed Redeemer, O save me at the cross.
No. 247 Now I Feel the Sacred Fire
Fine
1 Now I feel the sa - cred fire, Kind-ling, flam - ing, glow - ing,
High - er still and ris - ing higher, All my soul o'er-flow - ing;
2 Now I am from bond - age freed, Ev - 'ry bond is riv - en;
Je - sus makes me free in - deed, Just as free as heav - en;
3 Let the tes - ti - mo - ny roll, Roll thru ev - 'ry na - tion,
Wit - ness - ing from soul to soul This im-mense sal - va - tion;
4 Glo - ry be to God on high, Glo - ry be to Je - sus!
He hath bro't sal - va - tion nigh, From all sin He frees us;
D.C.—I was dead but now I live, Glo - ry! glo - ry! glo - ry!
I was bound, but now I'm free, Glo - ry! glo - ry! glo - ry!
For I feel it sav - ing me, Glo - ry! glo - ry! glo - ry!
Let the pil - grim shout a - loud, Glo - ry! glo - ry! glo - ry!
D.C.
Life im - mor - tal I re - ceive; O the won - drous sto - ry!
'Tis a glo - rious lib - er - ty; O the won - drous sto - ry!
Now I know it's full and free; O the won - drous sto - ry!
Let the gold - en harps of God Ring the won - drous sto - ry!

No. 248
I'll Be Satisfied
Joe H. Pannell
T. N. Pannell, owner
T. N. Pannell
1. When my soul is sing-ing in that prom-ised land a-bove, Prais-ing Christ the Sav-ior for re-deem-ing grace and love,
2. Liv-ing in a ci-ty where the soul shall nev-er die, There to meet with loved ones, nev-er-more to say good-by,
3. When I meet the ran-somed o-ver on the gold-en shore, There I'll join the an-gels sing-ing prais-es ev-er-more,
I'll be sat-is-fied;
I'll be sat-is-fied.
D.S.—When my soul is rest-ing in the pres-ence of the Lord, I'll be sat-is-fied.
Fine
Chorus
I'll be sat-is-fied, (sat-is-fied,) I'll be sat-is-fied; (sat-is-fied;)
D.S.
No. 249
Take Higher Ground
Copyright. 1909, by J. W. Askew Used by per.
Miss Jennie Wilson
J. W. Askew
1. Seek the blessings of a heart made pure, In whose depth no e-vil shall be found;
2. Seek to lay a-side each sin-ful weight, And in bless-ed lib-er-ty a-rise;
3. Take the higher ground where joys abide, Which the world can never take away;

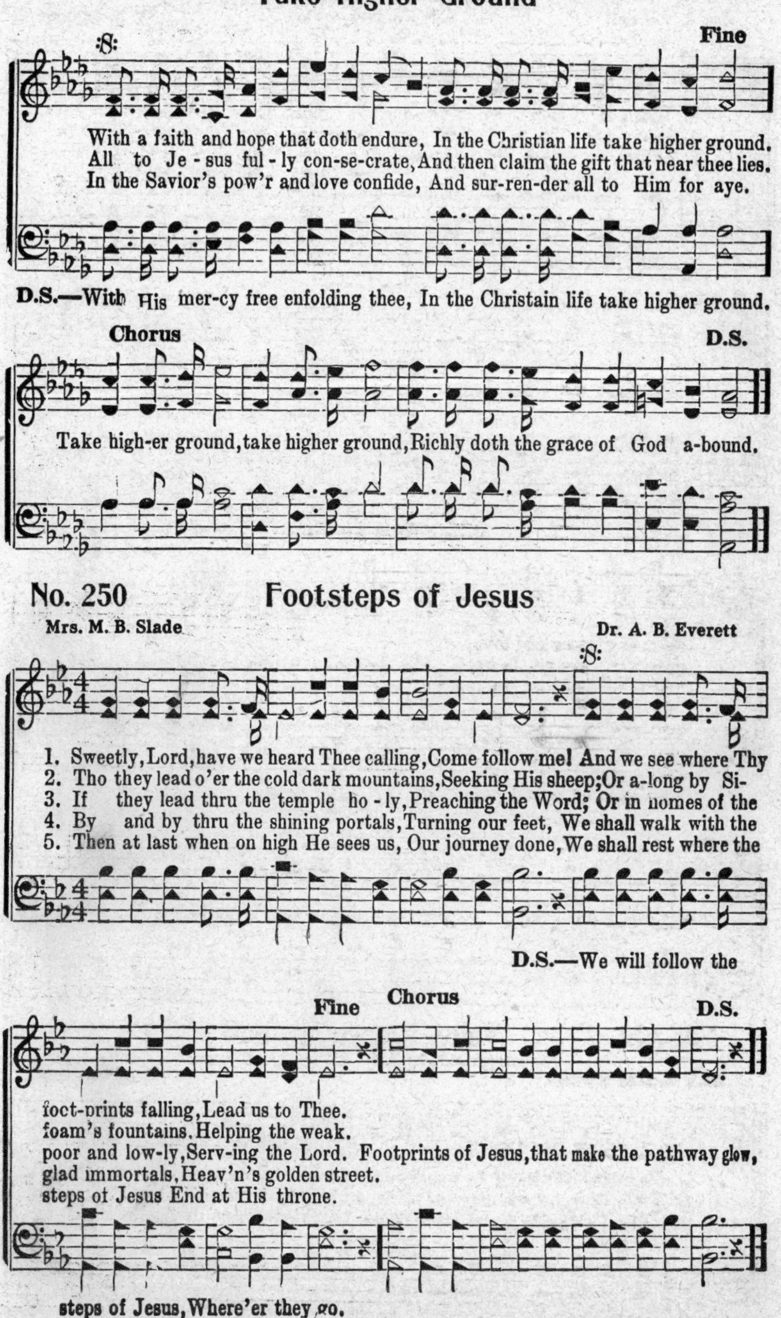
Take Higher Ground
Fine
With a faith and hope that doth endure, In the Christian life take higher ground.
All to Je - sus ful - ly con-se-crate, And then claim the gift that near thee lies.
In the Savior's pow'r and love confide, And sur-ren-der all to Him for aye.
D.S.—With His mer-cy free enfolding thee, In the Christain life take higher ground.
Chorus
D.S.
Take high-er ground, take higher ground, Richly doth the grace of God a-bound.
No. 250
Footsteps of Jesus
Mrs. M. B. Slade
Dr. A. B. Everett
1. Sweetly, Lord, have we heard Thee calling, Come follow me! And we see where Thy
2. Tho they lead o'er the cold dark mountains, Seeking His sheep; Or a-long by Si-
3. If they lead thru the temple ho - ly, Preaching the Word; Or in homes of the
4. By and by thru the shining portals, Turning our feet, We shall walk with the
5. Then at last when on high He sees us, Our journey done, We shall rest where the
D.S.—We will follow the
Fine
Chorus
D.S.
foot-prints falling, Lead us to Thee.
foam's fountains, Helping the weak.
poor and low-ly, Serv-ing the Lord. Footprints of Jesus, that make the pathway glow,
glad immortals, Heav'n's golden street.
steps of Jesus End at His throne.
steps of Jesus, Where'er they go.

No. 251 Take the Name of Jesus With You

Lydia Baxter — Copyright, 1899, by W. H. Doane, Renewal — William H. Doane

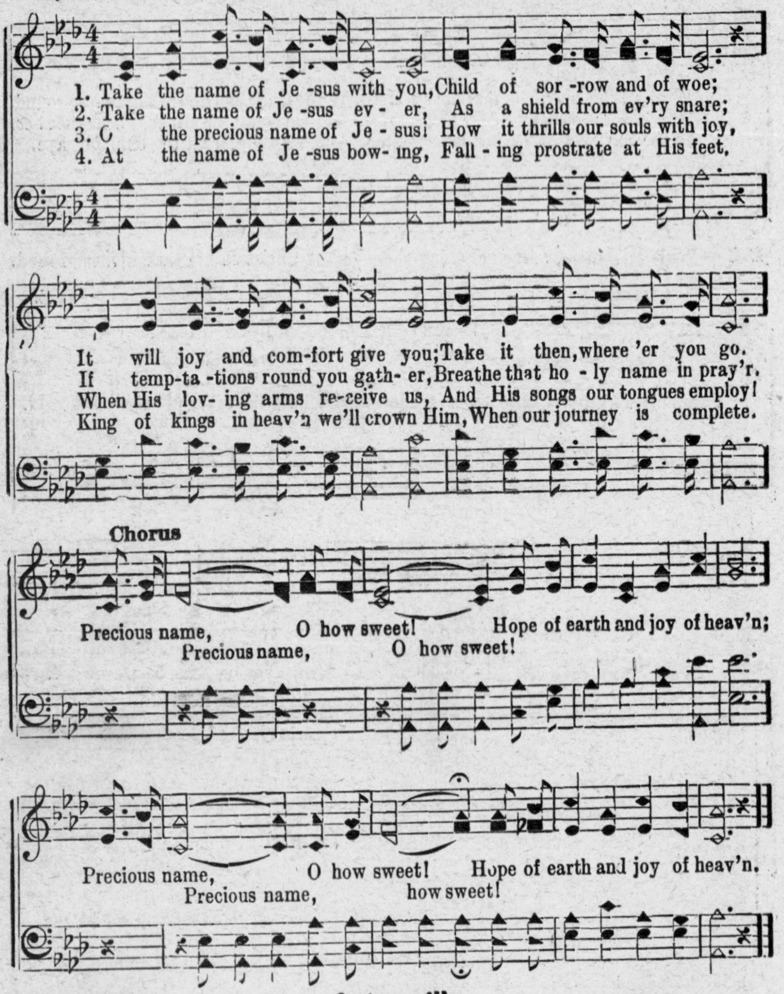

1. Take the name of Je-sus with you, Child of sor-row and of woe;
It will joy and com-fort give you; Take it then, where 'er you go.

2. Take the name of Je-sus ev-er, As a shield from ev'ry snare;
If temp-ta-tions round you gath-er, Breathe that ho-ly name in pray'r.

3. O the precious name of Je-sus! How it thrills our souls with joy,
When His lov-ing arms re-ceive us, And His songs our tongues employ!

4. At the name of Je-sus bow-ing, Fall-ing prostrate at His feet,
King of kings in heav'n we'll crown Him, When our journey is complete.

Chorus

Precious name, (Precious name,) O how sweet! (O how sweet!) Hope of earth and joy of heav'n;
Precious name, (Precious name,) O how sweet! (how sweet!) Hope of earth and joy of heav'n.

No. 252 Ortonville

John Newton — Dr. Thomas Hastings

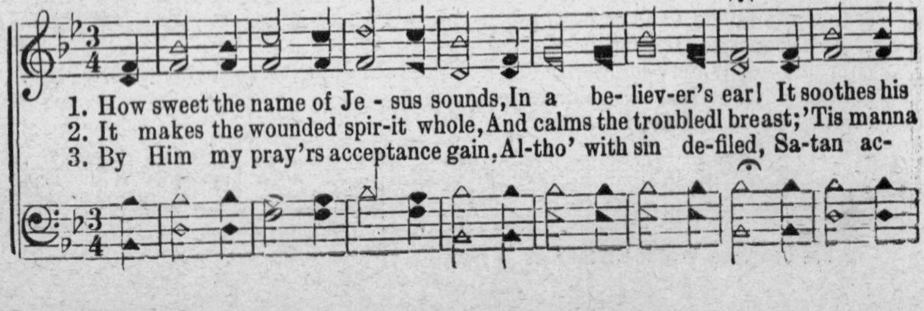

1. How sweet the name of Je-sus sounds, In a be-liev-er's ear! It soothes his
2. It makes the wounded spir-it whole, And calms the troubled breast; 'Tis manna
3. By Him my pray'rs acceptance gain, Al-tho' with sin de-filed, Sa-tan ac-

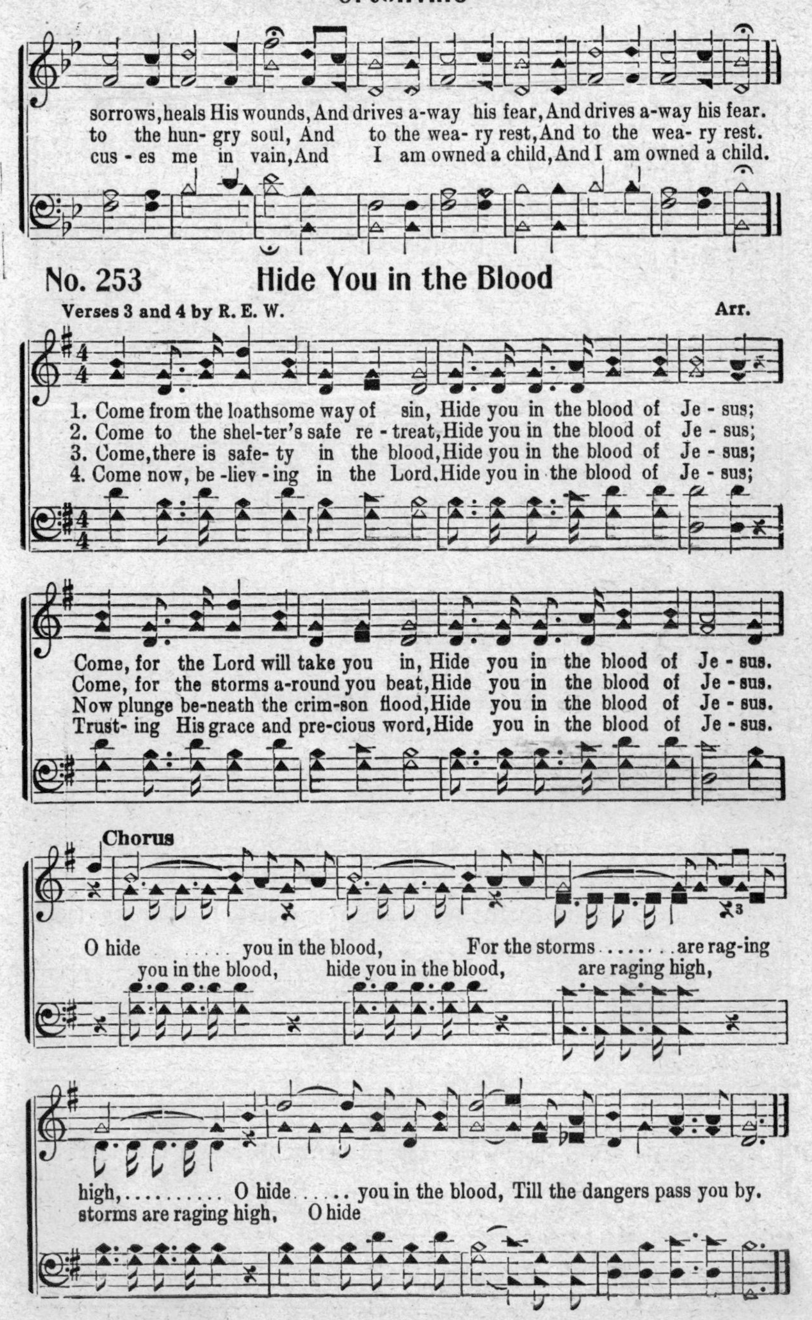
Ortonville
sorrows, heals His wounds, And drives a-way his fear, And drives a-way his fear.
to the hun- gry soul, And to the wea- ry rest, And to the wea- ry rest.
cus - es me in vain, And I am owned a child, And I am owned a child.
No. 253 Hide You in the Blood
Verses 3 and 4 by R. E. W.
Arr.
1. Come from the loathsome way of sin, Hide you in the blood of Je - sus;
2. Come to the shel-ter's safe re - treat, Hide you in the blood of Je - sus;
3. Come, there is safe- ty in the blood, Hide you in the blood of Je - sus;
4. Come now, be -liev - ing in the Lord, Hide you in the blood of Je - sus;
Come, for the Lord will take you in, Hide you in the blood of Je - sus.
Come, for the storms a-round you beat, Hide you in the blood of Je - sus.
Now plunge be-neath the crim-son flood, Hide you in the blood of Je - sus.
Trust- ing His grace and pre-cious word, Hide you in the blood of Je - sus.
Chorus
O hide ...... you in the blood, For the storms .... are rag-ing
you in the blood, hide you in the blood, are raging high,
high, ... O hide ..... you in the blood, Till the dangers pass you by.
storms are raging high, O hide

No. 254
Silent Night, Holy Night
Joseph Mohr
Franz Gruber
1. Si-lent night! Ho-ly night! All is calm, all is bright; Round yon virgin mother and Child, Ho-ly Infant so tender and mild,
2. Si-lent night! Ho-ly night! Shepherds quake at the sight; Glo-ries stream from heaven a-far, Heav-en-ly hosts sing Al-le-luia,
3. Si-lent night! Ho-ly night! Son of God, love's pure light; Radiant beams from Thy holy face With the dawn of redeeming grace,
Sleep in heav-en-ly peace, Sleep in heav-en-ly peace.
Christ, the Sav-ior, is born! Christ the Sav-ior is born!
Je-sus, Lord, at Thy birth, Je-sus, Lord, at Thy birth.
No. 255
O Why Not Tonight?
Used by permission
J. Calvin Bushey
1. O do not let the word de-part, And close thine eyes against the light;
2. To-mor-row's sun may nev-er rise To bless thy long de-lud-ed sight;
3. Our Lord in pit-y lin-gers still, And wilt thou thus His love re-quite?
4. Our bless-ed Lord re-fus-es none Who would to Him their souls u-nite;
Poor sin-ner, hard-en not your heart, Be saved, O to-night.
This is the time, O then, be wise, Be saved, O to-night.
Re-nounce at once thy stub-born will, Be saved, O to-night.
Be-lieve, o-bey, the work is done, Be saved, O to-night.

O Why Not Tonight?
Chorus
O why not to-night? O why not to-
not to-night? why not tonight? not tonight?
night? Wilt thou be saved? Then why not to-night?
why not tonight? be saved? wilt thou be saved? not, O why, not
No. 256
Why Not Now?
El Nathan
Copyright, 1919, Renewal. Homer A. Rodeheaver, owner
C. C. Case
1. While we pray and while we plead, While you see your soul's deep need,
2. You have wan-dered far a-way; Do not risk an-oth-er day;
3. In the world you've failed to find Aught of peace for trou-bled mind;
4. Come to Christ, con-fes-sion make; Come to Christ and par-don take;
While your Fa-ther calls you home, Will you not, my broth-er, come?
Do not turn from God your face, But to-day ac-cept His grace.
Come to Christ, on Him be-lieve, Peace and joy you shall re-ceive.
Trust in Him from day to day, He will keep you all the way.
Chorus
1
2
Why not now? why not now? Why not come to Jesus now?
Why not now? why not now? Je - - sus now?

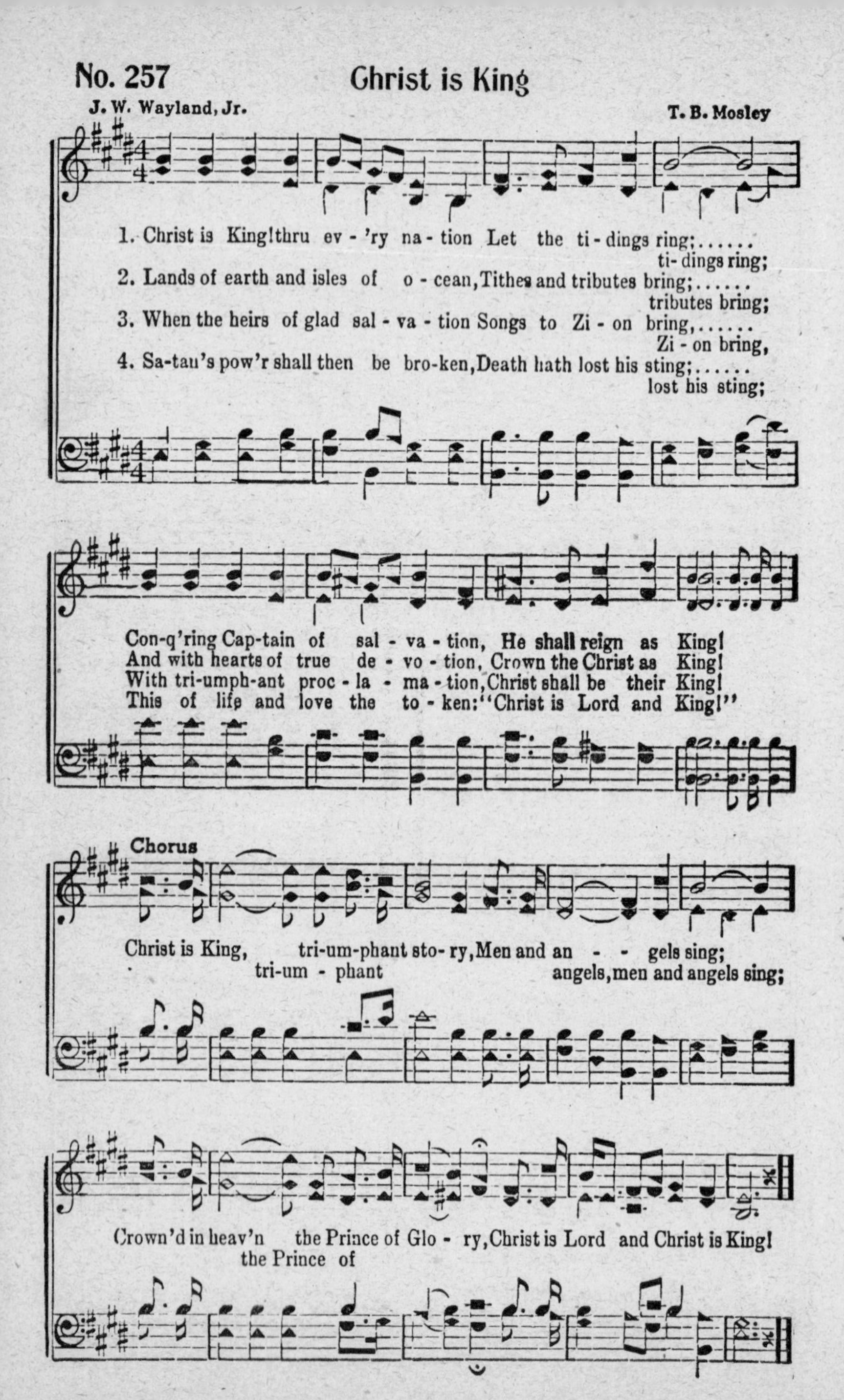
No. 257
Christ is King
J. W. Wayland, Jr.
T. B. Mosley
1. Christ is King! thru ev - 'ry na - tion Let the ti - dings ring;...... ti- dings ring;
2. Lands of earth and isles of o - cean, Tithes and tributes bring;...... tributes bring;
3. When the heirs of glad sal - va - tion Songs to Zi - on bring,...... Zi - on bring,
4. Sa-tan's pow'r shall then be bro-ken, Death hath lost his sting;...... lost his sting;
Con-q'ring Cap-tain of sal - va - tion, He shall reign as King!
And with hearts of true de - vo - tion, Crown the Christ as King!
With tri-umph-ant proc - la - ma - tion, Christ shall be their King!
This of life and love the to - ken: "Christ is Lord and King!"
Chorus
Christ is King, tri-um-phant sto- ry, Men and an - - gels sing;
tri-um - phant angels, men and angels sing;
Crown'd in heav'n the Prince of Glo - ry, Christ is Lord and Christ is King!
the Prince of

No. 258 The Great Glad Day

Mrs. J. M. Hunter T. B. Mosley, Albertville, Ala., owner T. B. Mosley

1. There will come a day when the Lord shall say To the saints of earth, "A-rise,"
2. O I look a-loft and I won-der oft When that blessed day shall dawn,
3. In the shin-ing ranks, giving praise and thanks, Sinner, don't you want a place?
4. Bells of heav-en chime, ush-er in the time, Come Thou, Christ, whom we a-dore;

With their wings unfurled they shall leave the world For their mansions in the skies.
It is hid-den yet, du-ty must be met, So in faith I'm pressing on.
Turn to Je-sus now, in con-tri-tion bow, He'll prepare you thru His grace.
Gold-en harps, ring out, all ye saved men, shout Glo-ry, glo-ry ev-er-more.

Chorus

O that great glad day, in His bright ar-ray, We shall then be-hold the King!
behold the King!

O the joy our souls shall in heav-en know, In that good and great glad day!

No. 259
In the Gospel Way
James Rowe
A. J. Showalter, owner, 1912
A. J. Showalter
1. Christ is dear to me always near to me, Safe - ly keep - ing
2. How He cares for me what He bears for me, How He strengthens
3. I will cling to Him trust Him, sing to Him, Till I meet Him
me from day to day; Nev - er chid - ing me, al - ways guid- ing me,
me to stand the fray. Grace up - hold - ing me, love en - fold - ing me,
on that bet- ter day; With the du - ti - ful, sin - less, beau - ti - ful,
In the glo - ry of the gos - pel way.
O how pleas-ant is the gos - pel way!
At the end - ing of the gos - pel way.
Chorus
Up - - - ward home - - ward, Christ is lead-ing and I shall not stray; March - ing, sing - ing, In the glo - ry of the gos - pel way.
Up- ward with Je - sus, home-ward with Je-sus, Marching with Je - sus, sing - ing of Je - sus,

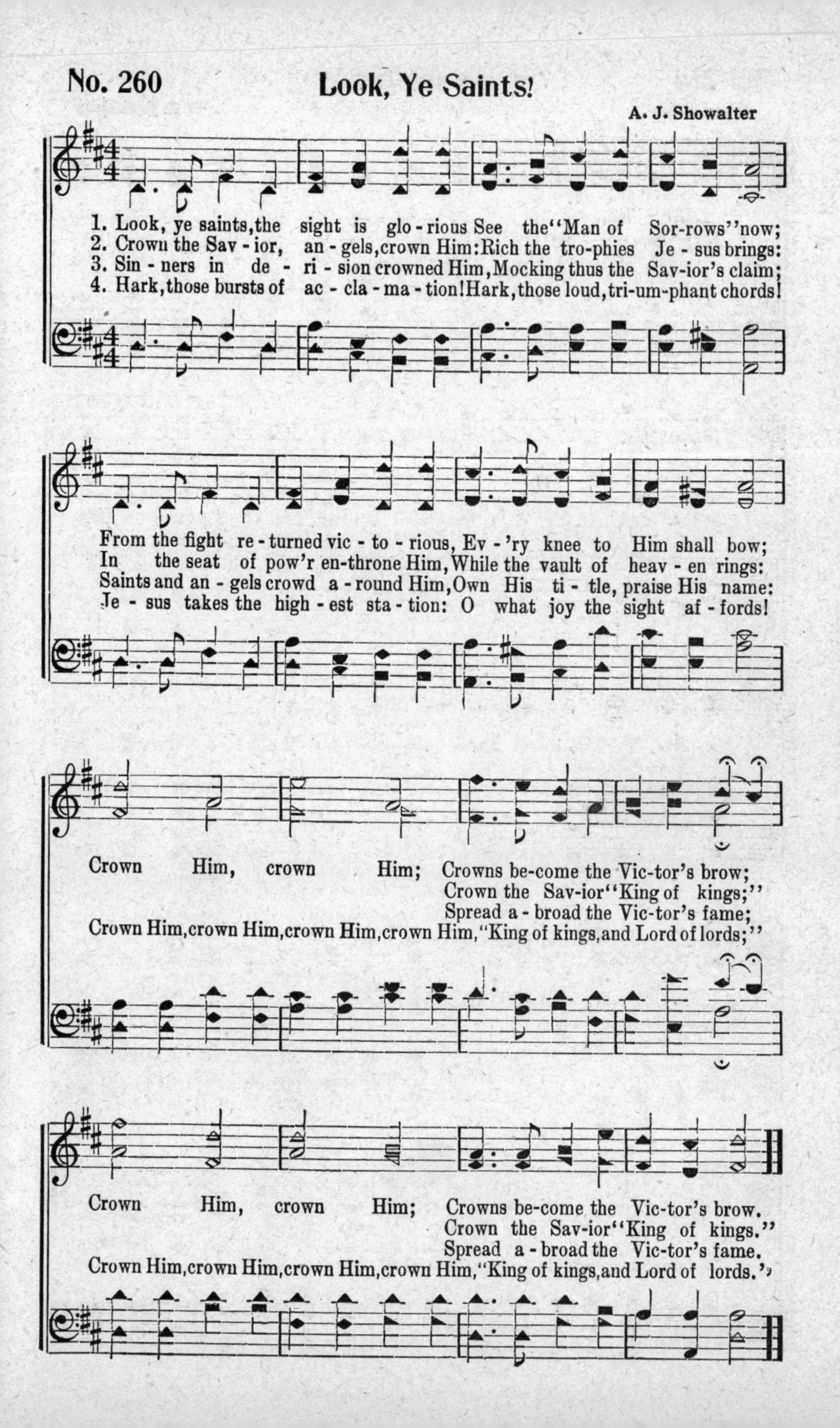
No. 260
Look, Ye Saints!
A. J. Showalter
1. Look, ye saints, the sight is glo-rious See the "Man of Sor-rows" now;
2. Crown the Sav-ior, an-gels, crown Him: Rich the tro-phies Je-sus brings:
3. Sin-ners in de-ri-sion crowned Him, Mocking thus the Sav-ior's claim;
4. Hark, those bursts of ac-cla-ma-tion! Hark, those loud, tri-um-phant chords!
From the fight re-turned vic-to-rious, Ev-'ry knee to Him shall bow;
In the seat of pow'r en-throne Him, While the vault of heav-en rings:
Saints and an-gels crowd a-round Him, Own His ti-tle, praise His name:
Je-sus takes the high-est sta-tion: O what joy the sight af-fords!
Crown Him, crown Him; Crowns be-come the Vic-tor's brow;
Crown the Sav-ior "King of kings;"
Spread a-broad the Vic-tor's fame;
Crown Him, crown Him, crown Him, crown Him, "King of kings, and Lord of lords;"
Crown Him, crown Him; Crowns be-come the Vic-tor's brow.
Crown the Sav-ior "King of kings."
Spread a-broad the Vic-tor's fame.
Crown Him, crown Him, crown Him, crown Him, "King of kings, and Lord of lords."

No. 261
At the Cross
Isaac Watts
R. E. Hudson
1. A - las, and did my Sav - ior bleed, And did my Sov-ereign die;
2. Was it for crimes that I have done, He groaned up - on the tree?
3. Well might the sun in dark-ness hide, And shut His glo - ries in,
4. But drops of grief can ne'er re - pay The debt of love I owe:
Would He de - vote that sa - cred head For such a worm as I?
A - maz - ing pit - y, grace un-known! And love be - yond de - gree!
When Christ, the might - y Mak - er, died For man the crea-ture's sin.
Here, Lord, I give my - self a - way, 'Tis all that I can do!
Chorus
At the cross, at the cross where I first saw the light, And the
bur-den of my heart rolled a - way, rolled a-way, It was there by
faith I re-ceived my sight, And now I am hap-py all the day!

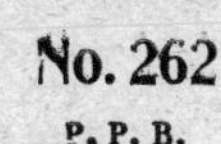

No. 262 Hold the Fort

P. P. B. P. P. Bliss

1. Ho, my com-rades, see the sig - nal Wav-ing in the sky!
2. See the might - y host ad - vanc - ing, Sa - tan lead - ing on;
3. See the glo - rious ban - ner wav - ing! Hear the trump - et blow!
4. Fierce and long the bat - tle rag - es, But our help is near;

Re - in - force-ments now ap - pear - ing, Vic - to - ry is nigh.
Might - y men a - round us fall - ing Cour - age al - most gone!
In our lead - er's name we tri - umph O - ver ev - 'ry foe.
On - ward comes our great Com-mand - er, Cheer, my com-rades, cheer!

Chorus

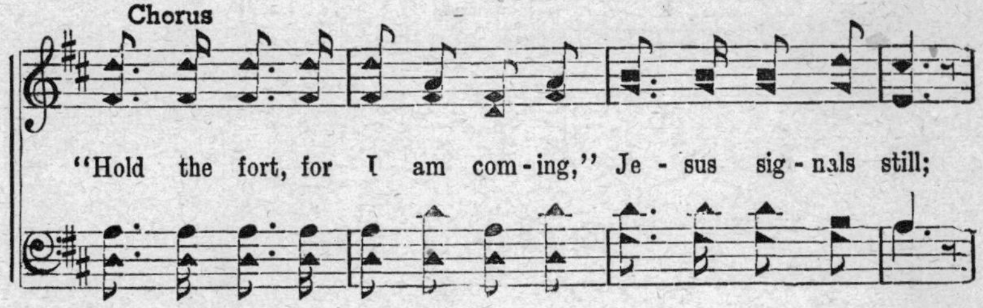

"Hold the fort, for I am com - ing," Je - sus sig - nals still;

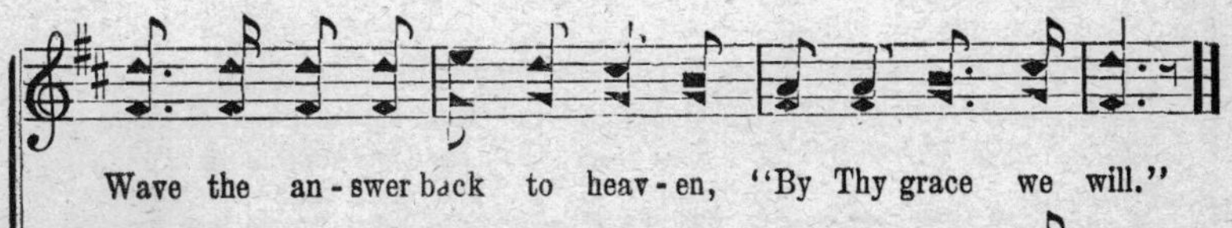

Wave the an - swer back to heav - en, "By Thy grace we will."

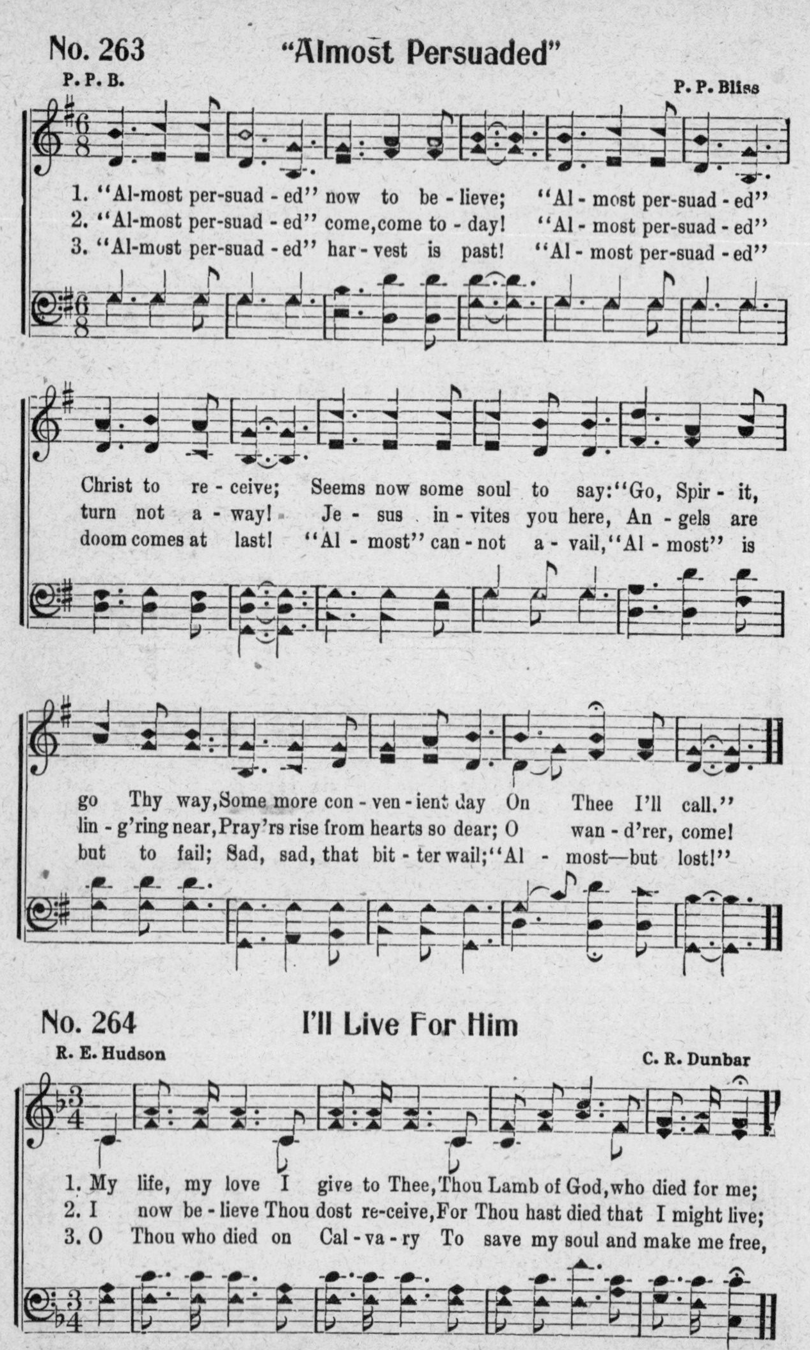
No. 263
"Almost Persuaded"
P. P. B.
P. P. Bliss
1. "Al-most per-suad - ed" now to be - lieve; "Al - most per-suad - ed"
2. "Al-most per-suad - ed" come,come to - day! "Al - most per-suad - ed"
3. "Al-most per-suad - ed" har - vest is past! "Al - most per-suad - ed"
Christ to re - ceive; Seems now some soul to say:"Go, Spir - it,
turn not a - way! Je - sus in - vites you here, An - gels are
doom comes at last! "Al - most" can - not a - vail,"Al - most" is
go Thy way,Some more con - ven - ient day On Thee I'll call."
lin - g'ring near,Pray'rs rise from hearts so dear; O wan - d'rer, come!
but to fail; Sad, sad, that bit - ter wail;"Al - most—but lost!"
No. 264
I'll Live For Him
R. E. Hudson
C. R. Dunbar
1. My life, my love I give to Thee,Thou Lamb of God,who died for me;
2. I now be - lieve Thou dost re-ceive,For Thou hast died that I might live;
3. O Thou who died on Cal - va - ry To save my soul and make me free,
Cho.—I'll live for Him who died for me, How hap - py then my life shall be!

I'll Live for Him
D.C. for Chorus
O may I ev - er faith - ful be, My Sav - ior and my God!
And now hence-forth I'll trust in Thee, My Sav - ior and my God!
I con - se - crate my life to Thee, My Sav - ior and my God!
I'll live for Him who died for me, My Sav - ior and my God!
No. 265 Shall We Gather at the River?
R. L.
Rev. Robert Lowry
1. Shall we gath - er at the riv - er, Where bright an - gel feet have trod;
2. On the mar - gin of the riv - er, Wash - ing up its sil - ver spray,
3. Ere we reach the shin - ing riv - er, Lay we ev - 'ry bur - den down;
4. Soon we'll reach the shin - ing riv - er, Soon our pil - grim - age will cease,
With its crys - tal tide for - ev - er Flowing by the throne of God?
We will walk and wor - ship ev - er, All the hap - py gold - en day.
Grace our spir - its will de - liv - er, And pro - vide a robe and crown.
Soon our hap - py hearts will quiv - er With the mel - o - dy of peace.
Chorus
Yes, we'll gath - er at the riv - er, The beau - ti - ful, the beau - ti - ful riv - er;
Gath - er with the saints at the riv - er That flows by the throne of God.

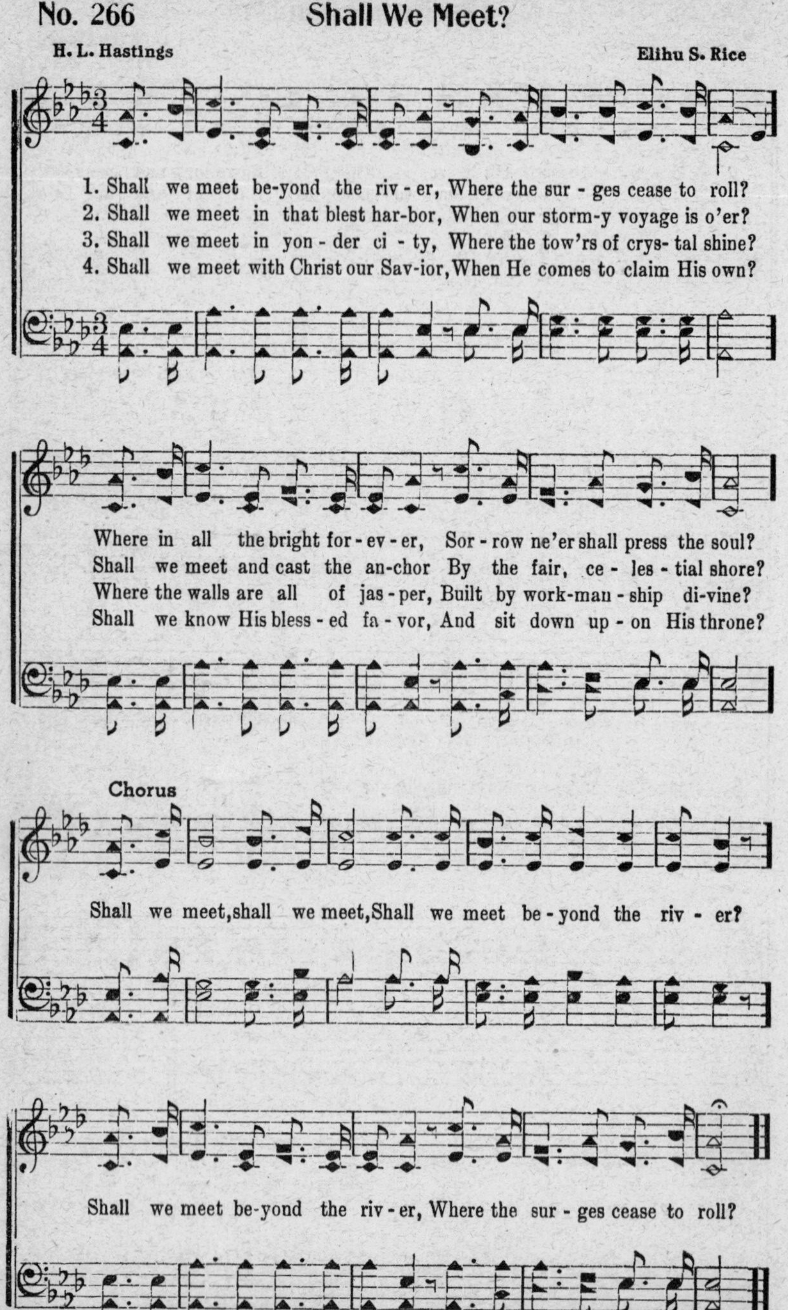
No. 266
Shall We Meet?
H. L. Hastings
Elihu S. Rice
1. Shall we meet be-yond the riv - er, Where the sur - ges cease to roll?
2. Shall we meet in that blest har-bor, When our storm-y voyage is o'er?
3. Shall we meet in yon - der ci - ty, Where the tow'rs of crys- tal shine?
4. Shall we meet with Christ our Sav-ior, When He comes to claim His own?
Where in all the bright for - ev - er, Sor - row ne'er shall press the soul?
Shall we meet and cast the an-chor By the fair, ce - les - tial shore?
Where the walls are all of jas - per, Built by work-man - ship di-vine?
Shall we know His bless - ed fa - vor, And sit down up - on His throne?
Chorus
Shall we meet, shall we meet, Shall we meet be - yond the riv - er?
Shall we meet be-yond the riv - er, Where the sur - ges cease to roll?

No. 267 Savior, More Than Life

Fanny J. Crosby — W. H. Doane

1. Sav - ior, more than life to me, I am cling-ing, cling-ing close to Thee;
2. Thru this changing world be-low, Lead me gen-tly, gen-tly as I go;
3. Let me love Thee more and more, Till this fleet-ing, fleet-ing life is o'er:
Let Thy pre-cious blood ap plied, Keep me ev - er, ev - er near Thy side.
Trusting Thee, I can-not stray, I can nev -er, nev - er lose my way.
Till my soul is lost in love, In a bright- er, bright-er world a - bove.
Chorus
Ev-'ry day, ev-'ry hour, Let me feel Thy cleansing pow'r;
and hour, ev-'ry day and hour,
May Thy ten - der love to me Bind me clos - er, clos - er, Lord, to Thee.

4. Savior, teach me day by day
Love's sweet lesson, lesson to obey,
Sweeter lesson cannot be,
For my Savior, Savior first loved me.

5. With a child-like heart I love,
At Thy bidding, bidding may I move,
Prompt to serve and follow Thee,
For my Savior, Savior first loved me.

6. Love in loving finds employ,
In true service, service all her joy;
Ever new that joy will be,
For my Savior, Savior first loved me.

7. Thus may I rejoice to show
That to Jesus, Jesus all I owe,
Singing till His face I see,
For my Savior, Savior first loved me.

No. 268 Close to Thee

Fanny J. Crosby

Silas J. Vail

1. Thou, my ev - er - last - ing por - tion, More than friend or life to me;
2. Not for ease or world - ly pleas-ure, Nor for fame my pray'r shall be;
3. Lead me thru the vale of shad-ows, Bear me o'er life's fit - ful sea;
All a - long my pil - grim jour - ney, Sav - ior, let me walk with Thee.
Glad - ly will I toil and suf - fer, On - ly let me walk with Thee.
Then the gate of life e - ter - nal May I en - ter, Lord, with Thee.
Chorus
Close to Thee, close to Thee, Close to Thee, close to Thee;
All a - long my pil - grim jour - ney Sav - ior, let me walk with Thee.
Glad - ly will I toil and suf - fer, On - ly let me walk with Thee.
Then the gate of life e - ter - nal May I en - ter, Lord, with Thee.

4. In the Rock I would be resting,
Safely sheltered to abide;
There no foes can e'er molest me
While within the cleft I hide.

5. Tho pursued by sin and Satan,
Weary, sad, I long for rest;
Let me find this heav'nly shelter,
Opened in my Savior's breast.

6. Peace which passeth understanding,
Joy the world can never give,
Let me find my blessed Savior,
In Thy smiles O let me live.

7. In the rifted Rock O hide me
Till the storms of life are past,
All secure in this blest refuge,
Heeding not the fiercest blast.

No. 269 I Love Him

English Hymn Book S. C. Foster

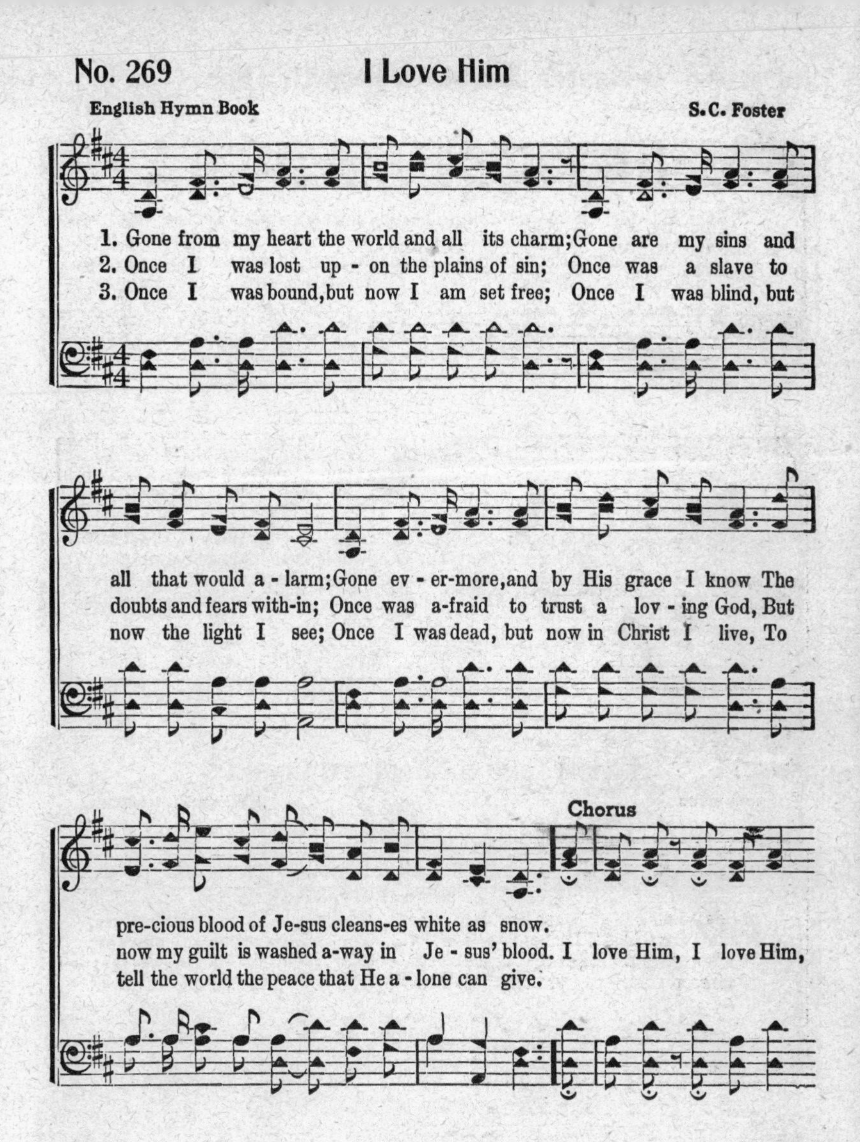

1. Gone from my heart the world and all its charm; Gone are my sins and all that would a-larm; Gone ev-er-more, and by His grace I know The pre-cious blood of Je-sus cleans-es white as snow.
2. Once I was lost up-on the plains of sin; Once was a slave to doubts and fears with-in; Once was a-fraid to trust a lov-ing God, But now my guilt is washed a-way in Je-sus' blood.
3. Once I was bound, but now I am set free; Once I was blind, but now the light I see; Once I was dead, but now in Christ I live, To tell the world the peace that He a-lone can give.
Chorus
I love Him, I love Him,

be-cause He first loved me, And purchased my sal-va-tion on Calv'ry's tree.

No. 270 O Master, Let Me Walk with Thee
W. Gladden
H. P. Smith
1. O Mas-ter, let me walk with Thee In low-ly paths of ser - vice free;
2. Help me the slow of heart to move By some clear, winning word of love;
3. Teach me Thy patience! still with Thee In clos-er, dear-er com - pa - ny,
4. In hope that sends a shin - ing ray Far down the fu-ture's broadening way,
Tell me Thy se - cret; help me bear The strain of toil, the fret of care.
Teach me the wayward feet to stay, And guide them in the homeward way.
In work that keeps faith sweet and strong, In trust that triumphs o - ver wrong.
In peace that on - ly Thou canst give, With Thee, O Mas-ter, let me live.
No. 271 Savior, Like a Shepherd Lead Us
Anonymous
William B. Bradbury
1. Sav - ior, like a shep-herd lead us, Much we need Thy ten-der care;
2. We are Thine; do Thou be-friend us, Be the Guardian of our way;
3. Thou hast promised to re-ceive us, Poor and sin - ful tho we be;
4. Ear - ly let us seek Thy fa - vor; Ear - ly let us do Thy will;
In Thy pleas-ant pas-tures feed us, For our use Thy folds pre-pare:
Keep Thy flock, from sin de - fend us, Seek us when we go a-stray:
Thou hast mer - cy to re - lieve us, Grace to cleanse, and pow'r to free:
Bless - ed Lord and on - ly Sav - ior, With Thy love our bos- oms fill:

Savior, Like a Shepherd Lead Us

Bless-ed Je - sus, bless-ed Je - sus, Thou hast bought us, Thine we are;
Bless-ed Je - sus, bless-ed Je - sus, Hear Thy chil-dren when they pray;
Bless-ed Je - sus, bless-ed Je - sus, Ear - ly let us turn to Thee;
Bless-ed Je - sus, bless-ed Je - sus, Thou hast loved us, love us still;
Bless-ed Je - sus, bless-ed Je - sus, Thou hast bought us, Thine we are.
Bless-ed Je - sus, bless-ed Je - sus, Hear Thy chil-dren when they pray.
Bless-ed Je - sus, bless-ed Je - sus, Ear - ly let us turn to Thee.
Bless-ed Je - sus, bless-ed Je - sus, Thou hast loved us, love us still.
No. 272 More Love to Thee
Elizabeth Prentiss
W. H. Doane
1. More love to Thee, O Christ, More love to Thee! Hear Thou the
2. Once earth - ly joy I craved, Sought peace and rest; Now Thee a-
3. Then shall my lat - est breath Whis-per Thy praise; This be the
pray'r I make On bend - ed knee; This is my ear - nest plea:
lone I seek, Give what is best; This all my pray'r shall be;
part - ing cry My heart shall raise; This still its pray'r shall be;
More love, O Christ, to Thee, More love to Thee, More love to Thee!

No. 273
Near the Cross
Fanny J. Crosby
W. H. Doane
1. Je - sus keep me near the cross, There a pre - cious foun - tain
2. Near the cross, a trem-bling soul, Love and mer - cy found me;
3. Near the cross! O Lamb of God, Bring its scenes be - fore me;
4. Near the cross I'll watch and wait, Hop - ing, trust - ing, ev - er,
Free to all— a heal - ing stream, Flows from Cal - v'ry's moun-tain.
There the Bright and Morn-ing Star Sheds its beams a - round me.
Help me walk from day to day, With its shad - ows o'er me.
Till I reach the gold - en strand, Just be - yond the riv - er.
Chorus
In the cross, in the cross, Be my glo - ry ev - er;
Till my rap - tured soul shall find Rest be - yond the riv - er.
No. 274
No, Not One
Rev. Johnston Oatman, Jr.
Geo. C. Hugg
1. There's not a friend like the low - ly Je - sus, No, not one! no, not one!
2. No friend like Him is so high and ho - ly, No, not one! no, not one!
3. There's not an hour that He is not near us, No, not one! no, not one!
4. Did ev - er saint find this Friend forsake him? No, not one! no, not one!
5. Was e'er a gift like the Sav - ior giv - en? No, not one! no, not one!

No, Not One
Fine
None else could heal all our soul's dis - eas - es, No, not one! no, not one!
And yet no friend is so meek and low - ly, No, not one! no, not one!
No night so dark but His love can cheer us, No, not one! no, not one!
Or sin - ner find that He would not take him, No, not one! no, not one!
Will He re-fuse us a home in heav-en? No, not one! no, not one!
D.S.-There's not a friend like the low-ly Je - sus, No, not one! no, not one!
Chorus
D.S.
Je - sus knows all a - bout our struggles, He will guide till the day is done;
No. 275
Hallelujah! What a Savior!
P. P. B.
P. P. Bliss
1. "Man of sor-rows," what a name For the Son of God who came
2. Bear - ing shame and scoff - ing rude, In my place condemned He stood,
3. Guilt - y, vile and help - less we; Spot - less Lamb of God was He;
4. Lift - ed up was He to die, "It is fin - ished," was His cry;
5. When He comes, our glo - rious King, All His ran-somed home to bring,
Ru - ined sin - ners to re - claim! Hal - le - lu - jah! what a Sav - ior!
Sealed my par - don with His blood; Hal - le - lu - jah! what a Sav - ior!
"Full a - tone-ment!" can it be? Hal - le - lu - jah! what a Sav - ior!
Now in heav'n ex - alt - ed high, Hal - le - lu - jah! what a Sav - ior!
Then a - new this song we'll sing, Hal - le - lu - jah! what a Sav - ior!

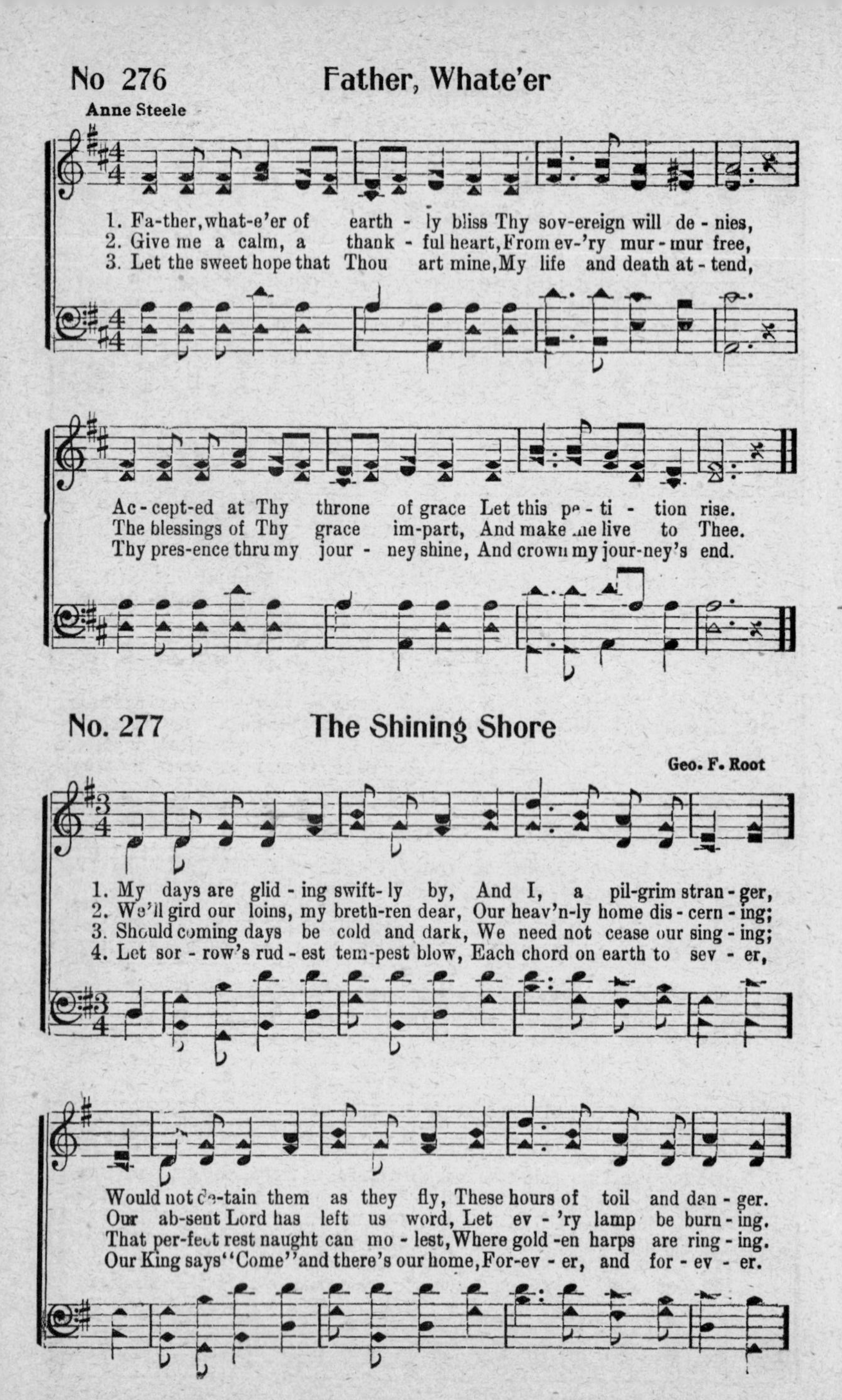
No 276 Father, Whate'er
Anne Steele
1. Fa-ther, what-e'er of earth - ly bliss Thy sov-ereign will de - nies,
2. Give me a calm, a thank - ful heart, From ev-'ry mur - mur free,
3. Let the sweet hope that Thou art mine, My life and death at - tend,
Ac-cept-ed at Thy throne of grace Let this pe - ti - tion rise.
The blessings of Thy grace im-part, And make me live to Thee.
Thy pres-ence thru my jour - ney shine, And crown my jour-ney's end.
No. 277 The Shining Shore
Geo. F. Root
1. My days are glid - ing swift- ly by, And I, a pil-grim stran - ger,
2. We'll gird our loins, my breth-ren dear, Our heav'n-ly home dis - cern - ing;
3. Should coming days be cold and dark, We need not cease our sing - ing;
4. Let sor - row's rud - est tem-pest blow, Each chord on earth to sev - er,
Would not de-tain them as they fly, These hours of toil and dan - ger.
Our ab-sent Lord has left us word, Let ev - 'ry lamp be burn - ing.
That per-fect rest naught can mo - lest, Where gold -en harps are ring - ing.
Our King says "Come" and there's our home, For-ev - er, and for - ev - er.

The Shining Shore

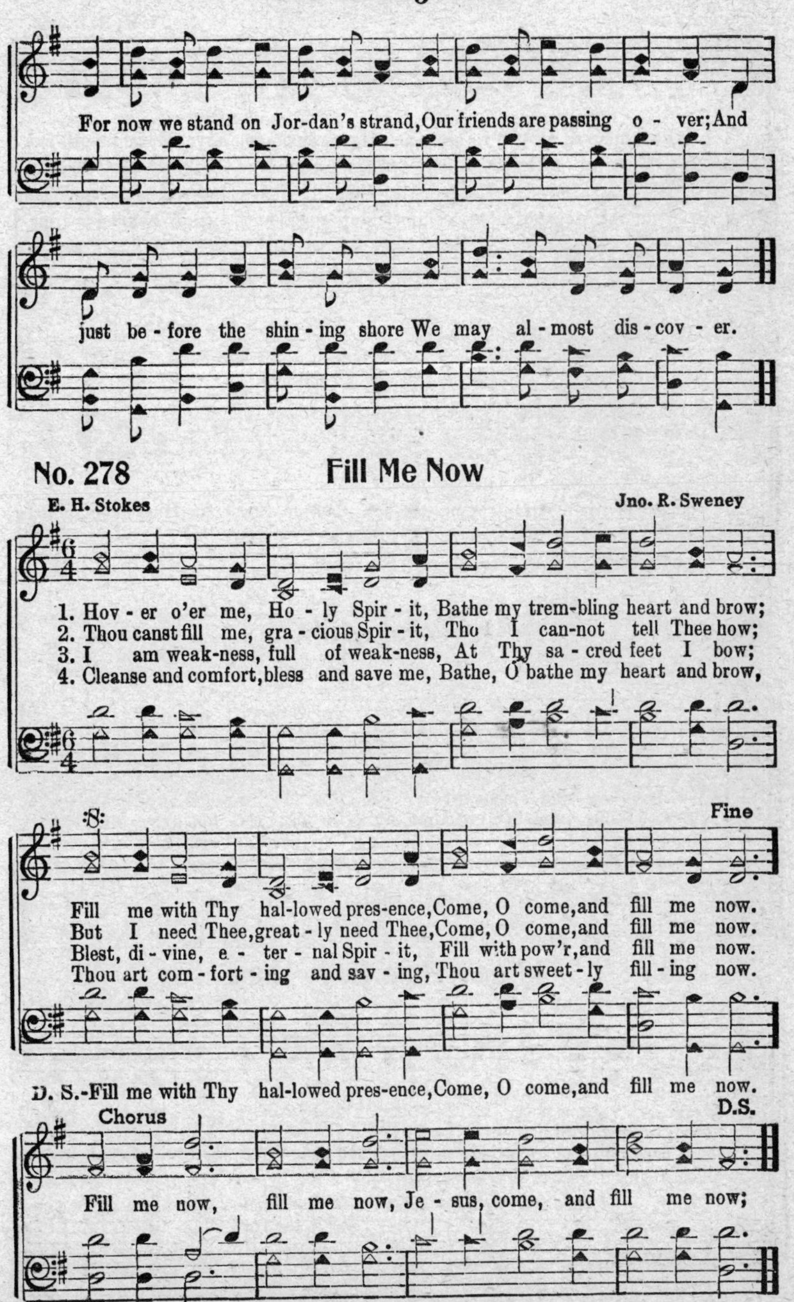
For now we stand on Jor-dan's strand, Our friends are passing o - ver; And
just be - fore the shin - ing shore We may al - most dis - cov - er.
No. 278
Fill Me Now
E. H. Stokes
Jno. R. Sweney
1. Hov - er o'er me, Ho - ly Spir - it, Bathe my trem-bling heart and brow;
2. Thou canst fill me, gra - cious Spir - it, Tho I can-not tell Thee how;
3. I am weak-ness, full of weak-ness, At Thy sa - cred feet I bow;
4. Cleanse and comfort, bless and save me, Bathe, O bathe my heart and brow,
Fine
Fill me with Thy hal-lowed pres-ence, Come, O come, and fill me now.
But I need Thee, great - ly need Thee, Come, O come, and fill me now.
Blest, di - vine, e - ter - nal Spir - it, Fill with pow'r, and fill me now.
Thou art com - fort - ing and sav - ing, Thou art sweet - ly fill - ing now.
D. S.-Fill me with Thy hal-lowed pres-ence, Come, O come, and fill me now.
Chorus
D.S.
Fill me now, fill me now, Je - sus, come, and fill me now;

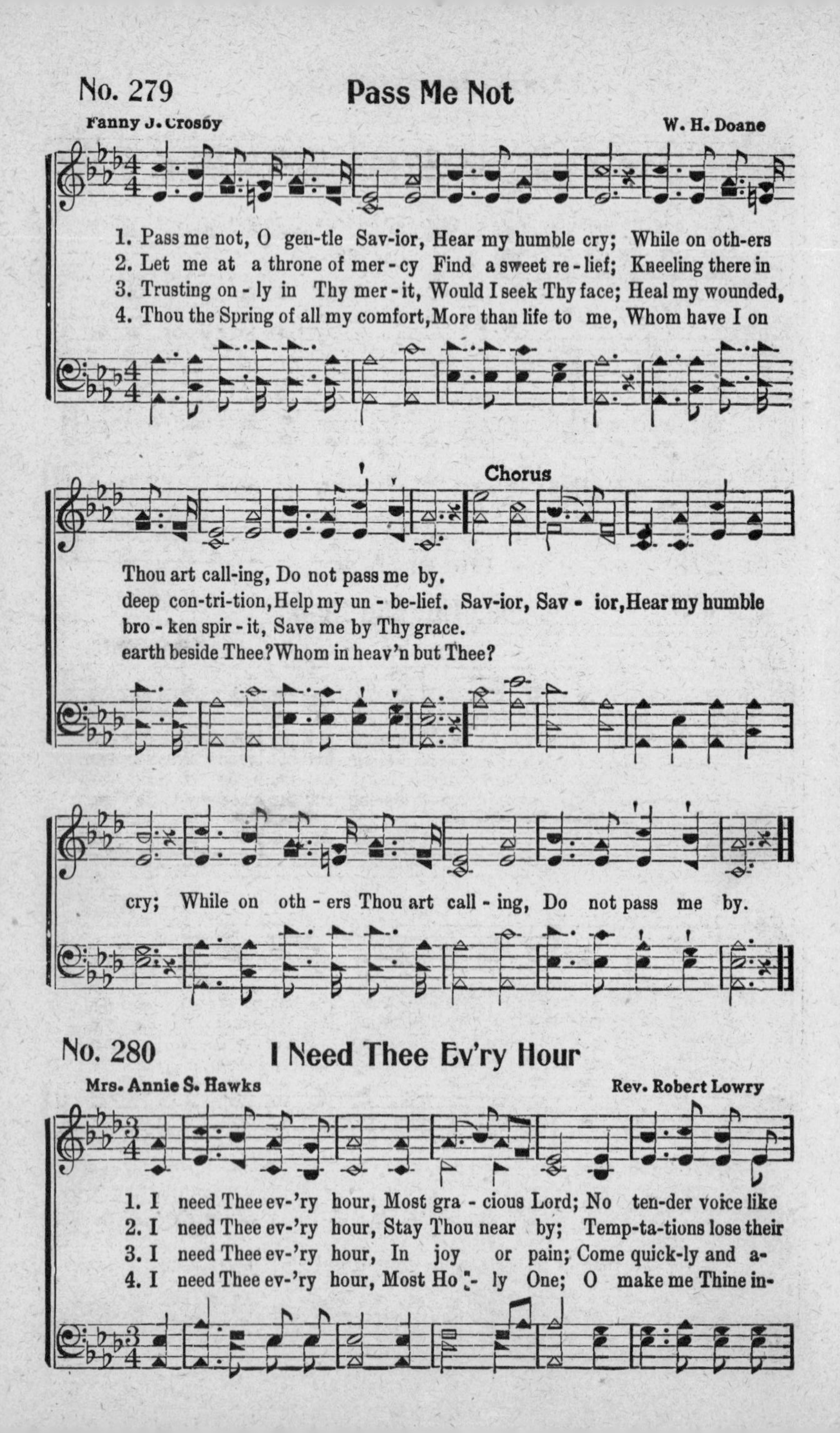
No. 279
Pass Me Not
Fanny J. Crosby
W. H. Doane
1. Pass me not, O gen-tle Sav-ior, Hear my humble cry; While on oth-ers Thou art call-ing, Do not pass me by.
2. Let me at a throne of mer-cy Find a sweet re-lief; Kneeling there in deep con-tri-tion, Help my un-be-lief.
3. Trusting on-ly in Thy mer-it, Would I seek Thy face; Heal my wounded, bro-ken spir-it, Save me by Thy grace.
4. Thou the Spring of all my comfort, More than life to me, Whom have I on earth beside Thee? Whom in heav'n but Thee?
Chorus
Sav-ior, Sav-ior, Hear my humble cry; While on oth-ers Thou art call-ing, Do not pass me by.
No. 280
I Need Thee Ev'ry Hour
Mrs. Annie S. Hawks
Rev. Robert Lowry
1. I need Thee ev-'ry hour, Most gra-cious Lord; No ten-der voice like
2. I need Thee ev-'ry hour, Stay Thou near by; Temp-ta-tions lose their
3. I need Thee ev-'ry hour, In joy or pain; Come quick-ly and a-
4. I need Thee ev-'ry hour, Most Ho-ly One; O make me Thine in-

I Need Thee Ev'ry Hour

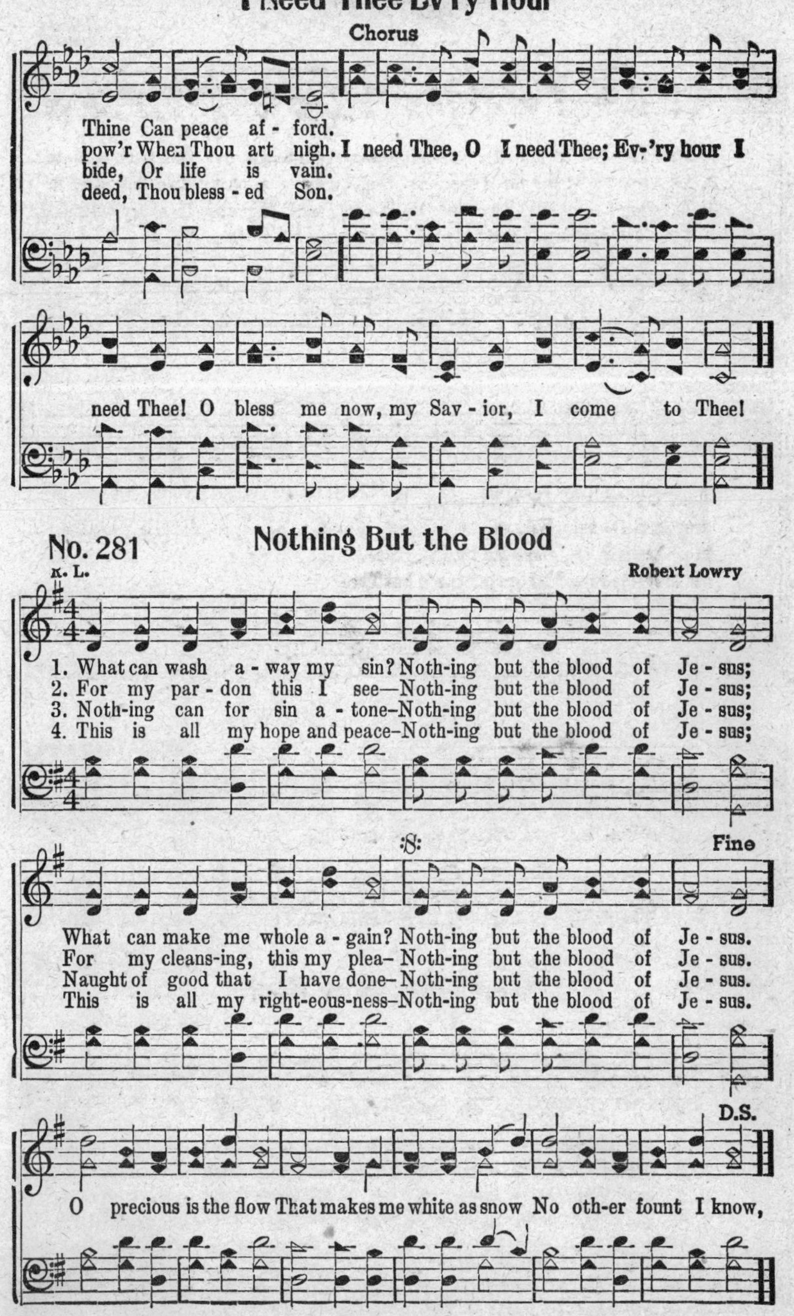
Chorus
Thine Can peace af - ford.
pow'r When Thou art nigh. I need Thee, O I need Thee; Ev-'ry hour I
bide, Or life is vain.
deed, Thou bless - ed Son.
need Thee! O bless me now, my Sav - ior, I come to Thee!
No. 281
Nothing But the Blood
R. L.
Robert Lowry
1. What can wash a - way my sin? Noth-ing but the blood of Je - sus;
2. For my par - don this I see—Noth-ing but the blood of Je - sus;
3. Noth-ing can for sin a - tone—Noth-ing but the blood of Je - sus;
4. This is all my hope and peace—Noth-ing but the blood of Je - sus;
Fine
What can make me whole a - gain? Noth-ing but the blood of Je - sus.
For my cleans-ing, this my plea— Noth-ing but the blood of Je - sus.
Naught of good that I have done—Noth-ing but the blood of Je - sus.
This is all my right-eous-ness—Noth-ing but the blood of Je - sus.
D.S.
O precious is the flow That makes me white as snow No oth-er fount I know,

No. 282
Where He Leads Me
E. W. Blandly
J. S. Norris
1. I can hear my Sav - ior call-ing, I can hear my Sav - ior call- ing,
2. I'll go with Him thru the gar-den, I'll go with Him thru the gar- den,
3. I'll go with Him thru the judgment, I'll go with Him thru the judgment,
4. He will give me grace and glo - ry, He will give me grace and glo - ry,
Cho.-Where He leads me I will fol-low, Where He leads me I will fol - low,
D.C. for Chorus
I can hear my Sav - ior call-ing, "Take thy cross and fol-low, fol-low Me."
I'll go with Him thru the gar-den, I'll go with Him, with Him all the way.
I'll go with Him thru the judgment, I'll go with Him, with Him all the way.
He will give me grace and glo - ry, And go with me, with me all the way.
Where He leads me I will fol - low, I'll go with Him, with Him all the way.
No. 283
Softly and Tenderly
W. L. T.
Will L. Thompson
1. Soft - ly and ten-der-ly Je - sus is call-ing, Call-ing for you and for me;
2. Why should we tarry when Jesus is pleading, Pleading for you and for me?
3. Time is now fleeting, the moments are passing, Passing from you and from me;
4. Oh! for the won-der-ful love He has promised, Promised for you and for me;
See, on the portals He's waiting and watching, Watching for you and for me.
Why should we linger and heed not His mercies, Mercies for you and for me?
Shadows are gathering, death-beds are coming, Coming for you and for me.
Tho we have sinned, He has mercy and pardon, Pardon for you and for me.

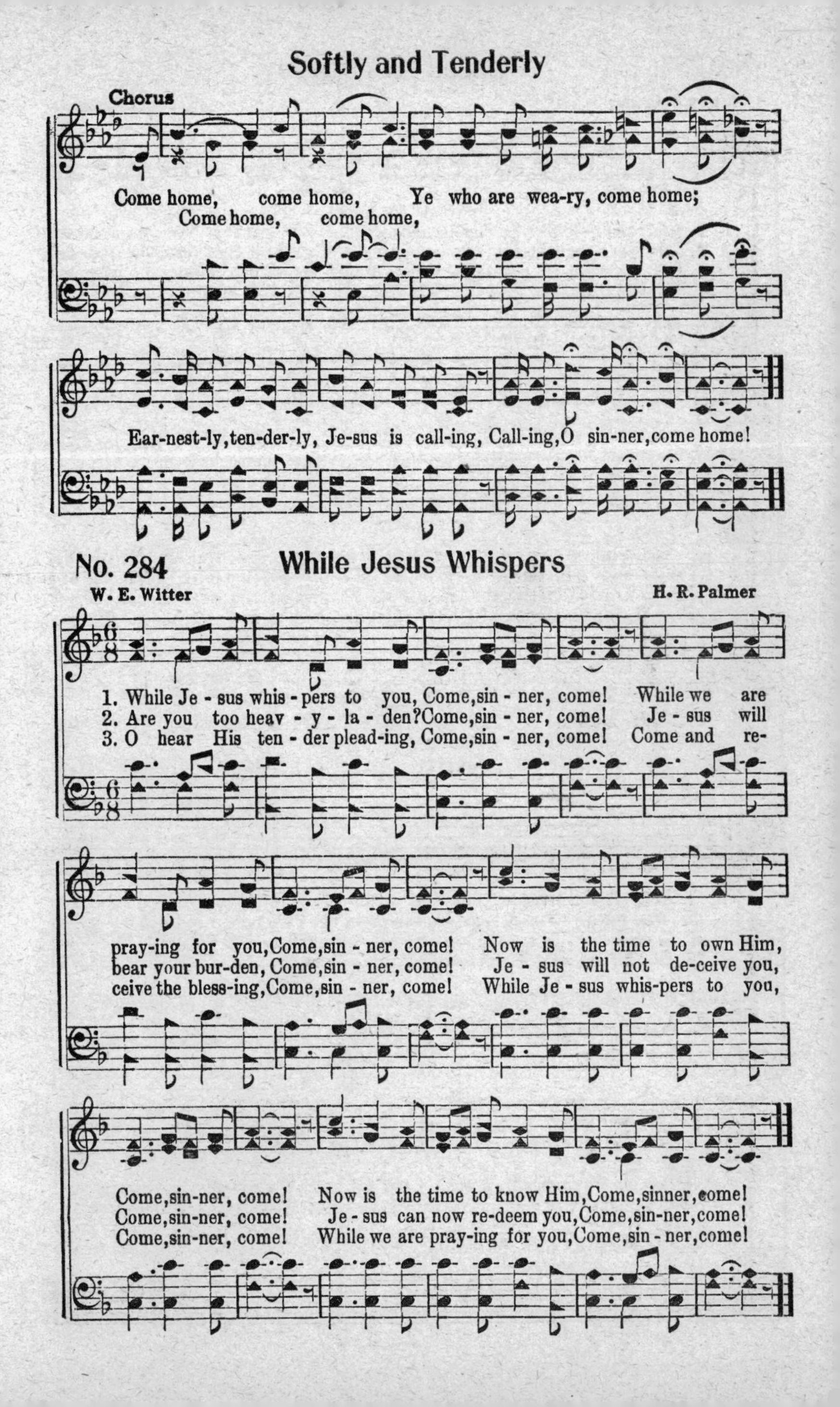
Softly and Tenderly
Chorus
Come home, come home, Ye who are wea-ry, come home;
Come home, come home,
Ear-nest-ly, ten-der-ly, Je-sus is call-ing, Call-ing, O sin-ner, come home!
No. 284 While Jesus Whispers
W. E. Witter
H. R. Palmer
1. While Je - sus whis - pers to you, Come, sin - ner, come! While we are
2. Are you too heav - y - la - den? Come, sin - ner, come! Je - sus will
3. O hear His ten - der plead-ing, Come, sin - ner, come! Come and re-
pray-ing for you, Come, sin - ner, come! Now is the time to own Him,
bear your bur-den, Come, sin - ner, come! Je - sus will not de-ceive you,
ceive the bless-ing, Come, sin - ner, come! While Je - sus whis-pers to you,
Come, sin-ner, come! Now is the time to know Him, Come, sinner, come!
Come, sin-ner, come! Je - sus can now re-deem you, Come, sin-ner, come!
Come, sin-ner, come! While we are pray-ing for you, Come, sin - ner, come!

No. 285 Blessed Assurance

Fanny J. Crosby | Mrs. J. F. Knapp

1. Bless-ed as - sur - ance, Je - sus is mine! O what a fore-taste of glo - ry di - vine! Heir of sal - va - tion, pur-chase of God, Born of His Spir - it, washed in His blood.
2. Per-fect sub - mis - sion, per-fect de - light, Vi-sions of rap-ture now burst on my sight; An - gels de - scend - ing, bring from a - bove Ech - oes of mer - cy, whis-pers of love.
3. Per-fect sub - mis - sion, all is at rest, I in my Sav - ior am hap - py and blest; Watch-ing and wait - ing, look - ing a - bove, Filled with His good-ness, lost in His love.

Chorus

This is my sto - ry,

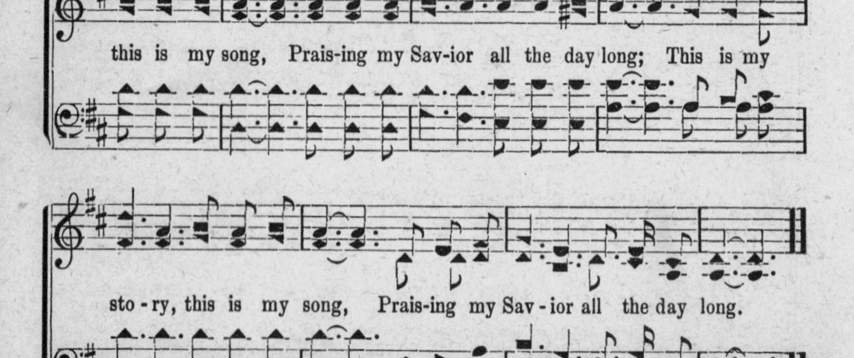
this is my song, Prais-ing my Sav-ior all the day long; This is my
sto - ry, this is my song, Prais-ing my Sav - ior all the day long.

No. 286
He Leadeth Me
Joseph H. Gilmore
William B. Bradbury
1. He lead-eth me! O bless-ed tho't! O words with heav'nly comfort fraught!
2. Sometimes 'mid scenes of deepest gloom, Sometimes where Eden's bowers bloom,
3. Lord, I would clasp Thy hand in mine, Nor ev - er mur-mur nor re-pine,
4. And when my task on earth is done, When, by Thy grace, the vic'try's won,
What-e'er I do, wher-e'er I be, Still 'tis God's hand that lead-eth me.
By wa - ters still, o'er troubled sea, Still 'tis His hand that lead-eth me!
Con-tent, what-ev - er lot I see, Since 'tis my God that lead-eth me!
E'en death's cold wave I will not flee, Since God thru Jor - dan lead-eth me.
Chorus
He lead-eth me, He lead-eth me, By His own hand He lead-eth me:
His faith-ful fol-low'r I would be, For by His hand He lead-eth me.

No. 287 On Jordan's Stormy Banks
Rev. Samuel Stennett
T. C. O'Kane
1. On Jor-dan's storm-y banks I stand, And cast a wish - ful eye
2. O'er all those wide ex - tend-ed plains Shines one e - ter - nal day;
3. When shall I reach that hap - py place, And be for - ev - er blest?
4. Filled with de-light, my rap-tured soul Would here no long - er stay;
To Ca-naan's fair and hap - py land, Where my pos - ses - sions lie.
There God the Son for - ev - er reigns, And scat - ters night a - way.
When shall I see my Fa-ther's face, And in His bos - om rest?
Tho Jor-dan's waves a - round me roll, Fear-less I'd launch a - way.
Chorus
We will rest in the fair and hap - py land, Just a-
by and by,
cross on the ev - er-green shore, Sing the song of
ev - er-green shore,
Mo-ses and the Lamb, by and by, And dwell with Je - sus ev - er - more.

No. 288 The Home Over There
D. W. C. Huntington
Tullius C. O'Kane
1. O think of a home o-ver there, By the side of the riv-er of light,
2. O think of the friends over there, Who before us the journey have trod,
3. My Sav-ior is now o-ver there, There my kindred and friends are at rest;
4. I'll soon be at home o-ver there, For the end of my journey I see;
o-ver there,
Where the saints all immortal and fair Are robed in their garments of white.
Of the songs that they breathe on the air, In their home in the palace of God.
Then a-way from my sorrow and care, Let me fly to the land of the blest.
Man - y dear to my heart o-ver there Are watching and waiting for me.
over there.
Chorus
O-ver there, o-ver there, O think of the home over there,
O-ver there, o-ver there, O think of the friends over there,
O-ver there, o-ver there, My Sav-ior is now o-ver there,
O-ver there, o-ver there, I'll soon be at home o-ver there,
Over there, over there, o-ver there,
O-ver there, o-ver there, o-ver there, O think of a home o-ver there.
O-ver there, o-ver there, o-ver there, O think of the friends over there.
O-ver there, o-ver there, o-ver there, My Sav-ior is now o- ver there.
O-ver there, o-ver there, o-ver there, I'll soon be at home over there.
O-ver there,

No. 289 Battle Hymn of the Republic
Julia Ward Howe
William Steffe
1. Mine eyes have seen the glo - ry of the com - ing of the Lord;
2. I have seen Him in the watch-fires of a hun - dred cir-cling camps;
3. He has sound - ed forth the trump-et that shall nev - er sound re-treat;
4. In the beau - ty of the lil - ies Christ was born a - cross the sea,
He is tram-pling out the vin-tage where the grapes of wrath are stored;
They have build - ed Him an al - tar in the eve - ning dews and damps;
He is sift - ing out the hearts of men be - fore His judg-ment seat;
With a glo - ry in His bos - om that trans-fig - ures you and me;
He hath loosed the fate - ful light-ning of His ter - ri - ble swift sword;
I can read His righteous sen-tence by the dim and flar - ing lamps;
O be swift, my soul, to an - swer Him! be ju - bi - lant, my feet!
As He died to make men ho - ly, let us die to make men free;
His truth is marching on.
Chorus
Glo - ry, glo - ry, hal - le - lu - jah, Glo - ry, glo - ry,
hal - le - lu - jah, Glo - ry, glo - ry, hal - le - lu - jah, His truth is marching on.

No. 290
God Be With You
J. E. Rankin, D. D.
W. G. Tomer
1. God be with you till we meet a - gain, By His coun - sels
2. God be with you till we meet a - gain, 'Neath His wings se-
3. God be with you till we meet a - gain, When life's per - ils
4. God be with you till we meet a - gain, Keep love's ban - ner
guide, up - hold you, With His sheep se - cure - ly fold you, God be
cure - ly hide you, Dai - ly man-na still pro-vide you, God be
thick confound you, Put His arms un - fail - ing round you, God be
float - ing o'er you, Smite death's threat'ning wave be-fore you, God be
Chorus
with you till we meet a - gain. Till we meet, till we
Till we meet, till we
meet, Till we meet at Je - sus' feet, Till we
meet a - gain, till we meet,
meet, till we meet, God be with you till we meet a-gain.
Till we meet, till we meet a-gain,

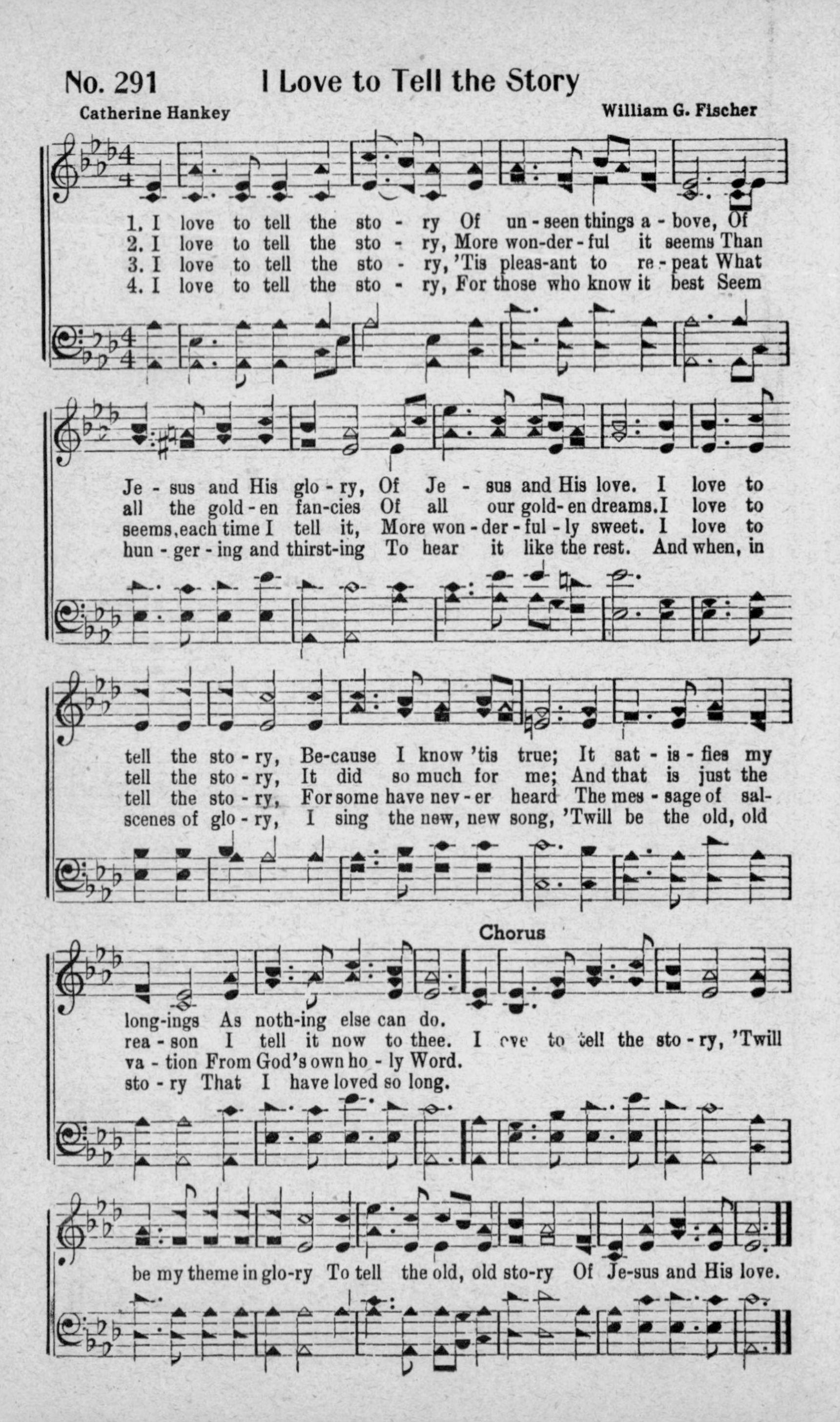
No. 291 I Love to Tell the Story
Catherine Hankey
William G. Fischer
1. I love to tell the sto - ry Of un-seen things a-bove, Of
2. I love to tell the sto - ry, More won-der-ful it seems Than
3. I love to tell the sto - ry, 'Tis pleas-ant to re-peat What
4. I love to tell the sto - ry, For those who know it best Seem
Je - sus and His glo - ry, Of Je - sus and His love. I love to
all the gold - en fan-cies Of all our gold-en dreams. I love to
seems, each time I tell it, More won - der - ful - ly sweet. I love to
hun - ger - ing and thirst-ing To hear it like the rest. And when, in
tell the sto - ry, Be-cause I know 'tis true; It sat - is - fies my
tell the sto - ry, It did so much for me; And that is just the
tell the sto - ry, For some have nev - er heard The mes - sage of sal-
scenes of glo - ry, I sing the new, new song, 'Twill be the old, old
long-ings As noth-ing else can do.
rea - son I tell it now to thee.
va - tion From God's own ho - ly Word.
sto - ry That I have loved so long.
Chorus
I ove to tell the sto - ry, 'Twill
be my theme in glo-ry To tell the old, old sto-ry Of Je-sus and His love.

No. 292
Even Me
Mrs. Elizabeth Codner
Wm. B. Bradbury
1. Lord, I hear of show'rs of bless - ing Thou art scatt'ring full and free;
2. Pass me not, O God, my Fa - ther Sin - ful tho my heart may be;
3. Pass me not, O gra - cious Sav - ior, Let me live and cling to Thee;
4. Love of God, so pure and change-less, Blood of Christ, so rich and free;
Show'r, the thirst-y land re - fresh - ing; Let some drops now fall on me;
Thou mightst leave me, but the rath - er; Let Thy mer - cy light on me;
I am long - ing for Thy fa - vor, Whilst Thou'rt calling, O call me;
Grace of God, so strong and bound-less Mag - ni - fy them all in me;
E - ven me, e - ven me, Let some drops now fall on me,
E - ven me, e - ven me, Let Thy mer - cy light on me;
E - ven me, e - ven me, Whilst Thou'rt call-ing, O call me;
E - ven me, e - ven me, Mag - ni - fy them all in me;
E - ven me, e - ven me, Let some drops now fall on me.
E - ven me, e - ven me, Let Thy mer - cy light on me.
E - ven me, e - ven me, Whilst Thou'rt call-ing. O call me.
E - ven me, e - ven me, Mag - ni - fy them all in me.

No. 293 Glory to His Name

Rev. E. A. Hoffman — Rev. J. H. Stockton

1. Down at the cross where my Savior died, Down where for cleansing from sin I cried,
There to my heart was the blood applied; (Omit.......................)
2. I am so wondrous-ly saved from sin, Je-sus so sweetly a-bides with-in,
There at the cross where He took me in; (Omit.......................)
3. O precious fountain that saves from sin, I am so glad I have en-tered in;
There Je-sus saves me and keeps me clean; (Omit.......................)
4. Come to this fountain so rich and sweet, Cast thy poor soul at the Savior's feet;
Plunge in to - day and be made complete; (Omit.......................)

D.C.—There to my heart was the blood applied; (Omit.......................)

Fine Chorus — D.C.

Glo-ry to His name. Glo-ry to His name, Glo-ry to His name;

No. 294 I am Trusting, Lord, in Thee

William McDonald — William G. Fischer

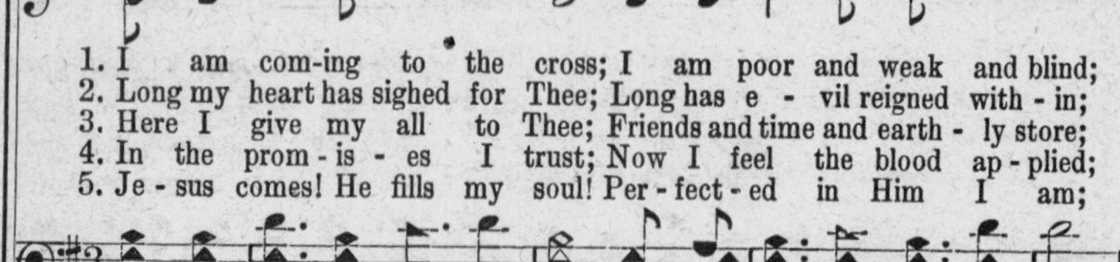

1. I am com-ing to the cross; I am poor and weak and blind;
2. Long my heart has sighed for Thee; Long has e - vil reigned with - in;
3. Here I give my all to Thee; Friends and time and earth - ly store;
4. In the prom - is - es I trust; Now I feel the blood ap - plied;
5. Je - sus comes! He fills my soul! Per - fect - ed in Him I am;

Cho.- I am trust - ing, Lord, in Thee, Bless-ed Lamb of Cal - va - ry;

D.C. for Chorus

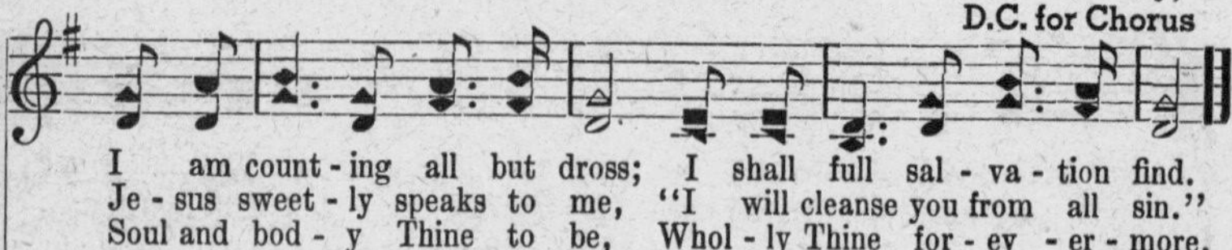

I am count - ing all but dross; I shall full sal - va - tion find.
Je - sus sweet - ly speaks to me, "I will cleanse you from all sin."
Soul and bod - y Thine to be, Whol - ly Thine for - ev - er - more.
I am pros - trate in the dust; I with Christ am cru - ci - fied.
I am ev - 'ry whit made whole: Glo - ry, glo - ry to the Lamb!

Hum-bly at Thy cross I bow, Save me, Je - sus, save me now.

No. 295 How Tedious and Tasteless
John Newton
Lewis Edson
1. How te - dious and taste-less the hours When Je-sus no long-er I see!
2. His name yields the rich - est per-fume, And sweet-er than mu-sic His voice,
3. Con-tent with be-hold - ing His face, My all to His pleas-ure re-signed,
4. Dear Lord, if in - deed I am Thine, If Thou art my sun and my song,
Sweet prospects, sweet birds, and sweet flow'rs, Have all lost their sweetness for me.
His pres-ence dis - pers-es my gloom, And makes all with-in me re - joice:
No chang-es of sea - son or place Would make an-y change in my mind:
Say, why do I lan-guish and pine, And why are my win-ters so long?
The mid - sum-mer sun shines but dim; The fields strive in vain to look gay;
I should, were He al - ways thus nigh, Have noth-ing to wish or to fear;
While blest with a sense of His love, A pal - ace a toy would ap-pear;
O drive these dark clouds from my sky; Thy soul-cheer-ing presence re-store;
But when I am hap-py in Him, De - cem-ber's as pleas-ant as May.
No mor-tal so hap-py as I; My sum-mer would last all the year.
And prisons would pal - a - ces prove, If Je - sus would dwell with me there.
Or take me un - to Thee on high, Where win-ter and clouds are no more.

No. 296 Come, Thou Fount

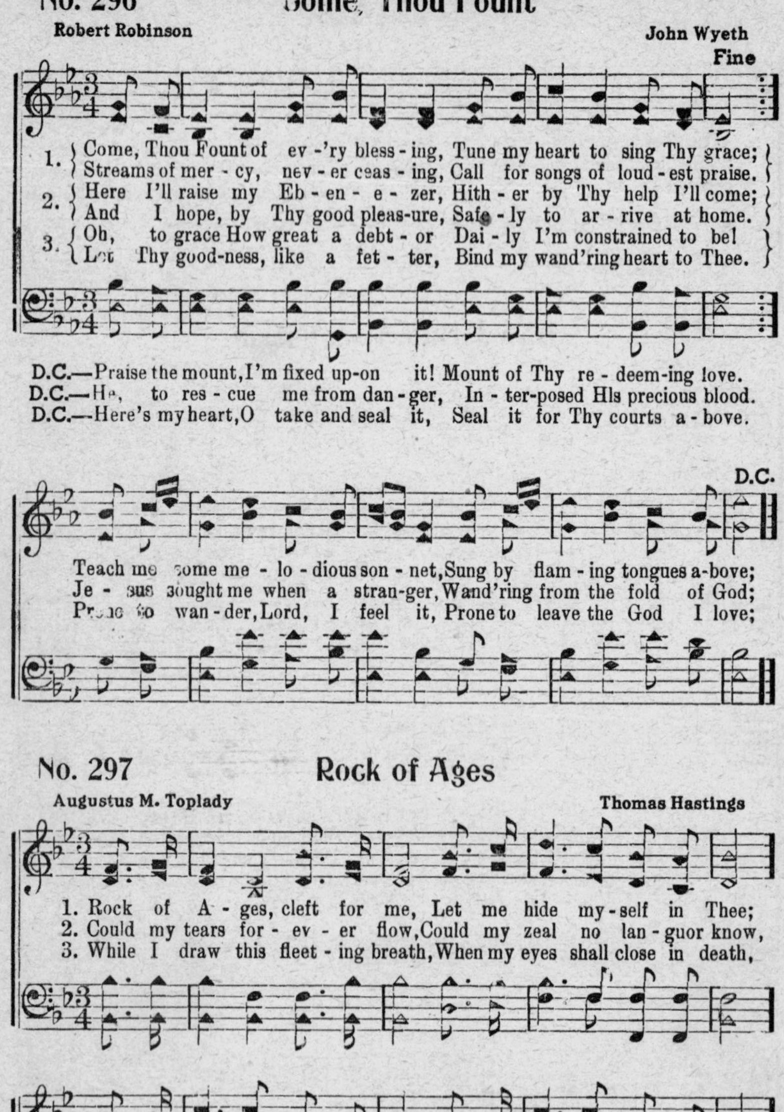

Robert Robinson
John Wyeth
Fine
1. Come, Thou Fount of ev-'ry bless-ing, Tune my heart to sing Thy grace;
Streams of mer-cy, nev-er ceas-ing, Call for songs of loud-est praise.
2. Here I'll raise my Eb-en-e-zer, Hith-er by Thy help I'll come;
And I hope, by Thy good pleas-ure, Safe-ly to ar-rive at home.
3. Oh, to grace How great a debt-or Dai-ly I'm constrained to be!
Let Thy good-ness, like a fet-ter, Bind my wand'ring heart to Thee.
D.C.—Praise the mount, I'm fixed up-on it! Mount of Thy re-deem-ing love.
D.C.—He, to res-cue me from dan-ger, In-ter-posed His precious blood.
D.C.—Here's my heart, O take and seal it, Seal it for Thy courts a-bove.
D.C.
Teach me some me-lo-dious son-net, Sung by flam-ing tongues a-bove;
Je-sus sought me when a stran-ger, Wand'ring from the fold of God;
Prone to wan-der, Lord, I feel it, Prone to leave the God I love;
No. 297 Rock of Ages
Augustus M. Toplady
Thomas Hastings
1. Rock of A-ges, cleft for me, Let me hide my-self in Thee;
2. Could my tears for-ev-er flow, Could my zeal no lan-guor know,
3. While I draw this fleet-ing breath, When my eyes shall close in death,
Let the wa-ter and the blood, From Thy wound-ed side which flowed,
These for sin could not a-tone, Thou must save, and Thou a-lone:
When I rise to worlds un-known, And be-hold Thee on Thy throne,

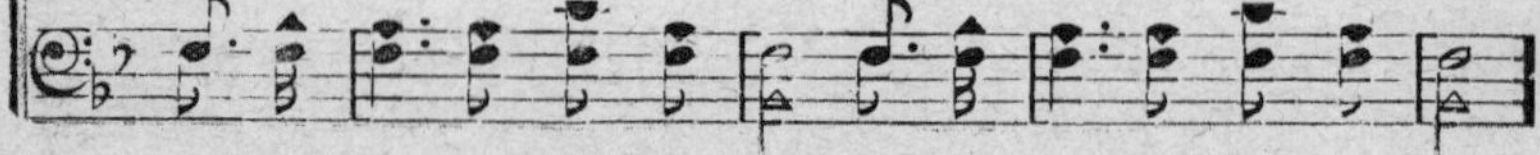

Rock of Ages

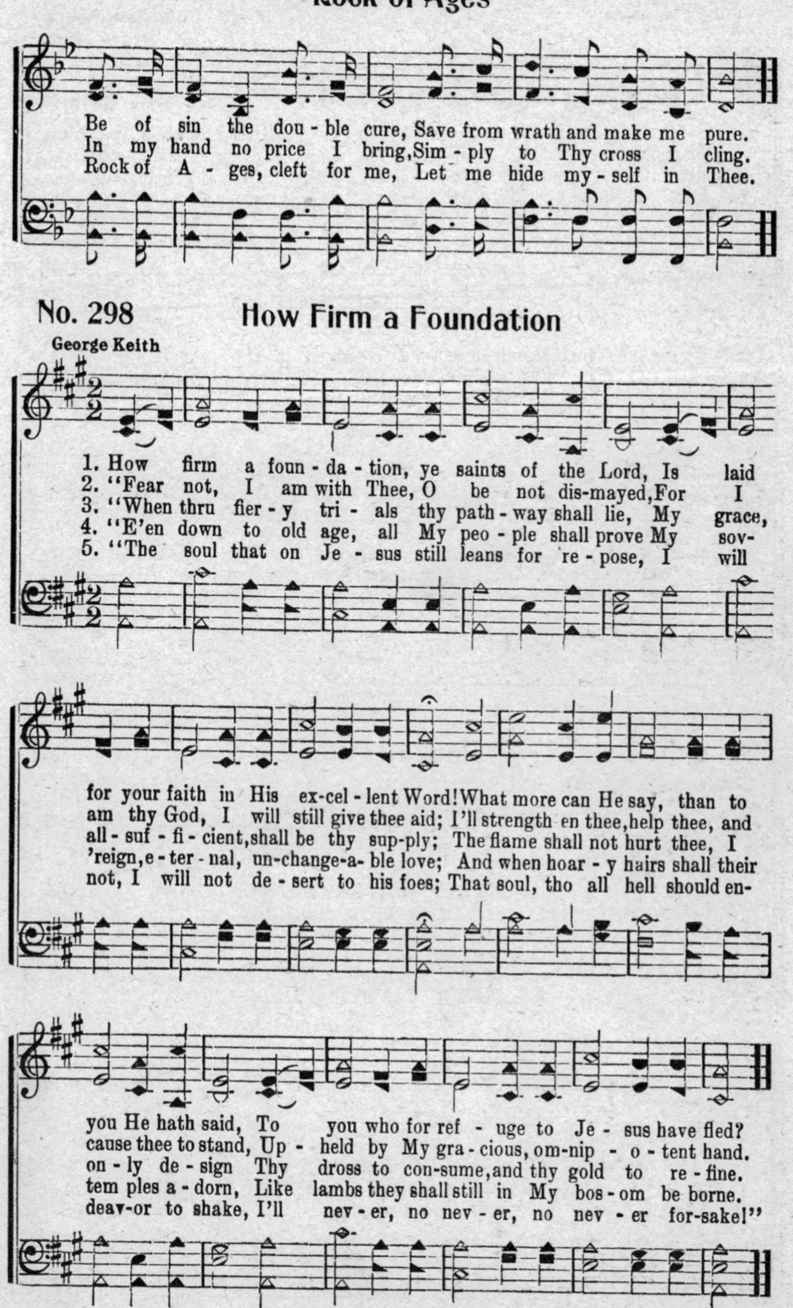

Be of sin the dou - ble cure, Save from wrath and make me pure.
In my hand no price I bring, Sim - ply to Thy cross I cling.
Rock of A - ges, cleft for me, Let me hide my - self in Thee.
No. 298
How Firm a Foundation
George Keith
1. How firm a foun - da - tion, ye saints of the Lord, Is laid
2. "Fear not, I am with Thee, O be not dis-mayed, For I
3. "When thru fier - y tri - als thy path - way shall lie, My grace,
4. "E'en down to old age, all My peo - ple shall prove My sov-
5. "The soul that on Je - sus still leans for re - pose, I will
for your faith in His ex-cel - lent Word! What more can He say, than to
am thy God, I will still give thee aid; I'll strength en thee, help thee, and
all - suf - fi - cient, shall be thy sup-ply; The flame shall not hurt thee, I
'reign, e - ter - nal, un-change-a - ble love; And when hoar - y hairs shall their
not, I will not de - sert to his foes; That soul, tho all hell should en-
you He hath said, To you who for ref - uge to Je - sus have fled?
cause thee to stand, Up - held by My gra - cious, om-nip - o - tent hand.
on - ly de - sign Thy dross to con-sume, and thy gold to re - fine.
tem ples a - dorn, Like lambs they shall still in My bos - om be borne.
deav-or to shake, I'll nev - er, no nev - er, no nev - er for-sake!"

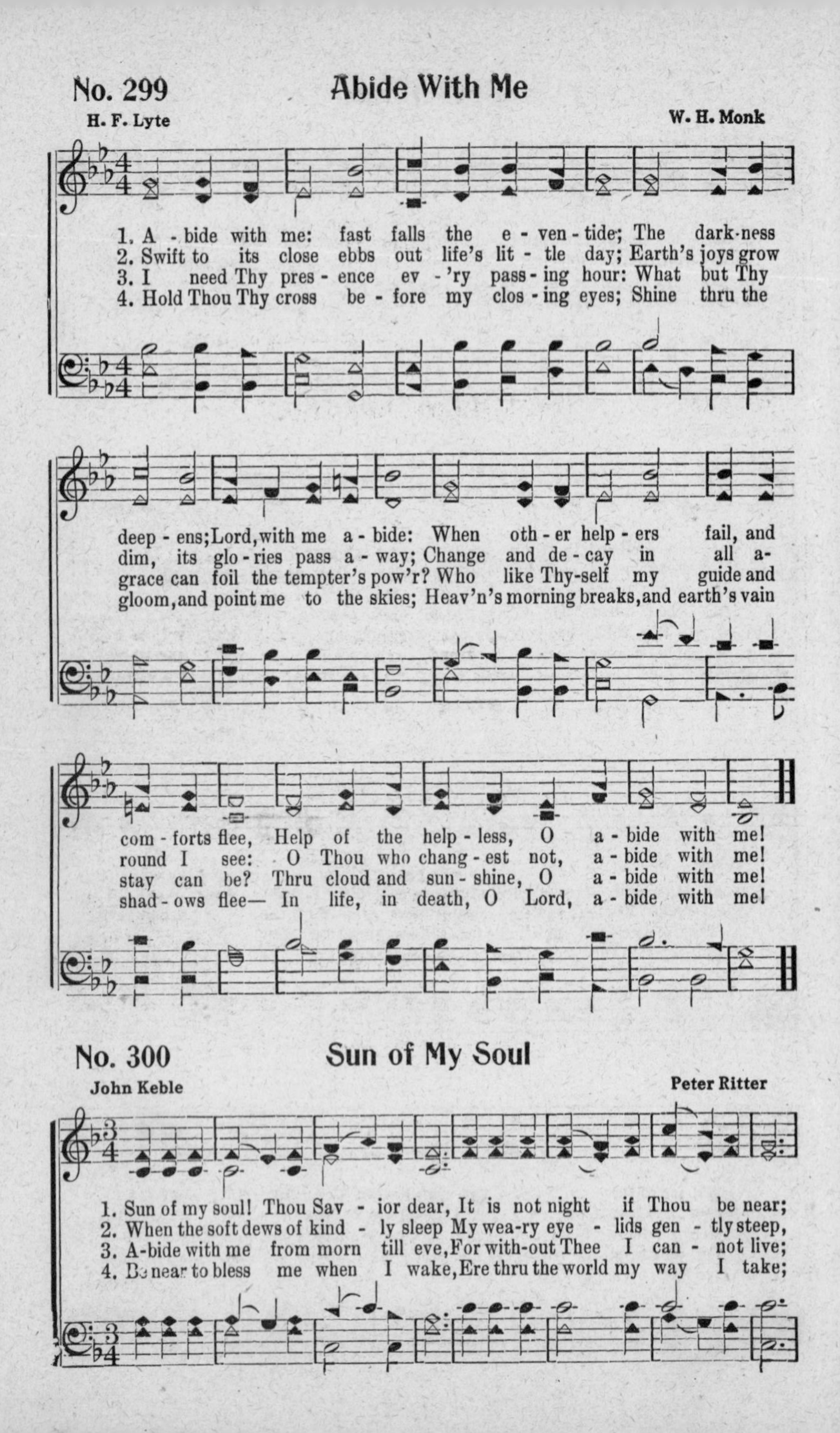
No. 299
Abide With Me
H. F. Lyte
W. H. Monk
1. A - bide with me: fast falls the e - ven - tide; The dark-ness
2. Swift to its close ebbs out life's lit - tle day; Earth's joys grow
3. I need Thy pres - ence ev - 'ry pass - ing hour: What but Thy
4. Hold Thou Thy cross be - fore my clos - ing eyes; Shine thru the
deep - ens; Lord, with me a - bide: When oth - er help - ers fail, and
dim, its glo - ries pass a - way; Change and de - cay in all a-
grace can foil the tempter's pow'r? Who like Thy-self my guide and
gloom, and point me to the skies; Heav'n's morning breaks, and earth's vain
com - forts flee, Help of the help - less, O a - bide with me!
round I see: O Thou who chang - est not, a - bide with me!
stay can be? Thru cloud and sun - shine, O a - bide with me!
shad - ows flee— In life, in death, O Lord, a - bide with me!
No. 300
Sun of My Soul
John Keble
Peter Ritter
1. Sun of my soul! Thou Sav - ior dear, It is not night if Thou be near;
2. When the soft dews of kind - ly sleep My wea-ry eye - lids gen - tly steep,
3. A-bide with me from morn till eve, For with-out Thee I can - not live;
4. Be near to bless me when I wake, Ere thru the world my way I take;

Sun of My Soul
O may no earth-born cloud a-rise To hide Thee from Thy serv-ant's eyes!
Be my last tho't–how sweet to rest For-ev-er on my Sav-ior's breast!
A-bide with me when night is nigh, For with-out Thee I dare not die.
A-bide with me till in Thy love I lose my-self in heav'n a-bove.
No. 301 My Faith Looks Up to Thee
Ray Palmer
Lowell Mason
1. My faith looks up to Thee, Thou Lamb of Cal-va-ry,
2. May Thy rich grace im-part Strength to my faint-ing heart,
3. While life's dark maze I tread, And griefs a-round me spread,
4. When ends life's tran-sient dream, When death's cold, sul-len stream
Sav-ior di-vine! Now hear me while I pray, Take all my
My zeal in-spire; As Thou hast died for me, O may my
Be Thou my Guide; Bid dark-ness turn to day, Wipe sor-row's
Shall o'er me roll; Blest Sav-ior, then, in love, Fear and dis-
guilt a-way, O let me from this day Be whol-ly Thine!
love to Thee Pure, warm and change-less be, A liv-ing fire!
tears a-way, Nor let me ev-er stray From Thee a-side.
trust re-move; O bear me safe a-bove, A ran-somed soul!

No. 302
Holy Spirit, Faithful Guide
M. M. W.
Marcus M. Wells
1. Ho - ly Spir - it, faith - ful Guide, Ev - er near the Chris- tian's side;
2. Ev - er pres - ent, tru - est Friend, Ev - er near Thine aid to lend,
3. When our days of toil shall cease, Wait - ing still for sweet re-lease,
Gen - tly lead us by the hand, Pil - grims in a des - ert land;
Leave us not to doubt and fear, Grop - ing on in dark - ness drear;
Noth - ing left but heav'n and pray'r, Won-d'ring if our names are there;
Wea - ry souls for-e'er re - joice, While they hear that sweet - est voice,
When the storms are rag - ing sore, Hearts grow faint and hopes give o'er,
Wad - ing deep the dis - mal flood, Plead-ing naught but Je - sus' blood,
Whis - per soft - ly, "Wan-d'rer, come! Fol - low me, I'll guide thee home."
No. 303
Holy Ghost, With Light Divine
Andrew Reed
L. M. Gottschalk
1. Ho - ly Ghost, with light di - vine, Shine up - on this heart of mine;
2. Ho - ly Ghost, with pow'r di - vine, Cleanse this guil - ty heart of mine;
3. Ho - ly Ghost, with joy di - vine, Cheer this saddened heart of mine;
4. Ho - ly Spir - it, all di - vine, Dwell with-in this heart of mine;

Holy Ghost, With Light Divine

Chase the shades of night a - way, Turn my dark - ness in - to day.
Long hath sin, with-out con - trol, Held do - min - ion o'er my soul.
Bid my man - y woes de - part, Heal my wound-ed, bleed-ing heart.
Cast down ev - 'ry i - dol-throne, Reign su-preme, and reign a - lone.
No. 304
Holy, Holy, Holy
Reginald Heber
Rev. John B. Dykes
1. Ho - ly, Ho - ly, Ho - ly, Lord God Al-might - y! Ear - ly in the
2. Ho - ly, Ho - ly, Ho - ly! All the saints a - dore Thee, Cast-ing down their
3. Ho - ly, Ho - ly, Ho - ly! Tho the darkness hide Thee, Tho the eye of
4. Ho - ly, Ho - ly, Ho - ly, Lord God Al-might - y! All Thy works shall
morn - ing our song shall rise to Thee; Ho - ly, Ho - ly, Ho - ly!
gold-en crowns a-round the glass-y sea; Cher-u - bim and sera - phim
sin - ful man Thy glo - ry may not see, On - ly Thou art ho - ly;
praise Thy name, in earth, and sky, and sea; Ho - ly, Ho - ly, Ho - ly!
Mer - ci-ful and Might - y! God in Three per-sons, bless-ed Trin - i - ty!
fall - ing down be-fore Thee, Who wert, and art, and ev - er more shalt be.
there is none be side Thee Per - fect in pow'r, in love, and pu - ri - ty.
Mer - ci-ful and Might - y! God in Three per-sons, bless-ed Trin - i - ty!

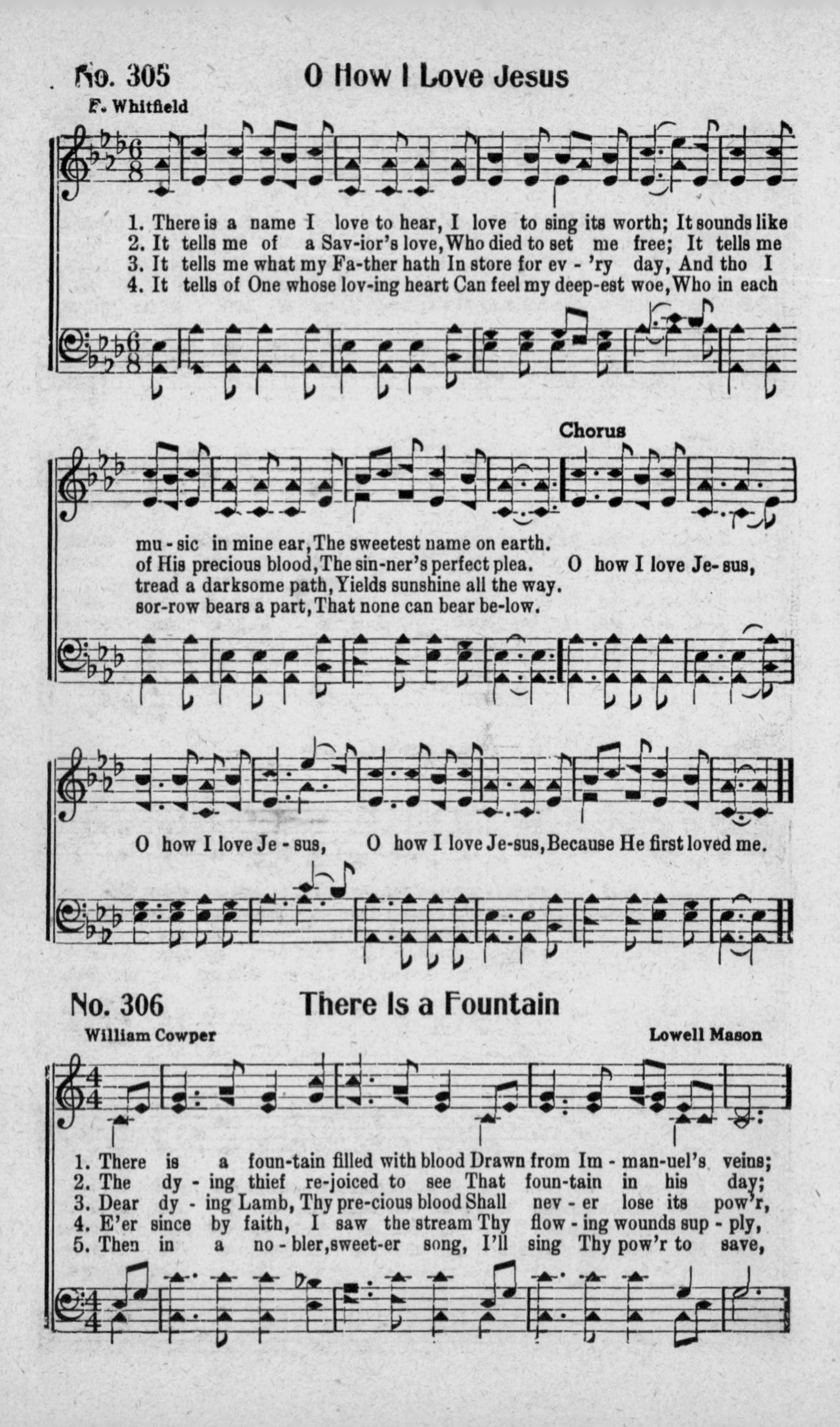
No. 305
O How I Love Jesus
F. Whitfield
1. There is a name I love to hear, I love to sing its worth; It sounds like
2. It tells me of a Sav-ior's love, Who died to set me free; It tells me
3. It tells me what my Fa-ther hath In store for ev - 'ry day, And tho I
4. It tells of One whose lov-ing heart Can feel my deep-est woe, Who in each
Chorus
mu - sic in mine ear, The sweetest name on earth.
of His precious blood, The sin-ner's perfect plea.
tread a darksome path, Yields sunshine all the way.
sor-row bears a part, That none can bear be-low.
O how I love Je- sus,
O how I love Je - sus, O how I love Je-sus, Because He first loved me.
No. 306
There Is a Fountain
William Cowper
Lowell Mason
1. There is a foun-tain filled with blood Drawn from Im - man-uel's veins;
2. The dy - ing thief re-joiced to see That foun-tain in his day;
3. Dear dy - ing Lamb, Thy pre-cious blood Shall nev - er lose its pow'r,
4. E'er since by faith, I saw the stream Thy flow - ing wounds sup - ply,
5. Then in a no - bler, sweet-er song, I'll sing Thy pow'r to save,

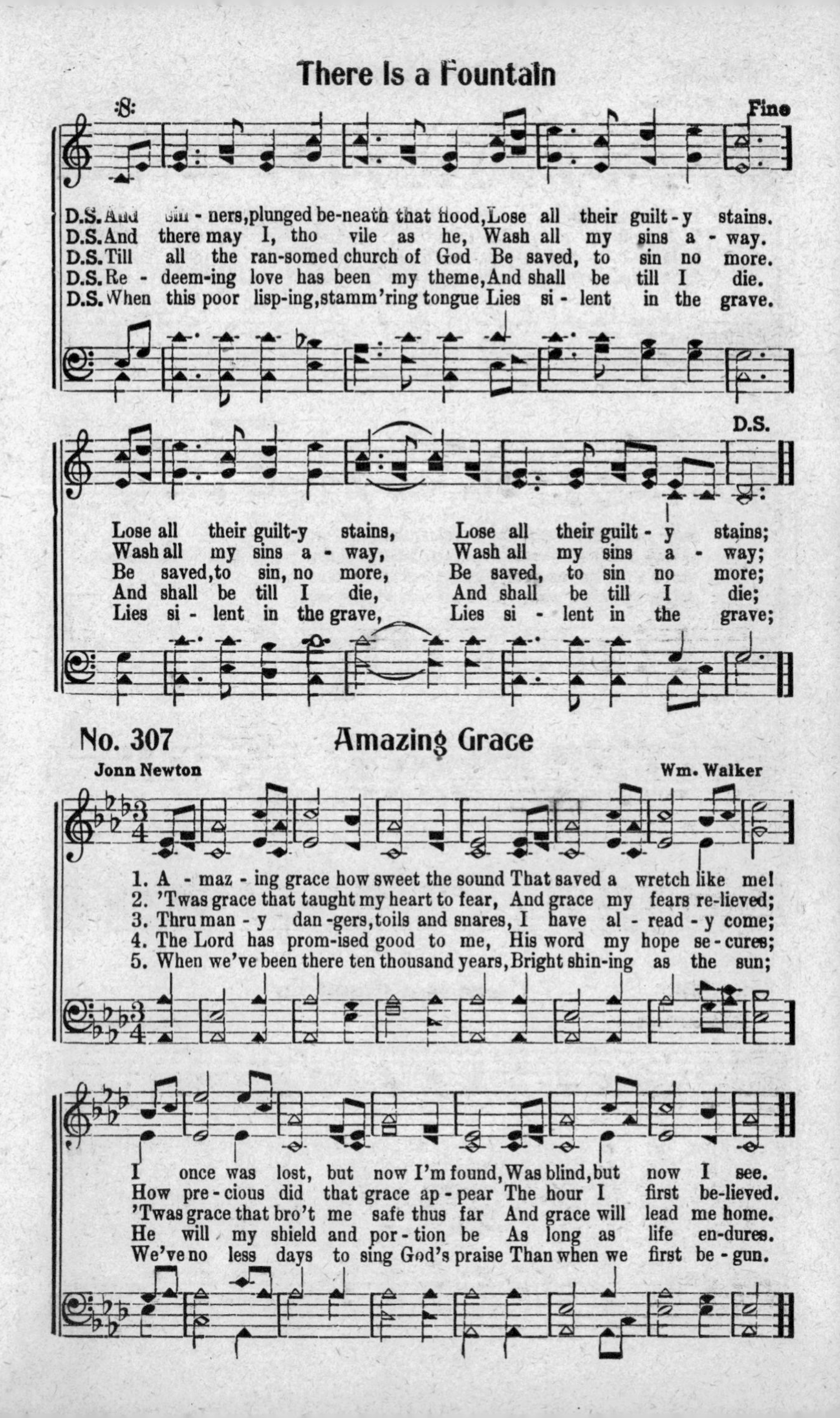
There Is a Fountain
Fine
D.S. And sin - ners, plunged be-neath that flood, Lose all their guilt - y stains.
D.S. And there may I, tho vile as he, Wash all my sins a - way.
D.S. Till all the ran-somed church of God Be saved, to sin no more.
D.S. Re - deem-ing love has been my theme, And shall be till I die.
D.S. When this poor lisp-ing, stamm'ring tongue Lies si - lent in the grave.
D.S.
Lose all their guilt-y stains, Lose all their guilt - y stains;
Wash all my sins a - way, Wash all my sins a - way;
Be saved, to sin, no more, Be saved, to sin no more;
And shall be till I die, And shall be till I die;
Lies si - lent in the grave, Lies si - lent in the grave;
No. 307 Amazing Grace
Jonn Newton
Wm. Walker
1. A - maz - ing grace how sweet the sound That saved a wretch like me!
2. 'Twas grace that taught my heart to fear, And grace my fears re-lieved;
3. Thru man - y dan - gers, toils and snares, I have al - read - y come;
4. The Lord has prom-ised good to me, His word my hope se - cures;
5. When we've been there ten thousand years, Bright shin-ing as the sun;
I once was lost, but now I'm found, Was blind, but now I see.
How pre - cious did that grace ap - pear The hour I first be-lieved.
'Twas grace that bro't me safe thus far And grace will lead me home.
He will my shield and por - tion be As long as life en-dures.
We've no less days to sing God's praise Than when we first be - gun.

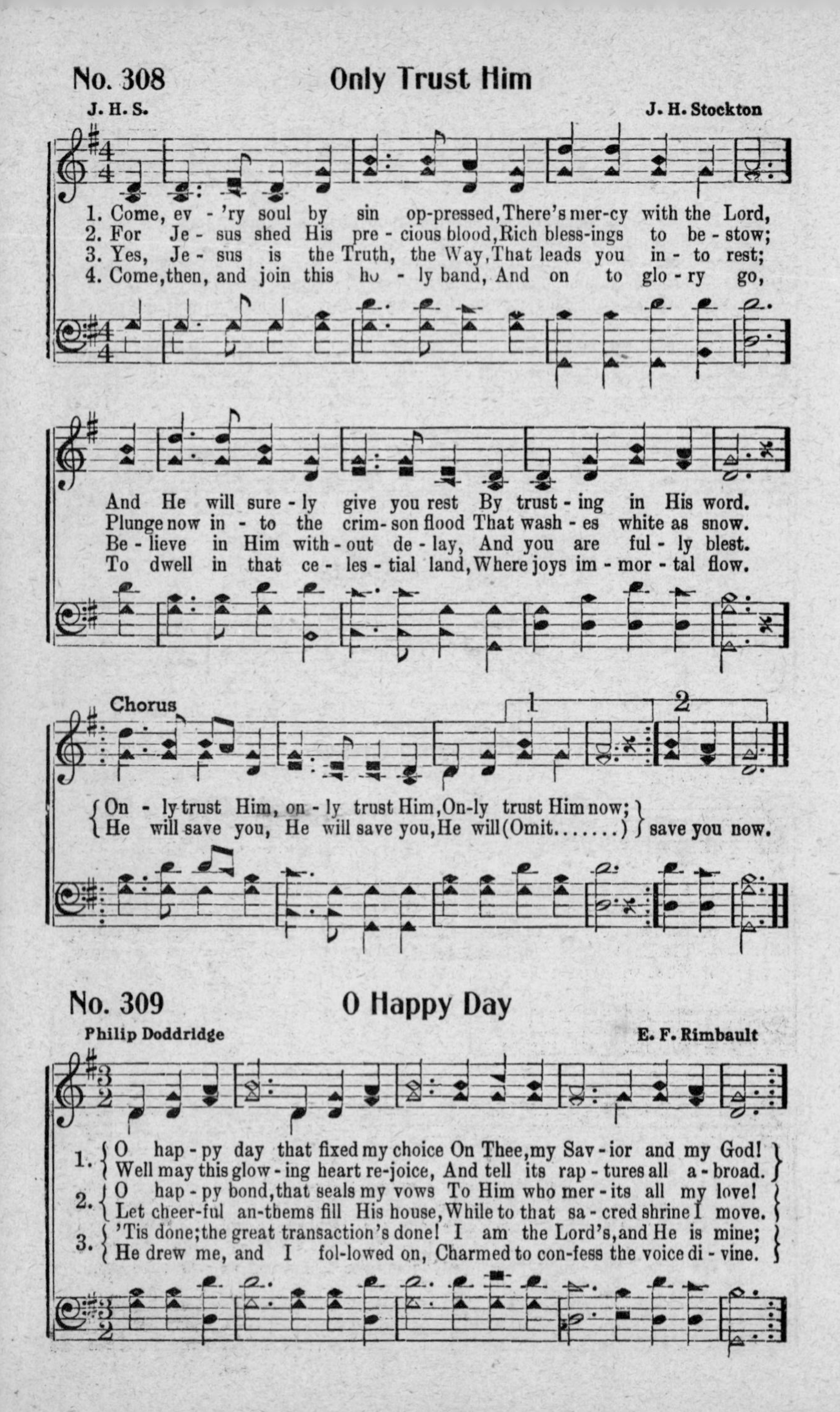
No. 308
Only Trust Him
J. H. S.
J. H. Stockton
1. Come, ev - 'ry soul by sin op-pressed, There's mer-cy with the Lord,
2. For Je - sus shed His pre - cious blood, Rich bless-ings to be - stow;
3. Yes, Je - sus is the Truth, the Way, That leads you in - to rest;
4. Come, then, and join this ho - ly band, And on to glo - ry go,
And He will sure - ly give you rest By trust - ing in His word.
Plunge now in - to the crim - son flood That wash - es white as snow.
Be - lieve in Him with - out de - lay, And you are ful - ly blest.
To dwell in that ce - les - tial land, Where joys im - mor - tal flow.
Chorus
On - ly trust Him, on - ly trust Him, On-ly trust Him now;
He will save you, He will save you, He will (Omit.......) save you now.
1
2
No. 309
O Happy Day
Philip Doddridge
E. F. Rimbault
1. O hap - py day that fixed my choice On Thee, my Sav - ior and my God!
Well may this glow - ing heart re-joice, And tell its rap - tures all a - broad.
2. O hap - py bond, that seals my vows To Him who mer - its all my love!
Let cheer-ful an-thems fill His house, While to that sa - cred shrine I move.
3. 'Tis done; the great transaction's done! I am the Lord's, and He is mine;
He drew me, and I fol-lowed on, Charmed to con-fess the voice di - vine.

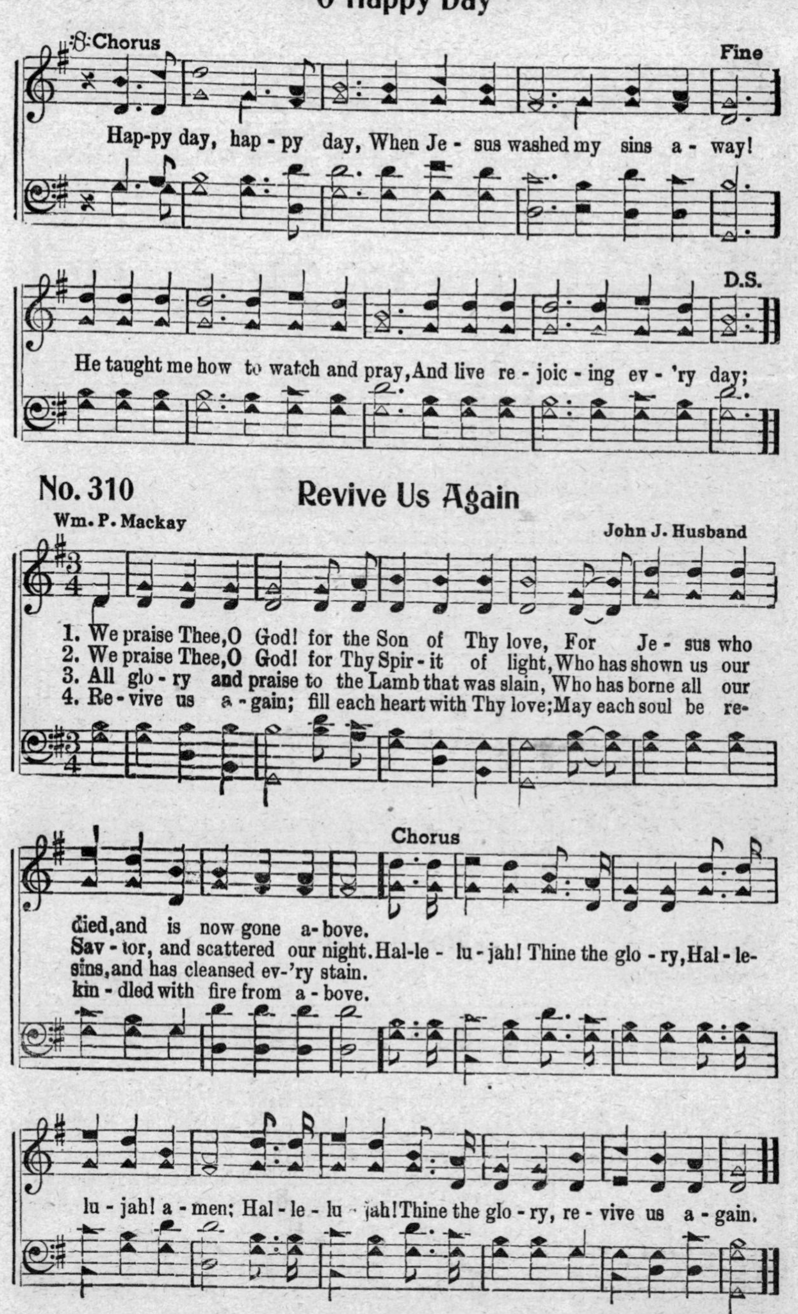
O Happy Day
Chorus
Fine
Hap-py day, hap - py day, When Je - sus washed my sins a - way!
D.S.
He taught me how to watch and pray, And live re - joic - ing ev - 'ry day;
No. 310
Revive Us Again
Wm. P. Mackay
John J. Husband
1. We praise Thee, O God! for the Son of Thy love, For Je - sus who died, and is now gone a - bove.
2. We praise Thee, O God! for Thy Spir - it of light, Who has shown us our Sav - ior, and scattered our night.
3. All glo - ry and praise to the Lamb that was slain, Who has borne all our sins, and has cleansed ev - 'ry stain.
4. Re - vive us a - gain; fill each heart with Thy love; May each soul be re - kin - dled with fire from a - bove.
Chorus
Hal-le - lu - jah! Thine the glo - ry, Hal - le - lu - jah! a - men; Hal - le - lu - jah! Thine the glo - ry, re - vive us a - gain.

No. 311
I Am Coming, Lord
L. H.
L. Hartsough
1. I hear Thy welcome voice, That calls me, Lord, to Thee, For cleansing
2. Tho com-ing weak and vile, Thou dost my strength assure; Thou dost my
3. 'Tis Je - sus calls me on To per-fect faith and love, To per-fect
in Thy pre-cious blood That flowed on Cal-va - ry.
vile - ness ful - ly cleanse, Till spot-less all and pure.
hope, and peace and trust, For earth and heav'n above.
Chorus
I am com-ing, Lord!
Com-ing now to Thee! Wash me, cleanse me in the blood That flowed on Calvary!
No. 312
Just As I Am
Charlotte Elliott
William B. Bradbury
1. Just as I am, with - out one plea, But that Thy blood was shed for me,
2. Just as I am, and wait - ing not To rid my soul of one dark blot,
3. Just as I am, tho tossed about With many a con-flict, many a doubt,
4. Just as I am, poor, wretched, blind; Sight, rich-es, heal-ing of the mind,
5. Just as I am—Thou wilt re-ceive, welcome, pardon, cleanse, relieve;

Just As I Am

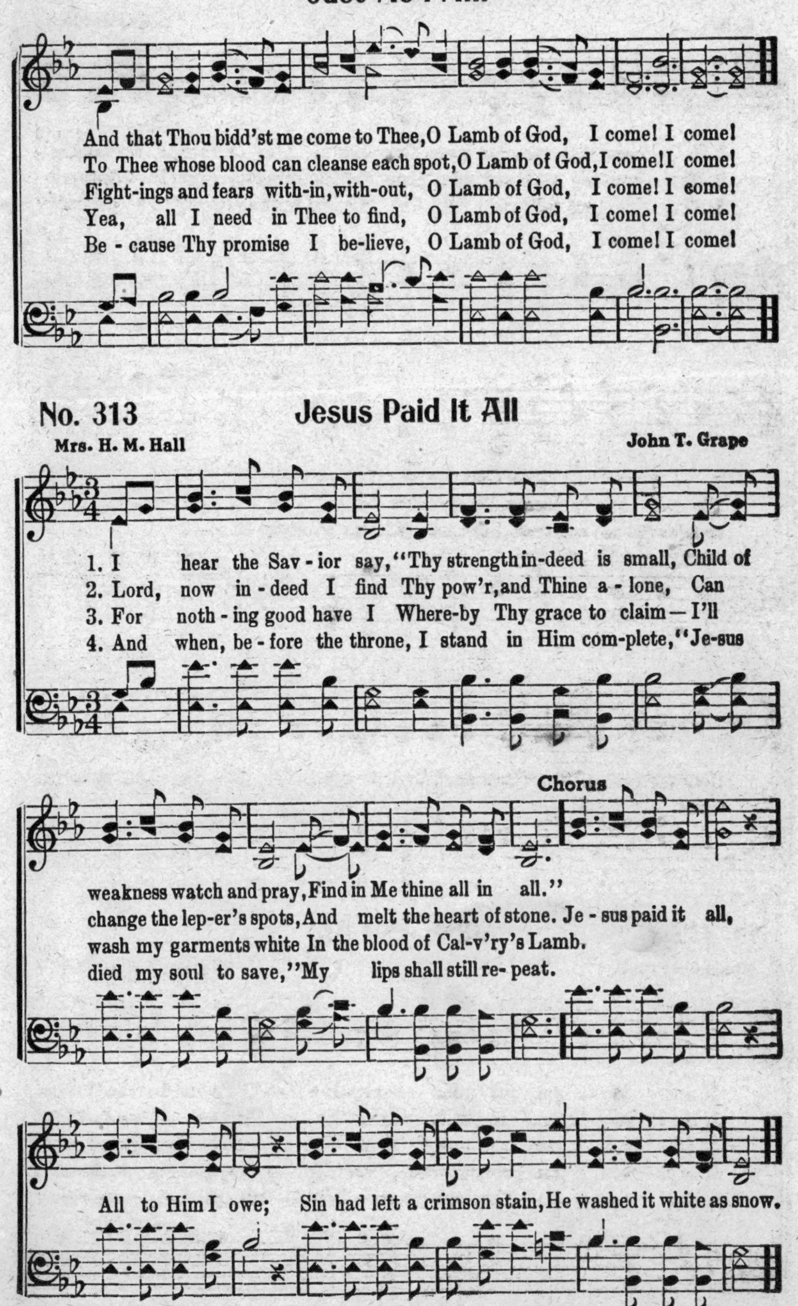
And that Thou bidd'st me come to Thee, O Lamb of God, I come! I come!
To Thee whose blood can cleanse each spot, O Lamb of God, I come! I come!
Fight-ings and fears with-in, with-out, O Lamb of God, I come! I come!
Yea, all I need in Thee to find, O Lamb of God, I come! I come!
Be - cause Thy promise I be-lieve, O Lamb of God, I come! I come!
No. 313
Jesus Paid It All
Mrs. H. M. Hall
John T. Grape
1. I hear the Sav - ior say, "Thy strength in-deed is small, Child of weakness watch and pray, Find in Me thine all in all."
2. Lord, now in - deed I find Thy pow'r, and Thine a - lone, Can change the lep-er's spots, And melt the heart of stone.
3. For noth - ing good have I Where-by Thy grace to claim — I'll wash my garments white In the blood of Cal-v'ry's Lamb.
4. And when, be - fore the throne, I stand in Him com-plete, "Je-sus died my soul to save," My lips shall still re- peat.
Chorus
Je - sus paid it all, All to Him I owe; Sin had left a crimson stain, He washed it white as snow.

No. 314
I Want to be a Worker
L. B.
L. Baltzell
1. I want to be a work - er for the Lord, I want to love and
2. I want to be a work - er ev - 'ry day, I want to lead the
3. I want to be a work - er strong and brave, I want to trust in
4. I want to be a work - er, help me, Lord, To lead the lost and
trust His ho - ly word; I want to sing and pray, and be bus - y ev - 'ry day
err - ing in the way That leads to heav'n a-bove, where all is peace and love,
Je - sus' pow'r to save; All who will tru - ly come, shall find a hap-py home
err - ing to Thy word That points to joys on high, where pleas-ures nev-er die
In the king-dom of the Lord. I will work, I will
Chorus
and pray,
pray In the vineyard, in the vine-yard of the Lord; I will
work and pray
of the Lord;
work I will pray, I will la - bor ev-'ry day In the vineyard of the Lord.

No. 315 The Gate Ajar For Me

Mrs. Lydia Baxter S. J. Vail

1. There is a gate that stands a - jar, And thru its por - tals gleam-ing
2. That gate a - jar stands free for all Who seek thru it sal - va - tion;
3. Press on - ward then, tho foes may frown, While mer-cy's gate is o - pen:
4. Be - yond the riv - er's brink we'll lay The cross that here is giv - en,

A ra-diance from the cross a - far, The Sav - ior's love re - veal - ing.
The rich and poor, the great and small, Of ev - 'ry tribe and na - tion.
Ac - cept the cross, and win the crown, Love's ev - er - last - ing to - ken.
And bear the crown of life a - way, And love Him more in heav - en.

Chorus

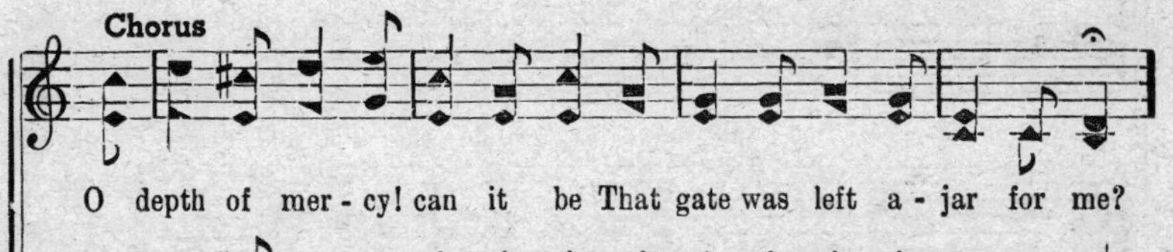

O depth of mer - cy! can it be That gate was left a - jar for me?

For me, for me? Was left a - jar for me?
For me, for me?

No. 316
Jesus Saves
Priscilla J. Owens
Wm. J. Kirkpatrick
1. We have heard the joy - ful sound: Je - sus saves! Je - sus saves!
2. Waft it on the roll - ing tide, Je - sus saves! Je - sus saves!
3. Sing a - bove the bat - tle strife, Je - sus saves! Je - sus saves!
4. Give the winds a might - y voice, Je - sus saves! Je - sus saves!
Spread the ti - dings all a - round; Je - sus saves! Je - sus saves!
Tell to sin - ners far and wide: Je - sus saves! Je - sus saves!
By His death and end - less life, Je - sus saves! Je - sus saves!
Let the na - tions now re - joice,—Je - sus saves! Je - sus saves!
Bear the news to ev - 'ry land, Climb the steeps and cross the waves;
Sing, ye is - lands of the sea; Ech - o back, ye o - cean caves;
Sing it soft - ly thru the gloom, When the heart for mer - cy craves;
Shout sal - va - tion full and free; High - est hills and deep - est caves;
On - ward! 'tis our Lord's command; Je - sus saves! Je - sus saves!
Earth shall keep her ju - bi - lee: Je - sus saves! Je - sus saves!
Sing in tri - umph o'er the tomb,—Je - sus saves! Je - sus saves!
This our song of vic - to - ry,— Je - sus saves! Je - sus saves!

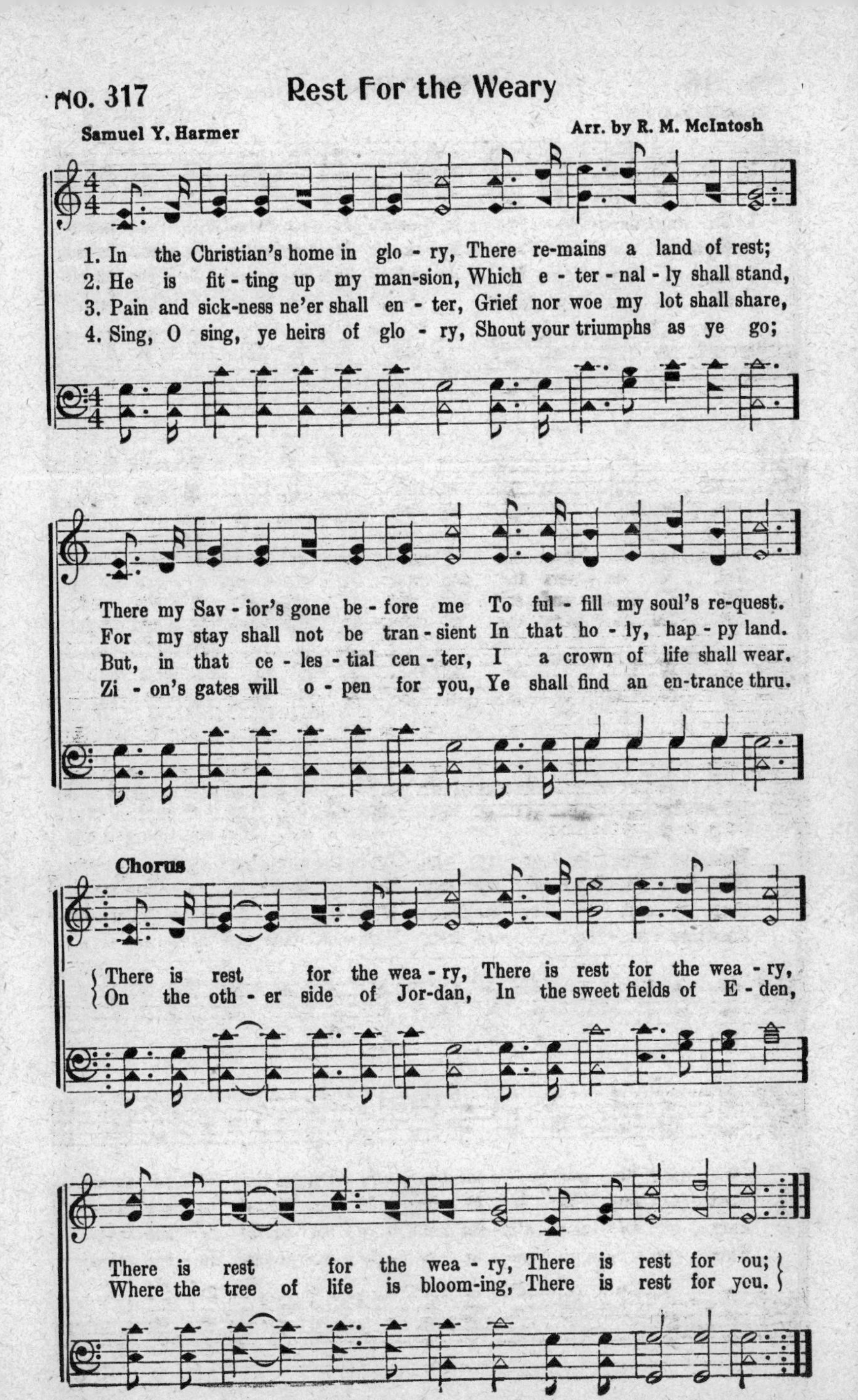
No. 317
Rest For the Weary
Samuel Y. Harmer
Arr. by R. M. McIntosh
1. In the Christian's home in glo - ry, There re-mains a land of rest;
2. He is fit - ting up my man-sion, Which e - ter - nal - ly shall stand,
3. Pain and sick-ness ne'er shall en - ter, Grief nor woe my lot shall share,
4. Sing, O sing, ye heirs of glo - ry, Shout your triumphs as ye go;
There my Sav - ior's gone be - fore me To ful - fill my soul's re-quest.
For my stay shall not be tran - sient In that ho - ly, hap - py land.
But, in that ce - les - tial cen - ter, I a crown of life shall wear.
Zi - on's gates will o - pen for you, Ye shall find an en-trance thru.
Chorus
There is rest for the wea - ry, There is rest for the wea - ry,
On the oth - er side of Jor-dan, In the sweet fields of E - den,
There is rest for the wea - ry, There is rest for you;
Where the tree of life is bloom-ing, There is rest for you.

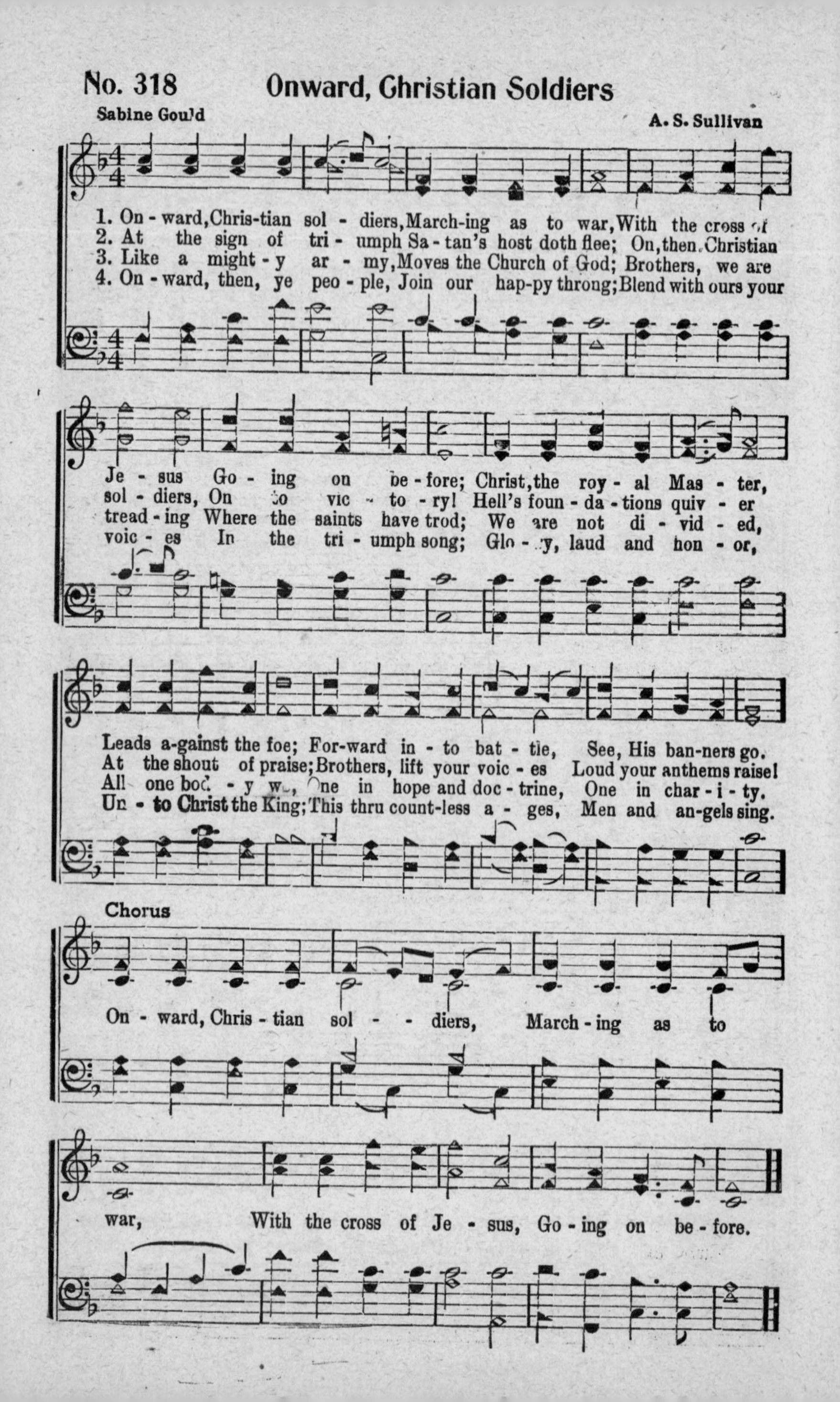
No. 318 Onward, Christian Soldiers
Sabine Gould
A. S. Sullivan
1. On - ward, Chris-tian sol - diers, March-ing as to war, With the cross of
2. At the sign of tri - umph Sa - tan's host doth flee; On, then, Christian
3. Like a might - y ar - my, Moves the Church of God; Brothers, we are
4. On - ward, then, ye peo - ple, Join our hap-py throng; Blend with ours your
Je - sus Go - ing on be - fore; Christ, the roy - al Mas - ter,
sol - diers, On to vic - to - ry! Hell's foun - da - tions quiv - er
tread - ing Where the saints have trod; We are not di - vid - ed,
voic - es In the tri - umph song; Glo - ry, laud and hon - or,
Leads a-gainst the foe; For-ward in - to bat - tle, See, His ban-ners go.
At the shout of praise; Brothers, lift your voic - es Loud your anthems raise!
All one bod - y we, One in hope and doc - trine, One in char - i - ty.
Un - to Christ the King; This thru count-less a - ges, Men and an-gels sing.
Chorus
On - ward, Chris - tian sol - - diers, March - ing as to
war, With the cross of Je - sus, Go - ing on be - fore.

No. 319 There's a Great Day Coming
W. L. T.
W. L. Thompson
1. There's a great day com-ing, a great day com-ing, There's a great day
2. There's a bright day com-ing, a bright day com-ing, There's a bright day
3. There's a sad day com-ing, a sad day com-ing, There's a sad day
com-ing by and by, When the saints and the sin-ners shall be
com-ing by and by, But its bright-ness shall on-ly come to
com-ing by and by, When the sin-ner shall hear his doom, "De-
part-ed, right and left,
them that love the Lord, Are you read-y for that day to come?
part, I know ye not,"
Chorus
Are you read-y, are you read-y? Are you read-y for the
judg-ment day? Are you ready, are you read-y For the judg-ment day?

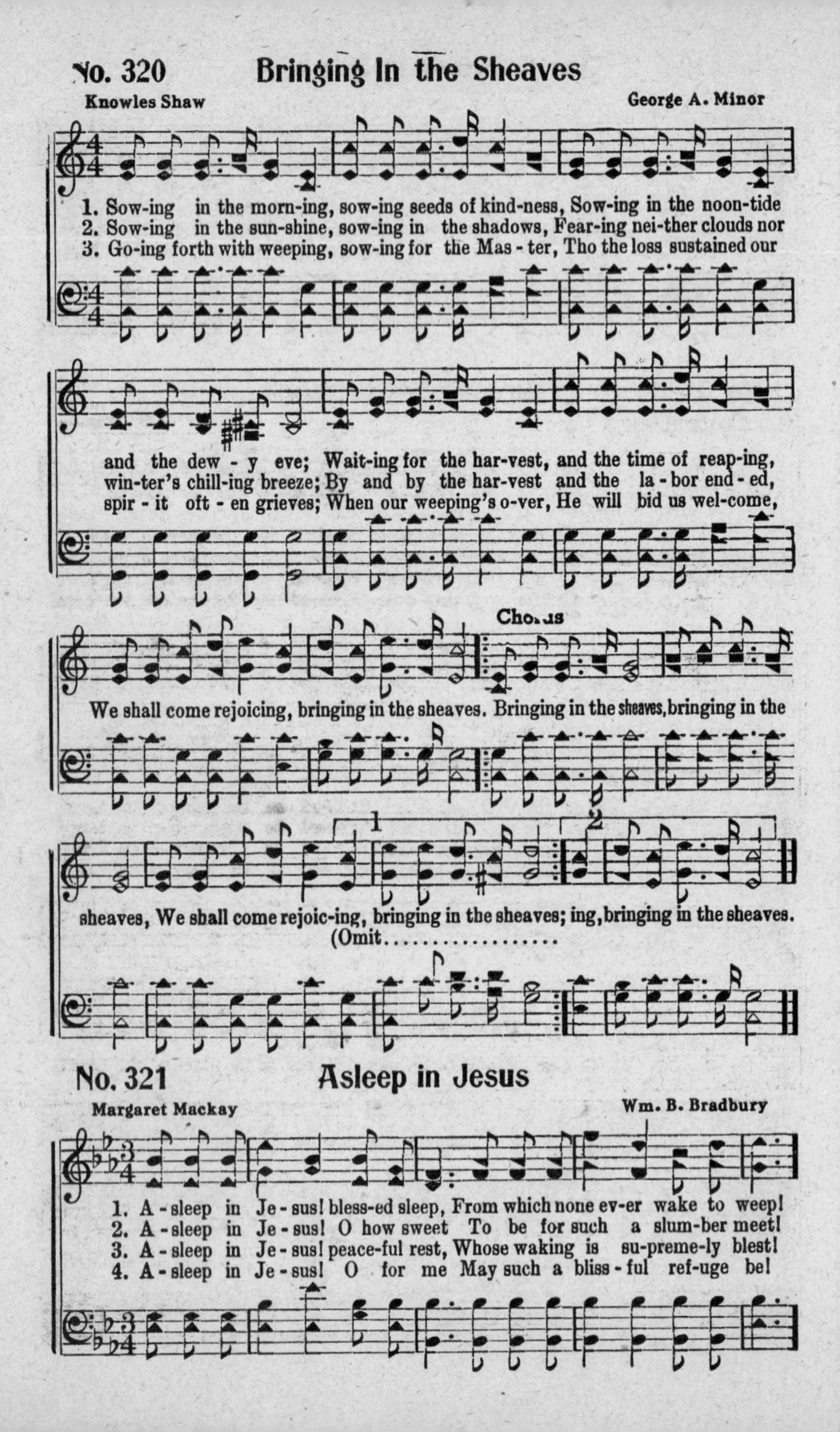
No. 320 Bringing In the Sheaves
Knowles Shaw
George A. Minor
1. Sow-ing in the morn-ing, sow-ing seeds of kind-ness, Sow-ing in the noon-tide and the dew - y eve; Wait-ing for the har-vest, and the time of reap-ing,
2. Sow-ing in the sun-shine, sow-ing in the shadows, Fear-ing nei-ther clouds nor win-ter's chill-ing breeze; By and by the har-vest and the la - bor end - ed,
3. Go-ing forth with weeping, sow-ing for the Mas - ter, Tho the loss sustained our spir - it oft - en grieves; When our weeping's o-ver, He will bid us wel-come,
We shall come rejoicing, bringing in the sheaves.
Chorus
Bringing in the sheaves, bringing in the sheaves, We shall come rejoic-ing, bringing in the sheaves; ing, bringing in the sheaves.
(Omit..................
1
2
No. 321 Asleep in Jesus
Margaret Mackay
Wm. B. Bradbury
1. A - sleep in Je - sus! bless-ed sleep, From which none ev-er wake to weep!
2. A - sleep in Je - sus! O how sweet To be for such a slum-ber meet!
3. A - sleep in Je - sus! peace-ful rest, Whose waking is su-preme-ly blest!
4. A - sleep in Je - sus! O for me May such a bliss - ful ref-uge be!

Asleep in Jesus

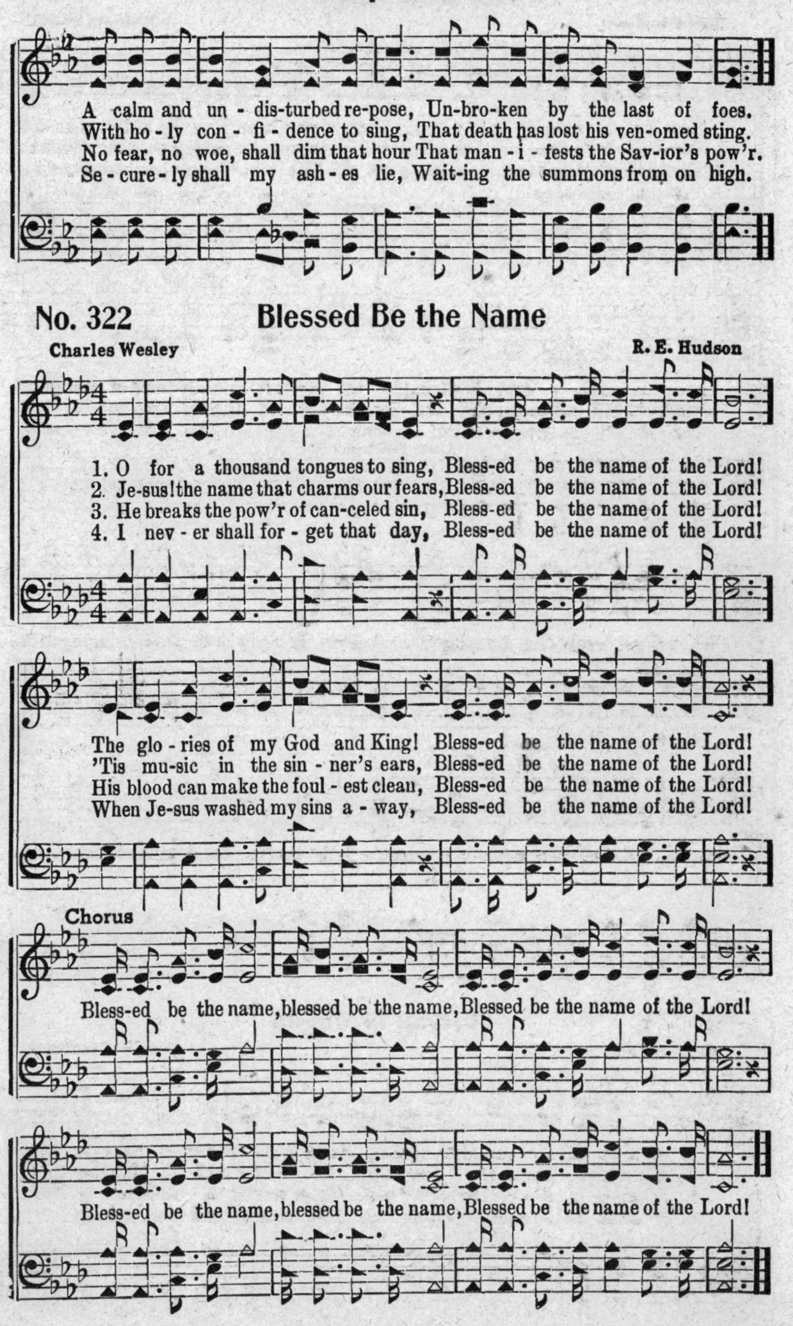
A calm and un - dis-turbed re-pose, Un-bro-ken by the last of foes.
With ho - ly con - fi - dence to sing, That death has lost his ven-omed sting.
No fear, no woe, shall dim that hour That man - i - fests the Sav-ior's pow'r.
Se - cure - ly shall my ash - es lie, Wait-ing the summons from on high.
No. 322 Blessed Be the Name
Charles Wesley
R. E. Hudson
1. O for a thousand tongues to sing, Bless-ed be the name of the Lord!
2. Je-sus! the name that charms our fears, Bless-ed be the name of the Lord!
3. He breaks the pow'r of can-celed sin, Bless-ed be the name of the Lord!
4. I nev - er shall for - get that day, Bless-ed be the name of the Lord!
The glo - ries of my God and King! Bless-ed be the name of the Lord!
'Tis mu-sic in the sin - ner's ears, Bless-ed be the name of the Lord!
His blood can make the foul - est clean, Bless-ed be the name of the Lord!
When Je-sus washed my sins a - way, Bless-ed be the name of the Lord!
Chorus
Bless-ed be the name, blessed be the name, Blessed be the name of the Lord!
Bless-ed be the name, blessed be the name, Blessed be the name of the Lord!

No. 323 We'll Work Till Jesus Comes
Elizabeth Mills
William Miller
1. O land of rest, for thee I sigh! When will the mo-ment come When
2. To Je - sus Christ I fled for rest! He bade me cease to roam, And
3. I sought at once my Sav-ior's-side, No more my steps shall roam; With
I shall lay my ar-mor by, And dwell in peace at home?
lean for suc-cor on His breast Till He con-duct me home.
Him I'll brave death's chilling tide, And reach my heav'nly home.
Chorus
We'll work till Je-sus comes, We'll work till Je-sus comes; And we'll be gathered home.
We'll work
We'll work
1
2
No. 324 Nearer, My God, to Thee
Sarah F. Adams
Lowell Mason
1. Near-er, my God, to Thee! Near-er to Thee, E'en tho it be a cross
2. Tho like a wan-der-er, The sun gone down, Dark-ness be o-ver me,
3. There let the way ap-pear, Steps un-to heav'n; All that thou send-est me,
4. Then, with my waking tho'ts Bright with Thy praise, Out of my ston-y griefs
5. Or if on joy-ful wing, Cleav-ing the sky, Sun, moon and stars for-got
D. S.—Near-er, my God, to Thee,

Nearer, My God, to Thee
Fine
D.S.
That rais-eth me; Still all my song shall be, Nearer, my God, to Thee,
My rest a stone, Yet in my dreams I'd be Nearer, my God, to Thee,
In mer-cy giv'n; An-gels to beck-on me Nearer, my God, to Thee,
Beth-el I'll raise; So by my woes to be Nearer, my God, to Thee,
Up-ward I fly; Still all my song shall be, Nearer, my God, to Thee,
Near-er to Thee.
No. 325
The Solid Rock
Edward Mote
William B. Bradbury
1. My hope is built on noth-ing less Than Je-sus' blood and righteousness;
2. When darkness veils His love-ly face, I rest on His un-chang-ing grace;
3. His oath, His cov-e-nant, His blood, Sup-port me in the whelming flood;
4. When He shall come with trumpet sound, O may I then in Him be found;
I dare not trust the sweet-est frame, But whol-ly lean on Je-sus' name.
In ev-'ry high and storm-y gale, My an-chor holds with-in the veil.
When all a-round my soul gives way, He then is all my hope and stay.
Dressed in His right-eous-ness a-lone, Fault-less to stand be-fore the throne.
Chorus
On Christ, the sol-id Rock, I stand; All oth-er ground is
sink-ing sand, All oth-er ground is sink-ing sand. A-men.

No. 326
All Hail the Power
Edward Perronet
Oliver Holden
1. All hail the pow'r of Je-sus' name! Let an-gels pros-trate fall!
2. Ye cho-sen seed of Is-rael's race, Ye ran-somed from the fall,
3. Let ev-'ry kin-dred, ev-'ry tribe; On this ter-res-trial ball,
4. O that with yon-der sa-cred throng We at His feet may fall!
Bring forth the roy-al di-a-dem,
Hail Him who saves you by His grace, And crown Him Lord of all!
To Him all maj-es-ty as-cribe,
We'll join the ev-er-last-ing song,
Bring forth the roy-al di-a-dem,
Hail Him who saves you by His grace, And crown Him Lord of all!
To Him all maj-es-ty as-cribe,
We'll join the ev-er-last-ing song,
Second Tune
William Shrubsole
1. All hail the pow'r of Je-sus' name! Let an-gels pros-trate fall! Bring forth the roy-
al di-a-dem, And crown Him, crown Him, crown Him, Crown Him Lord of all!

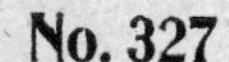
No. 327

Sweet Hour of Prayer

W. W. Walford — Wm. B. Bradbury

1. Sweet hour of prayer! sweet hour of prayer! That calls me from a world of care,
2. Sweet hour of prayer! sweet hour of prayer! Thy wings shall my pe - ti - tion bear
3. Sweet hour of prayer! sweet hour of prayer! May I thy con - so - la-tion share,

And bids me at my Fa-ther's throne Make all my wants and wish-es known;
To Him whose truth and faith-ful - ness En-gage the wait - ing soul to bless;
Till, from Mouut Pisgah's loft - y height, I view my home , and take .ny flight:

In sea - sons of dis-tress and grief, My soul has oft - en found re - lief,
And since He bids me seek His face, Be-lieve His word and trust His grace,
This robe of flesh I'll drop, and rise To seize the ev - er - last - ing prize;

And oft es-caped the tempter's snare By thy re-turn, sweet hour of prayer.
I'll cast on Him my ev - 'ry care, And wait for thee,sweet hour of prayer.
And shout, while passing thru the air, Farewell,farewell, sweet hour of prayer.

No. 328 What Wondrous Love

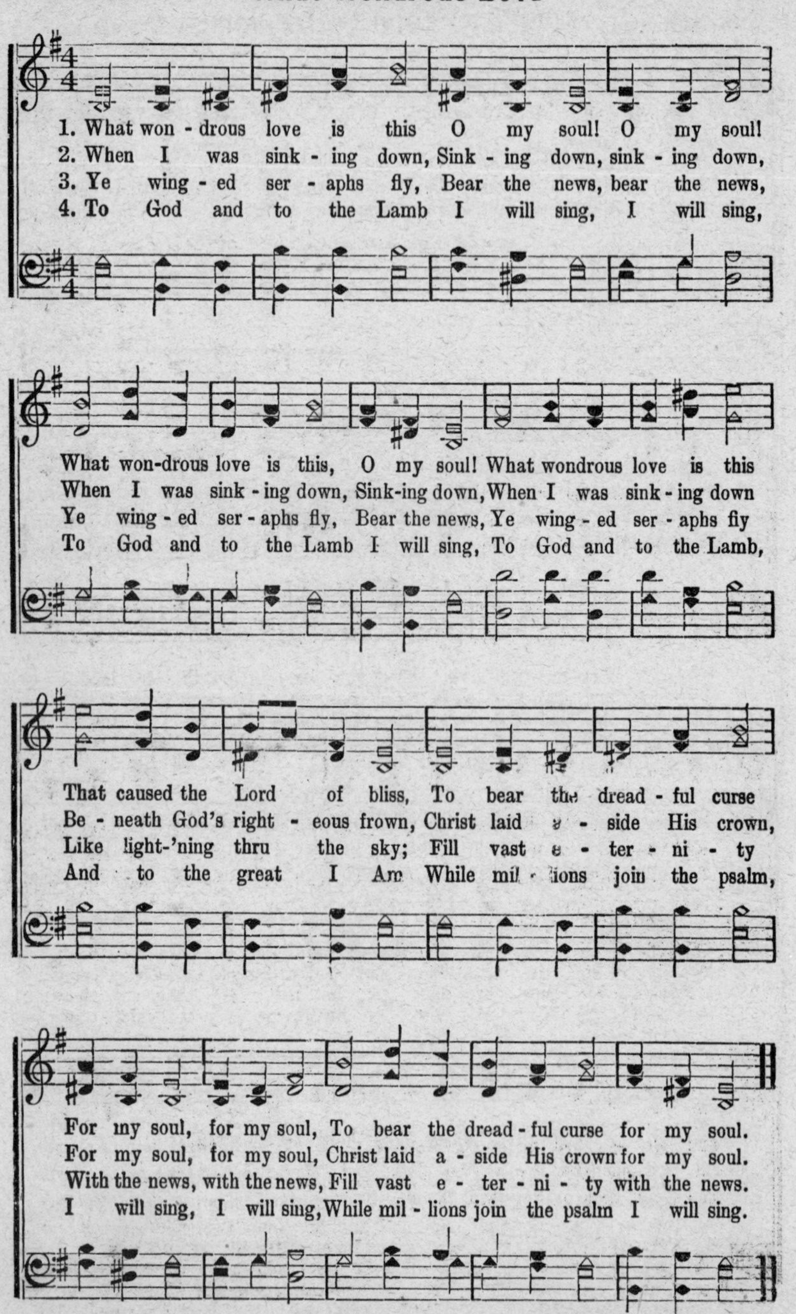

1. What won - drous love is this O my soul! O my soul!
2. When I was sink - ing down, Sink - ing down, sink - ing down,
3. Ye wing - ed ser - aphs fly, Bear the news, bear the news,
4. To God and to the Lamb I will sing, I will sing,
What won-drous love is this, O my soul! What wondrous love is this
When I was sink - ing down, Sink-ing down, When I was sink - ing down
Ye wing - ed ser - aphs fly, Bear the news, Ye wing - ed ser - aphs fly
To God and to the Lamb I will sing, To God and to the Lamb,
That caused the Lord of bliss, To bear the dread - ful curse
Be - neath God's right - eous frown, Christ laid a - side His crown,
Like light-'ning thru the sky; Fill vast e - ter - ni - ty
And to the great I Am While mil - lions join the psalm,
For my soul, for my soul, To bear the dread - ful curse for my soul.
For my soul, for my soul, Christ laid a - side His crown for my soul.
With the news, with the news, Fill vast e - ter - ni - ty with the news.
I will sing, I will sing, While mil - lions join the psalm I will sing.

No. 329 Stand Up, Stand Up for Jesus
George Duffield
George J. Webb
1. Stand up, stand up for Je - sus, Ye sol - diers of the cross!
2. Stand up, stand up for Je - sus, The trump - et call o - bey;
3. Stand up, stand up for Je - sus, Stand in His strength a - lone;
4. Stand up, stand up for Je - sus, The strife will not be long;
Lift high His roy - al ban - ner, It must not suf - fer loss:
Forth to the might - y con - flict, In this His glo - rious day:
The arm of flesh will fail you, Ye dare not trust your own:
This day, the noise of bat - tle, The next, the vic - tor's song:
From vic - t'ry un - to vic - t'ry, His ar - my shall He lead,
Ye that are men, now serve Him, A - gainst un - num-bered foes;
Put on the gos - pel ar - mor, And, watch - ing un - to pray'r,
To Him that o - ver - com - eth, A crown of life shall be;
Till ev - 'ry foe is vanquished And Christ is Lord in - deed.
Your cour - age rise with dan - ger, And strength to strength op - pose.
Where du - ty calls, or dan - ger, Be nev - er want - ing there.
He with the King of Glo - ry Shall reign e - ter - nal - ly!

No. 330 The Morning Light is Breaking

First or Second Tune

1 The morning light is breaking,
The darkness disappears,
The sons of earth are waking,
To penitential tears;
Each breeze that sweeps the ocean
Brings tidings from afar,
Of nations in commotion,
Prepared for Zion's war.

2 See heathen nations bending
Before the God of love,
And thousand hearts ascending
In gratitude above;
While sinners now confessing,
The gospel's call obey,
And seek a Savior's blessing,
A nation in a day.

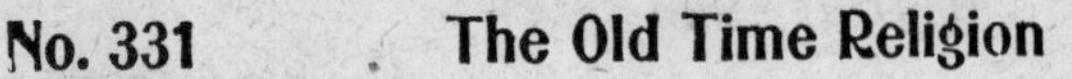

No. 331 The Old Time Religion

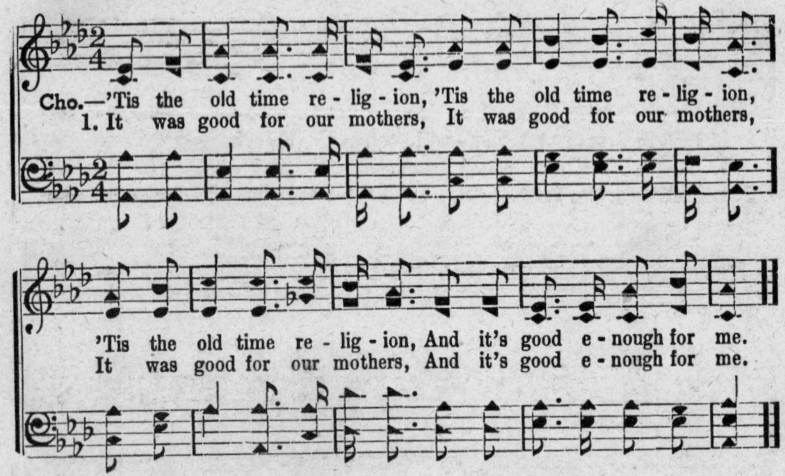

Cho.—'Tis the old time re - lig - ion, 'Tis the old time re - lig - ion,
1. It was good for our mothers, It was good for our mothers,
'Tis the old time re - lig - ion, And it's good e - nough for me.
It was good for our mothers, And it's good e - nough for me.

2. Makes me love ev'ry-body.
3. It has saved our fathers.
4. It was good for the Prophet Daniel.
5. It was good for the Hebrew children.
6. It was tried in the fiery furnace.
7. It was good for Paul and Silas.
8. It will do when I am dying.
9. It will take us all to heaven.

No. 332 The Great Physician

Wm. Hunter

J. H. Stockton

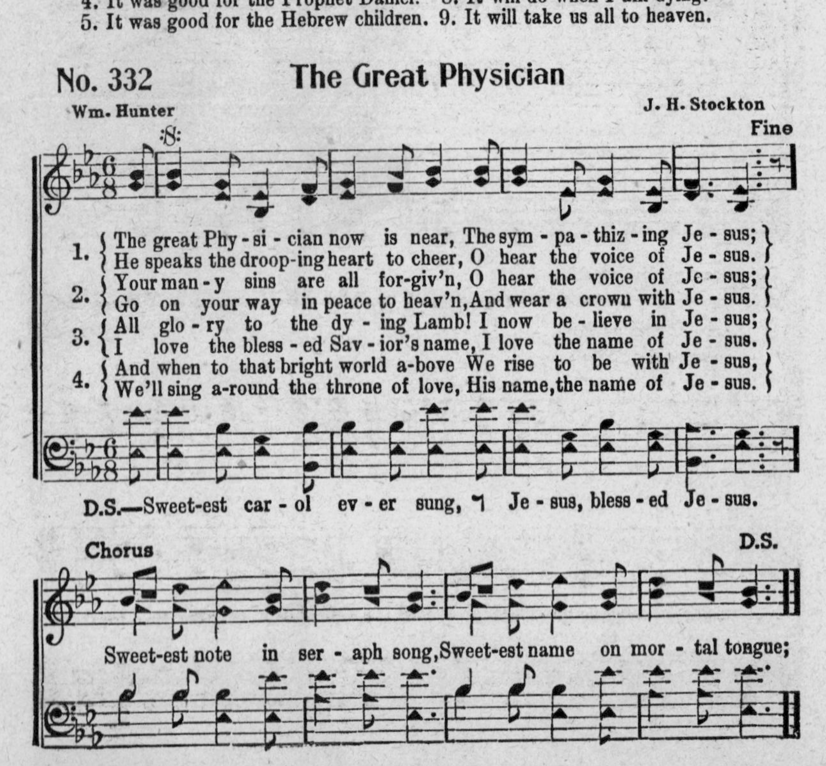

Fine
1. The great Phy - si - cian now is near, The sym - pa - thiz - ing Je - sus;
He speaks the droop-ing heart to cheer, O hear the voice of Je - sus.
2. Your man - y sins are all for-giv'n, O hear the voice of Je - sus;
Go on your way in peace to heav'n, And wear a crown with Je - sus.
3. All glo - ry to the dy - ing Lamb! I now be - lieve in Je - sus;
I love the bless - ed Sav - ior's name, I love the name of Je - sus.
4. And when to that bright world a-bove We rise to be with Je - sus,
We'll sing a-round the throne of love, His name, the name of Je - sus.
D.S.—Sweet-est car - ol ev - er sung, Je - sus, bless - ed Je - sus.
Chorus
D.S.
Sweet-est note in ser - aph song, Sweet-est name on mor - tal tongue;

No. 333 Whiter Than Snow

James Nicholson — Wm. G. Fischer

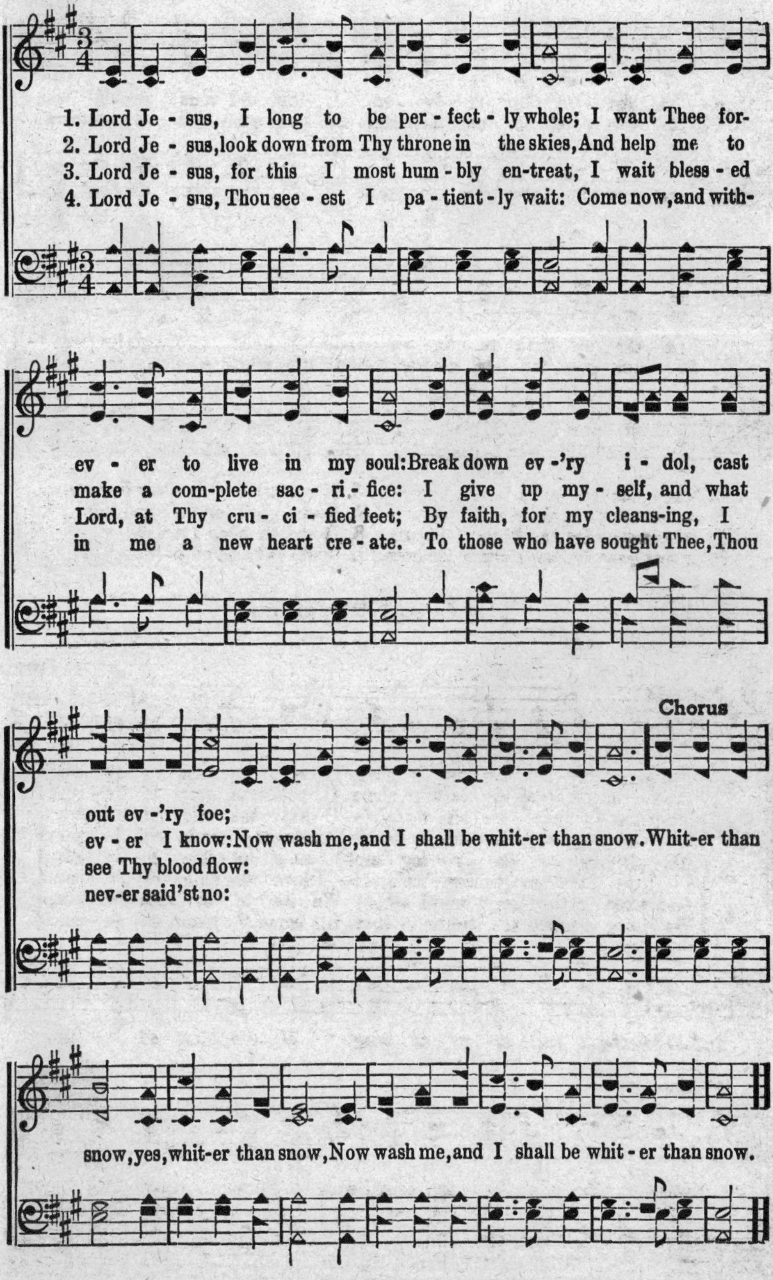

1. Lord Je - sus, I long to be per - fect - ly whole; I want Thee for- ev - er to live in my soul: Break down ev -'ry i - dol, cast out ev -'ry foe;
2. Lord Je - sus, look down from Thy throne in the skies, And help me to make a com-plete sac - ri - fice: I give up my - self, and what ev - er I know:
3. Lord Je - sus, for this I most hum - bly en-treat, I wait bless - ed Lord, at Thy cru - ci - fied feet; By faith, for my cleans-ing, I see Thy blood flow:
4. Lord Je - sus, Thou see - est I pa - tient - ly wait: Come now, and with- in me a new heart cre - ate. To those who have sought Thee, Thou nev-er said'st no:

Now wash me, and I shall be whit-er than snow.

Chorus

Whit-er than snow, yes, whit-er than snow, Now wash me, and I shall be whit - er than snow.

No. 334 Jesus, Savior, Pilot Me
Edward Hopper
J. E. Gould
Fine
1. Je - sus, Sav - ior, pi - lot me O - ver life's tem - pes - tuous sea;
2. As a moth - er stills her child, Thou canst hush the o - cean wild;
3. When at last I near the shore, And the fear - ful break - ers roar
D.C.—Chart and com - pass came from Thee, Je - sus, Sav - ior, pi - lot me.
D.C.—Won-drous Sov-'reign of the sea, Je - sus, Sav - ior, pi - lot me.
D.C.—May I hear Thee say to me, "Fear not, I will pi - lot Thee."
D.C.
Unknown waves be - fore me roll, Hid-ing rocks and treach'rous shoal;
Boist'rous waves o - bey Thy will When Thou say'st to them, "Be still!"
'Twixt me and the peace-ful rest, Then, while lean-ing on Thy breast,
No. 335 Is My Name Written There?
Mrs. Mary A. Kidder
Frank M. Davis
1. Lord, I care not for rich - es, Neither sil - ver nor gold, I would make sure
In the book of Thy kingdom With its pag - es so fair, Tell me, Je - sus
2. Lord, my sins they are man-y, Like the sands of the sea, But Thy blood, O
For Thy prom - ise is writ-ten In bright letters that glow, Tho your sins be
3. O that beau - ti - ful ci - ty With its mansions of light With its glo - ri-
Where no e - vil thing cometh To de-spoil what is fair, Where the an-gels
1
2
Fine
of heav - en, I would en - ter the fold;
my (Omit.........................) Sav-ior, Is my name writ-ten there?
my Sav - ior, Is su - fi - cient for me;
as (Omit.........................) scar-let, I will make them like snow.
fied be - ings In pure garments of white;
are (Omit.........................) watching, Is my name writ-ten there?
D.S.—Is my name writ-ten there?

Is My Name Written There?

Chorus
D.S.
Is my name written there, On the page white and fair? In the book of Thy kingdom,
No. 336
What a Friend
Joseph Scriven
Charles C. Converse
1. What a friend we have in Je - sus, All our sins and griefs to bea
2. Have we tri - als and temp - ta - tions? Is there trou - ble an - y - wher
3. Are we weak and heav - y la - den, Cumbered with a load of care?—
What a priv - i - lege to car - ry Ev - 'ry-thing to God in pray'r!
We should nev - er be dis - cour-aged, Take it to the Lord in pray'r.
Pre-cious Sav - ior, still our ref - uge,–Take it to the Lord in pray'r.
O what peace we oft - en for - feit, O what need-less pain we bear,
Can we find a friend so faith - ful, Who will all our sor-rows share?
Do thy friends despise, for - sake Thee? Take it to the Lord in pray'r;
All be-cause we do not car - ry Ev - 'ry-thing to God in pray'r!
Je - sus knows our ev - 'ry weak-ness, Take it to the Lord in pray'r
In His arms He'll take and shield thee, Thou wilt find a sol - ace there

No. 337
Sweet By and By
S. Fillmore Bennett
by per.
Jos. P. Webster
1. There's a land that is fair - er than day, And by faith we can see it a-
2. We shall sing on that beau-ti - ful shore The me - lo - di - ous songs of the
3. To our boun - ti - ful Fa - ther a-bove, We will of - fer our trib-ute of
far; For the Fa - ther waits o - ver the way, To pre - pare us a
blest, And our spir - its shall sor - row no more, Not a sigh for the
praise, For the glo - ri - ous gift of His love, And the bless-ings that
Chorus
dwell-ing place there. In the sweet by and by, We shall
bless - ing of rest.
hal - low our days. In the sweet by and by,
meet on that beau-ti - ful shore, In the sweet by and
by and by, In the sweet
by, We shall meet on that beau - ti - ful shore.
by and by,

No. 338
Blest Be the Tie
John Fawcett
Hans G. Nageli
1. Blest be the tie that binds Our hearts in Chris - tian love;
2. Be - fore our Fa - ther's throne, We pour our ar - dent pray'rs;
3. We share our mu - tual woes, Our mu - tual bur - dens bear;
4. When we a - sun - der part, It gives us in - ward pain;
The fel - low-ship of kin - dred minds Is like to that a - bove.
Our fears, our hopes, our aims are one, Our com - forts and our cares.
And oft - en for each oth - er flows The sym - pa - thiz - ing tear.
But we shall still be joined in heart, And hope to meet a - gain.
No. 339
My Soul, Be On Thy Guard
George Heath
Lowell Mason
1. My soul, be on Thy guard; Ten thou-sand foes a - rise; The
2. O watch, and fight, and pray; The bat - tle ne'er give o'er; Re-
3. Ne'er think the vic - t'ry won, Nor lay thine ar - mor down; The
4. Fight on, my soul, till death Shall bring thee to thy God; He'll
hosts of sin are press - ing hard To draw thee from the skies.
new it bold - ly ev - 'ry day, And help di - vine im - plore.
work of faith will not be done, Till thou ob - tain the crown.
take thee, at thy part - ing breath, To His di - vine a - bode.

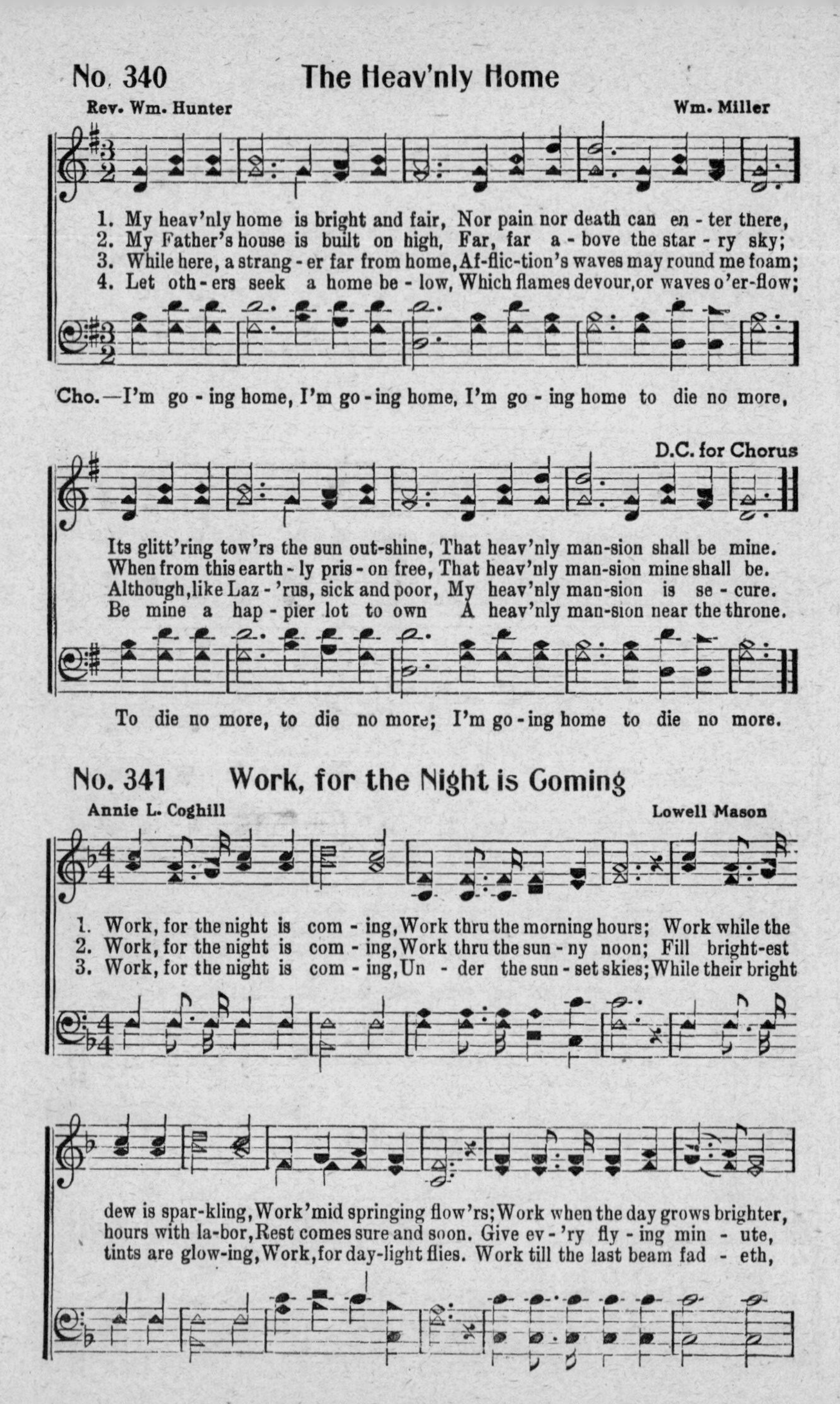
No. 340 The Heav'nly Home
Rev. Wm. Hunter
Wm. Miller
1. My heav'nly home is bright and fair, Nor pain nor death can en - ter there,
2. My Father's house is built on high, Far, far a - bove the star - ry sky;
3. While here, a strang - er far from home, Af-flic-tion's waves may round me foam;
4. Let oth - ers seek a home be - low, Which flames devour, or waves o'er-flow;
Cho.—I'm go - ing home, I'm go - ing home, I'm go - ing home to die no more,
D.C. for Chorus
Its glitt'ring tow'rs the sun out-shine, That heav'nly man-sion shall be mine.
When from this earth - ly pris - on free, That heav'nly man-sion mine shall be.
Although, like Laz - 'rus, sick and poor, My heav'nly man-sion is se - cure.
Be mine a hap - pier lot to own A heav'nly man-sion near the throne.
To die no more, to die no more; I'm go - ing home to die no more.
No. 341 Work, for the Night is Coming
Annie L. Coghill
Lowell Mason
1. Work, for the night is com - ing, Work thru the morning hours; Work while the
2. Work, for the night is com - ing, Work thru the sun - ny noon; Fill bright-est
3. Work, for the night is com - ing, Un - der the sun - set skies; While their bright
dew is spar-kling, Work 'mid springing flow'rs; Work when the day grows brighter,
hours with la-bor, Rest comes sure and soon. Give ev - 'ry fly - ing min - ute,
tints are glow-ing, Work, for day-light flies. Work till the last beam fad - eth,

Work, for the Night is Coming

Work in the glowing sun; Work, for the night is coming, When man's work is done.
Something to keep in store: Work, for the night is coming, When man works no more.
Fadeth to shine no more; Work while the night is dark'ning, When man's work is o'er.
No. 342
Gloria Patri, No. 1
Charles Meineke
Glo - ry be to the Fa - ther, and to the Son, and to the
Ho - ly Ghost; As it was in the be - gin - ning, is
now, and ev - er shall be, world with - out end. A - men, A - men.
No. 343
Gloria Patri, No. 2
Gregorian
Glory be to the Father, and to the Son, and to the Ho - ly Ghost;
As it was in the beginning, is now, and ev-er shall be, world with-out end. A - men.

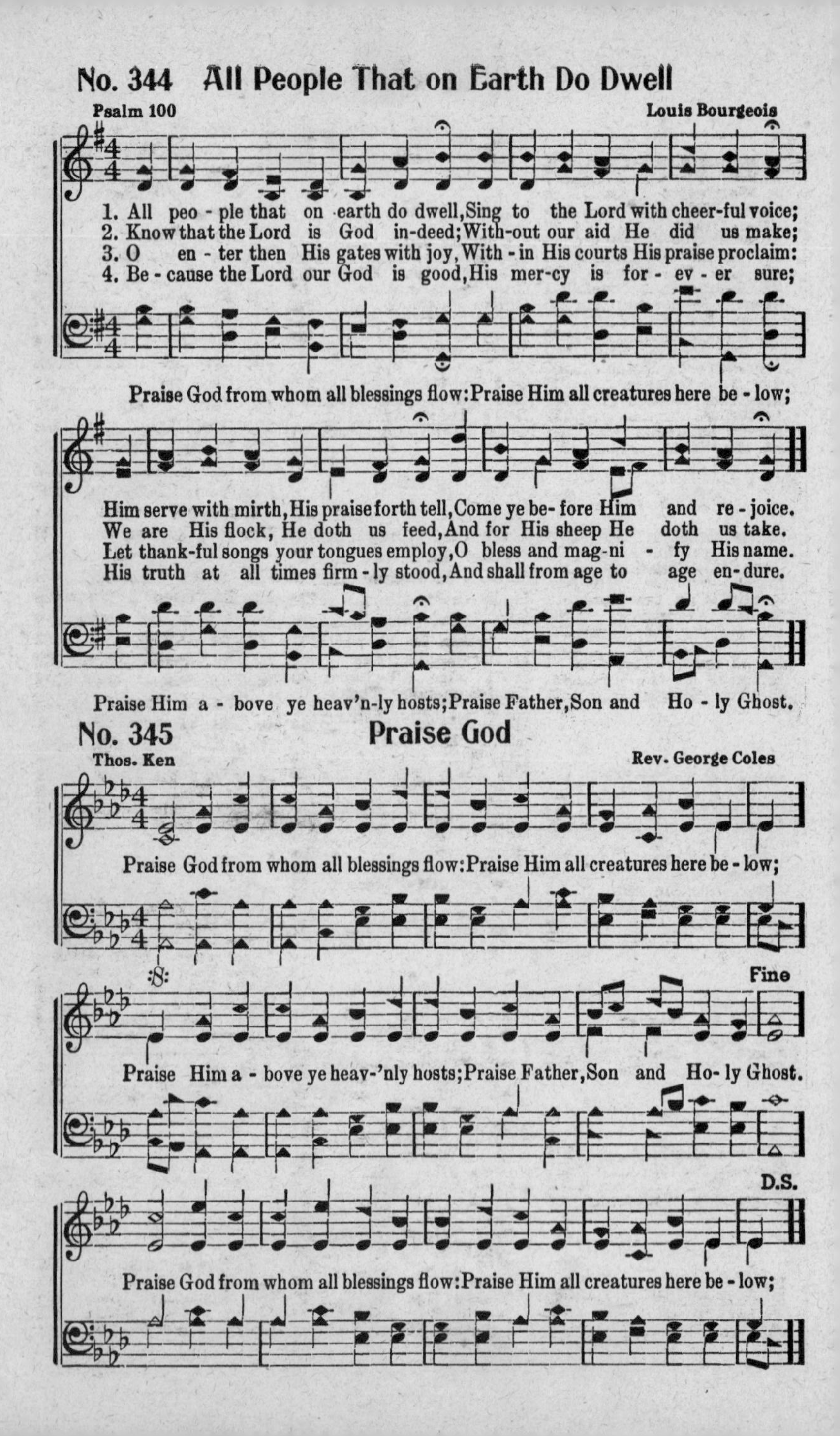
No. 344 All People That on Earth Do Dwell
Psalm 100
Louis Bourgeois
1. All peo - ple that on earth do dwell, Sing to the Lord with cheer-ful voice; Him serve with mirth, His praise forth tell, Come ye be- fore Him and re - joice.
2. Know that the Lord is God in-deed; With-out our aid He did us make; We are His flock, He doth us feed, And for His sheep He doth us take.
3. O en - ter then His gates with joy, With - in His courts His praise proclaim: Let thank-ful songs your tongues employ, O bless and mag-ni - fy His name.
4. Be - cause the Lord our God is good, His mer-cy is for - ev - er sure; His truth at all times firm - ly stood, And shall from age to age en- dure.
Praise God from whom all blessings flow: Praise Him all creatures here be - low;
Praise Him a - bove ye heav'n-ly hosts; Praise Father, Son and Ho - ly Ghost.
No. 345 Praise God
Thos. Ken
Rev. George Coles
Praise God from whom all blessings flow: Praise Him all creatures here be - low;
Fine
Praise Him a - bove ye heav-'nly hosts; Praise Father, Son and Ho- ly Ghost.
D.S.
Praise God from whom all blessings flow: Praise Him all creatures here be - low;

Index

A

A Million Years from.... 48
A Soul Winner.................168
A Wonderful Time........ 3
Abide With Me.................299
After Death What 99
After the Shadows 52
All Alone 85
All Hail the Power......326
All People that Dwell..344
Almost Persuaded 263
Amazing Grace 307
An Empty Mansion 33
An Old Account was......106
Anywhere Is Home 202
Are You Outside 225
Are You Washed 107
Arlington 131
Asleep In Jesus 321
At the Cross 261

B

Battle Hymn 289
Be a Light for Jesus....113
Beautiful Gleanings 184
Believe On the........Preface
Better Mind the Lord..212
Blessed Assurance 285
Blessed Be the Name..322
Blest Be the Tie 338
Bound for the Promised 83
Bringing in the 320
By His Stripes 72

C

Camping in Canaan 122
Children of the King....232
Christ Arose 89
Christ Is King 257
Christ Receiveth 59
Close to Thee 268
Coming 130
Come Humble Sinner..245
Come On, Let's All Go.. 46
Come Thou Fount 296
Come to Jesus..............112

D

Death Is Only a............188
Did You Think to..........199
Don't Let the Light....224
Dying from Home 240

E

Elijah's God 169
Enough for Me..............215
Even Me 292
Everybody Will Be........ 88

F

Face to Face 118
Farther Along 38
Father, What 276
Fill Me Now 278
Footsteps of Jesus........250
Free Waters 163
From the Garden to........117

G

Gathering Home 189
Gethsemane 13
Give Me Your Hand....119
Give Peace Again............101
Gloria Patri No. 1..........342
Gloria Patri No. 2..........343
Glory to His Name........293
Glory Will Be Mine.... 47
Go Into the Fields........ 80
God Be With You..........290
God Put a Rainbow....109
God's Tomorrow 9
Good Night and Good.. 41

H

Hallelujah, We Shall....137
Hallelujah, What 275
Heaven Holds All 63
Heaven Is Nearer 177
He Bore It All 124
He Leadeth Me 286
He Makes Me Forget ..161
He Whispers Sweet 195
He'll Wipe All Tears..148
Help Somebody Today.. 75
He's A Wonderful 157
Hide You in the 253
His Broken Body 95
His Way with Thee....102
His Yoke Is Easy..........243
Hold the Fort 262
Hold to God's Hand....141
Holy Ghost with Love..303
Holy, Holy, Holy............304
Holy Spirit, ...302
Home of the Soul........... 18
How Beautiful Heaven.. 68
How Firm a 298
How Tedious and 295
How Wonderful Jesus.. 61

I

I Am Coming Lord......311
I Am Praying for You..127
I Am Resolved 23
I Am So Glad 16
I Am Thine, O Lord.... 8
I Am Trusting Lord....294
I Choose Jesus 29
I Guess I'm Old 207
I Intend to Go Thru.... 73
I Know Somebody's 201
I Love Him 269
I Love My Savior 145
I Love to Tell the 291
I Need Thee 280
I Shall Not Be Moved..241
I Want to be a 314
I Will Arise 227
I Will Sing the.............. 28
I Would Not Be 19
I Would Not Miss It..210
I'd Rather Be an Old..204
I'd Rather Have 146
If I Could Hear 65
If Men Go to Hell 35
If the Light Has 66
I'll Be a Friend to........156
I'll Be Listening 25
I'll Be Ready to 81
I'll Be Satisfied 248
I'll Fly Away 179
I'll Go Where He.......... 49
I'll Live for Him............264
I'll Live In Glory.......... 90
I'll Live On 15
I'll Make It My 173
I'll Meet You in the....208
I'm Getting Ready 139
I'm Going that Way......132
I'm Going Through 183
I'm Moving Across 11
I'm Not Ashamed 82
I'm On the Rock 185
I'm Saved 174
I'm So Tired I Want.. 34
In Gethsemane Alone.... 4
In The Garden 12
In The Great Morning.. 17
In The Gospel Way ..259
In The Morning of Joy 170
In The Shadow of........ 32
It Is the Hour of..........147
It Is Well with My......186
It Won't Be Long........ 98
Is It Well 165
Is My Name Written..335
Is Thy Heart 182

J

Jesus Believes In You.. 24
Jesus Hold My Hand..203
Jesus Is Calling 181
Jesus Loves Even Me..234
Jesus Paid It all(new) 70
Jesus Paid It All 313
Jesus Saves 316
Jesus Savior Pilot Me..334
Jesus Will Save 111
Joy Unspeakable 30
Just As I Am 312
Just Over In 140
Just A Little While......205

K

Kneel at the Cross......172

L

Leaning on the 133
Let Him In 42
Lift Him Up 114
Listen to the Voice......223
Look for Me at the........ 5

Index continued

Look, Ye Saints 260
Lord, Revive Us 239
Lord, Send Me 144
Love Lifted Me 6
Love Took It Away.....134

M

Master the Tempest.....206
Mear 218
More Abundantly 67
More Love to Thee.....272
My Dreams Will Come..120
My Faith Looks Up.....301
My Redeemer 96
My Soul Be on Thy.....339

N

Nailed to the Cross....152
Near the Cross 273
Nearer, My God 324
No. Not One 274
No Tears In Heaven....103
Not Made with Hands..229
Nothing Between 56
Nothing But the 281
Now I Feel the Fire..247

O

O, Come Angel Band..226
O, Happy Day 309
O How I Love Jesus..305
O I Want to See Him 54
O, Master Let Me..........270
O Save Me at the 246
O Why Not Surrender 105
O Why Not Tonight....255
Oh, Glory to His..........222
Old Time Power 125
On Jordan's Stormy 287
On The Main Line 236
On The Jericho Road.. 94
Only Trust Him 308
Onward Christian 318
Ortonville 252
Our Coming King 235
Our King Immanuel.....100
Our Lord's Return 76
Our Savior Left Alone 187

P

Parting Hand 216
Passing Away 228
Pass Me Not 279
Praise God From..........345
Praise Him. Praise.....150
Precious Memories 123
Prepare to Meet Thy....194

R

Ready 221
Redeemed 164
Redeeming Love 217
Rescue the Perishing....104
Rest for the Weary.....317
Revive Us Again 310
Rock of Ages 297

S

Safe in the Arms 190
Savior in Thy Mercy..238
Savior, Lead Me 198
Savior, Like a 271
Savior, More than 267
Shake Hands with 135
Shall We Gather 265
Shall We Meet 266
Show Pity, Lord 213
Silent Night 254
Sin Can Never Enter....197
Since Jesus Came Into.. 22
Sitting at the Feet of.. 87
Softly and Tenderly.....283
Some Day 91
Some Glad Day 192
Some Glad Day 214
Some Time 93
Stand Up for Jesus....329
Standing on the 37
Sun of My Soul 300
Sweeping Thru the 84
Sweet By and By 337
Sweet Hour of Prayer..327
Sweetest Mother 176
Swing Out on the 110

T

Take Higher Ground 249
Take the Name of 251
Talk It Over 86
Tell It to Jesus 167
Tell Me the Old 153
Tell Me the Story of.. 64
Thank God for the 39
That Is Where I..........149
The Beautiful Garden.. 55
The Book that Never..175
The Cross of Calvary.. 92
The Eastern Gate 77
The Gate Ajar 315
The Glory Train 166
The Gloryland Way 26
The Great Glad Day.....258
The Great Physician 332
The Great Redeemer ..200
The Half Has Never.... 74
The Haven of Rest....... 97
The Heavenly Home 340
The Home Over There..288
The Kingdom Coming ..155
The Light of the 237
The Lily of the Valley 50
The Morning Light 330
The Old Gospel Ship.. 60
The Old Rugged 51
The Old Time Religion 331
The Palace of Prayer..211
The Pearly White City 160
The Royal Telephone 21
There Is a Fountain....306
There Is Power in the 14
There'll Be No Sorrow 219
There'll Be Shouting..128
There's A Crown 193
There's a Great Day....319
There Shall Be 180
The Shining Shore 277
The Solid Rock 325
The Son Hath Made.....142
The Unclouded Day 53
The Unseen Hand 233
The Way of the Cross.. 44
This World Is Not 1
Throw Out the Life 62
'Tis So Sweet to 158
To the Work 126

V

Victory Ahead 79

W

Watching You 154
We'll Work Till Jesus..323
We're Marching to 43
We Shall Understand ..209
What A Friend 336
What Did He Do? 71
What The Old World..115
What Wondrous Love ..328
What Would You Do?..143
What Would You 191
When All God's 108
When I Can Read 231
When I Make My Last 10
When I See the Blood..116
When I Walk the 69
When Morning Comes.. 57
When Our Lord Shall..162
When The Redeemed.. 159
When The Roll Is 138
When They Ring the.... 40
When The Saints Go....151
When We All Get to.. 78
Where He Leads..........121
Where He Leads Me....282
Where The Soul Never 27
Where We'll Never 20
While Jesus Whispers..284
Whiter Than Snow 333
Who At My Door Is..244
Who Is That 129
Why Not Now?..........256
Will Jesus Find Us.....196
Will The Circle Be 171
Will The Waters Be....220
Windham 230
Wonderful Jesus 178
Wonderful Story of.......... 45
Wonderful Words of ..242
Wondrous Saving 136
Won't It Be Wonderful 31
Work For the Night..341

Y

Ye Must Be Born.......... 58
You Can Shine.......... 36
You Can't Do Wrong.. 2
You Never Mentioned.... 7